NEW CROPS FOR THE NEW WORLD

EDITED BY

CHARLES MORROW WILSON

THE MACMILLAN COMPANY · NEW YORK

1945

To Martha and Her Gardens

Acknowledgments

The editor wishes to give due credit for the photographs listed below:

V. C. Dunlap—Plate 11; Plate 13; Plate 14; Plate 15.

Farm Security Administration—Plate 4, upper left and lower; Plate 6, upper right; Plate 7; Plate 8; Plate 9; Plate 10; Plate 18; Plate 25; Plate 26; Plate 28; Plate 32.

Giles G. Healey—Plate 1; Plate 27.

Middle America Information Bureau—Plate 5; Plate 6; upper left and lower; Plate 12; Plate 20, upper; Plate 23; Plate 24.

Wilson Popenoe—Plate 2; Plate 3; Plate 4, upper right; Plate 16; Plate 17.

Muriel Reis—Plate 30; Plate 31.

U.S. Dept of Agriculture—Plate 19, upper and lower left; Plate 20, lower left and lower right; Plate 21; Plate 22.

J. A. Weston—Plate 19, lower right.

Iris Woolcock—Plate 29.

Contents

Illustrations

ILLUSTRATIONS

Introduction

IN THE Americas today great and durable news is being written on the scrolls of producing fields. World War II has witnessed—in some measure is causing—the most widespread and potentially the most beneficial migration of crops in known history.

Indigenous plants of proved value to people are being brought or returned from the Old World to the New, and vice versa. The migration proceeds regardless of compass bearings and, on the whole, with skilled direction that would substitute the planned migration of benefitting plants and livestock for the repetitious pattern of frantic and unplanned migration of distressed peoples. In some instances the migration of crops is entirely local; in others it proceeds completely around the earth.

In general this emergence of new or renovated crops is encouraging. It supports specifically Secretary of Agriculture Wickard's maxim that food will win the war and write the peace. It suggests tangibly that more and better foods for all of the people, and more of the needed non-food products of fields, ranges, and forests can help keep a better and more lasting peace.

The Americas need more crops and better crops. In a great part of our hemisphere the existing list of cultivated crops is distressingly small, and constructive experimentation with species, genera, and families of economic plants which might become valuable crops has been chronically inadequate. Patently, more proved crops can mean fewer sick or underfed Americans, better homes, better lands, and better lives. All the more so, since about half of the people of this hemisphere live on or directly from the land. (In the United States before World War II, about a third of our census was rural, and most probably will be after the war. In the Americas south of the Rio Grande the proportion is nearly two-thirds.)

Thus, in money or any other measure of living standards a good and widely adaptable crop is immensely valuable—worth millions or even billions of dollars yearly, or more definitively, better lives for thousands or millions of people. As an over-all proposition the fields, ranges, and woodlands of this hemisphere can use new crops to advantage—dozens or scores or perhaps hundreds of them. For now, and in the future, the Americas require more fruitful and better-diversified food crops, more versatile farming practices, and more varied non-food crops and plant materials. Even during this high tide of synthetic production the uses for plant materials are increasing by the thousands and tens of thousands as the fact becomes ever more apparent that the census majority of synthetics is also made from crops and plant materials.

It is not reasonable to predict that all the new, experimental, or renovated crops that are now being set to American fields, gardens, or ranges will prove successful. Some are almost certain to fail. Perhaps the majority will not stand the practical and frequently unmerciful tests and demands of self-perpetuating agricultures. Some, likely to win as subsistence or local crops, may not prove feasible as staple crops for major farming areas or entire nations. Some may fulfil domestic needs of a community or province or country and fail to qualify for profitable export. In other instances successful export crops may not qualify as adequate subsistence or domestic crops. But winner's stakes are high. The Americas need new crops, and the Americas are getting them.

The title of this book, *New Crops for the New World,* takes for granted the working definition that a crop is any plant or animal species which considerable numbers of people can grow profitably, or with other benefit to themselves.

Some of the new crops discussed in this book are being grown in our hemisphere for the first time, as an immediate result of urgent wartime needs. For example, abacá, the banana-like Manila fiber plant that was formerly produced exclusively in the Philippines and other Pacific tropics, is being planted extensively in the American tropics for the first time. Others, including the Hevea tree, the decisive source of natural rubber, and the Cinchona tree, from whose bark quinine is made, are indigenous resources of the South American wilds. For good reason they had been put into cultivation and made principal crops in other and distant tropics, and now, also for good reason, they are being returned for selective cultivation in the Americas.

Still other new crops are native plants, formerly neglected or abandoned, and now because of reawakened or newly created demands they are being changed to crops, either in cultivation or in the wilds. Many of the indigenous American palm crops and drug crops are in this latter catalog, as is kapok, the lustrous and light floss of the common Ceiba tree of the American tropics. Others, including the enormously important hybrid corns and new breeds or crosses of cattle and swine, are new by virtue of skilfully directed genetic experiments and developments, many of which are now in progress.

Still others of the new or comparatively new crops for the New World are new only by happenstance and without apparent benefit of man's knowledge or work. Such botanical foundlings are sometimes called "sports." The common sweet yellow or Gros Michel banana, which one usually buys or tries to buy at the corner market, is a classic instance of an unexplained genetic accident that has grown to be one of the greatest export crops of this hemisphere.

The banana genera are one of man's oldest cultivated crops, if not his oldest. Presumably their homeland was the humid tropics of southeast Asia. When the banana finally reached the Americas a mere four centuries ago, many types had been recorded and were being grown in the wet tropics all around the equator.

Then on a day in 1836 a Jamaica planter named Jean François Pouyat, while strolling through farms in nearby Martinque, ran smack against a new kind of banana, which he carried back to his Jamaica estate, planted, and named with endearing modesty, "Banana-Pouyat." From that casual finding on a casual holiday stroll has grown the decisive banana acreage of the western hemisphere which ordinarily exports well over 150 million bunches of Gros Michel yearly, and so supplies bananas to the world.

But the fact stands that God alone knows, and during the past 109 years has not revealed, just how the Gros Michel came into being. Similar instances are also part of the continuing epic of new crops for the New World.

But regardless of origin or emergence, mere plants become valid crops for good and human reasons. People must select the species, genera, or families of plants; prepare them for cultivation; plan, station, till, and harvest them; or if the potential crop is "wild," people must be there and able to recognize the plant, to reap and process it. New crops for the New World are thus forever a part of the human equation. They cannot possibly succeed without the interest, the energy, the toil, sweat, and sometimes the tears and blood of workaday farmers who are game to contribute and risk their time and lands, their experience and skills to the cause of proving and establishing a mere growing plant as a beneficial and lasting crop.

Because the commonplace tillers and tenders of earth are preponderantly more or less poor men and women who must work without immediate benefit of elaborate educations, technical leadership, or money reserves, in order that crops may be widely established and perpetuated, it is usually advisable or essential that new crops be grown by independent citizen farmers of a given community or state or nation. There may be unique exceptions—crops which can be grown successfully only on extensive acreage and with the support of working capital, machinery, and other accessories that are definitely beyond the means of most farming citizens.

The latter instances are extremely few. In almost every case the everyday, dirt-turning farmer is essential to the success of the new crops or the valid betterment of the old. The truth is that the feat of nursing, coaxing, or otherwise helping a new or experimental crop to practical maturity and establishment, like that of helping raise a son or daughter, cannot be a casual or entirely carefree task. And however loyal, capable, and essential is the workaday farmer to the destinies and survival of a crop, he can hardly be expected to attend all the exacting, involved details thereby incurred.

Almost invariably the establishment of a crop also requires capable help from one or more skilled scientists, and usually the help of strong companies, or cooperatives, or governments, or groups of governments to sponsor or otherwise underwrite the work of the scientists. The particular plant or animal that is to be raised to the station of an experimental crop must be skilfully selected and painstakingly identified, and usually carried through a costly period of trial propagation which generally requires the services of several highly skilled scientists. There are no absolute formulas for plant introduction, and no over-all rules beyond the statement that the individual farmer cannot be expected to completely "develop" a new crop before he grows it.

In the United States, Soviet Russia, Brazil and several other American nations, agencies of government are working determinedly, frequently brilliantly, to facilitate the introduction of new crops. In the pre-war Netherlands Indies a great part of the introduction and improvement of new crops was accomplished by private research effected cooperatively by associations of land-owners. In the Americas commercial companies are also outstandingly active in the introduction of new crops which may better local economies and the fortunes of the every-day farmer, in keeping with the accredited tenets of this common-man's century.

A realistic estimate of new crops for the New World can overlook or underestimate what is due the sowers and reapers and tenders thereof. Time is required to change potentially economic plants to proved crops, and usually still more time to produce the crop in real and practical agriculture. And regardless of the donor, a capable Exhibit A is prerequisite; that is, the objective opportunity for the independent farmer to see the new crop growing, to learn and ponder its characteristics and so decide for himself whether or not he elects to grow the crop on his own land.

But nobody can overemphasize the reality that the grower is indispensable to the crop, which implies the bona fide recognition of the right of any American, whether in Minnesota, Uruguay, Arkansas, or Chile, to own and use land in his own name and to use it for the best possible advantage of himself and his neighbors. The prevailing migration of crops clearly implies that valid crops, regardless of how procured or developed, must be made freely available to all men of goodwill who would grow them. For if inter-American agriculture is to progress, neither it nor the Americas generally can endure the arbitrary monopoly of valid crops or planting material for the exclusive benefit of vested groups or privileged individuals. Western hemisphere agriculture cannot endure quinine monopolies, or spice monopoly, or fiber monopoly, or any other collusive establishment that would arbitrarily anchor the decisive production of a given crop to a particular area for the exclusive benefit of a favored few. Since common men must serve crops, crops must also serve common men.

To this end, and particularly in the instances of certain strategic crops that are required for hemisphere security, it may be necessary for American nations to effect or to enlarge the reciprocal trade agreements already established, and to provide them with adjustable and revisable preferential treatment in inter-American trade.

But the desired goal of new crops for the New World certainly is not one of engendering destructive competition between producing areas in the respective hemispheres or to otherwise overwhelm or smack down the agrarian strongholds of the eastern hemisphere. The desired goal is, for evident reasons of hemisphere security, to make possible inter-American production of a reasonable proportion of the various crop materials that are essential to Pan American survival in time of war and that are validly beneficial to Pan American agricultures in time of peace.

The feat of helping farmers of all the Americas and other lands to help themselves by means of better-adapted crops is no theorist's dream. It is horse sense and indispensable hemisphere policy. As never before, all the Americas are as one, and the good of each is inevitably the good of all. Whether or not you and I can grow any of these new or changing crops in our own particular flower pots or garden, or yardway or woodlands, fields or window boxes, the new crops for the New World are important to every one of us—more so today and tomorrow than ever before. For no one of us can live without the harvests from earth, and no nation is likely to flourish without the benefits of a good and ever-improving agriculture.

As a long-time reporter of agriculture in the Americas, I believe better farming is closely synonymous with better government and what we may call "social justice." I believe, too, that experienced scientific appraisal is essential to any competent appraisal of the inter-American life today and tomorrow.

This book is born of this belief. It includes the discussions of new or comparatively new crops for the New World as they seem to fourteen career scientists who are now doing significant work in many phases of inter-American and international agriculture. These contributors have written factually, carefully, and well. All fourteen of them are busy men except Dr. Miriam L. Bomhard ("Palm Oils and Waxes"), who is a busy woman. All of the contributors are immensely active in significant work, and all are crowded with wartime obligations. I am doubly grateful for their help.

CHARLES MORROW WILSON

New York, 1945

1

The Undeveloped Field
of Tropical Fruit

By WILSON POPENOE

DIRECTOR DE LA ESCUELA
AGRÍCOLA PANAMERICANA

IN the earlier stages of this book, one of our distinguished contributors warned that the content list was beginning to sound like a fruit salad. This warning has been heeded with solemn respect. Only this one chapter deals exclusively with fruits.

Maybe there is poetic justice in placing this chapter first. As any produce seller knows, and as almost any food statistician will avidly demonstrate with charts and curves, if given half a chance, ours is an age of fruits and a generation of fruit eaters. What is more relevant here is that many of the varied, enticing, and too little known tropical fruits are in the process of becoming real or potential new crops, changing from casual bounties of the wilderness; and thanks to improved refrigeration, accelerated shipping, and better horticulture, they are coming our way.

Dr. Wilson Popenoe, a distinguished career scientist of the American tropics, is particularly well qualified to write this chapter. Founder-director of the renowned Lancetilla Experiment Station of Honduras and long-time world traveler for the United States Department of Agriculture, he is now director of the new Escuela Agrícola Panamericana at Zamorano, Honduras—one of the newest and most useful schools of Pan American agriculture. Dr. Popenoe is also the owner and restorer of the House in Antigua (Guatemala) about which Louis Adamic wrote a book.

1

VISITORS to the tropics frequently remark that the fruits of this part of the world are in the main less delicious than those of the North. "Of course," it will be admitted, "there are exceptions: take, for example, the pineapple and the banana." The corollary is obvious to one who is familiar with the history of pomology. The handsome apples, the luscious peaches, the tasty plums of the North are the result of deliberate selection and improvement, and their perpetuation has been achieved through vegetative propagation.

Had tropical fruits in general received as much attention at the hands of skilful horticulturists as has been given to northern species, and had vegetative propagation been the rule rather than the exception, there would be a different story to tell. In those instances where nature did most of the work—where vegetative propagation was simple, as with the pineapple and the banana—superior varieties originating by chance were saved and passed on to succeeding generations. Where this was not the case—where it was necessary for man to develop horticultural techniques such as grafting—the tropics of the New World have brought up the rear.

Thus we are faced today with interesting and attractive possibilities in the field of tropical pomology: we are surrounded, in the first place, by many native fruits which through selection, breeding, and vegetative propagation can be made to equal if not surpass the fruits of the North; and in the second, we are drawing upon the tropics of the Old World for many which have already been improved, and which, where conditions of climate and soil are suitable, have only to be propagated and disseminated to increase our horticultural wealth. The citrus fruits and the banana are examples of this second group which have already achieved the commercial importance which their intrinsic merits warrant. The avocado and the annonas are examples of the first which are coming to the fore.

A century ago, bananas were unknown in the markets of the North; half a century ago, the same was true of the avocado. To a great extent it is still true of the mango, and of the cherimoya which Mark Twain called "deliciousness itself."

Rapid transportation and refrigeration have revolutionized tropical fruit culture in our own generation. Witness the banana industry, which annually places a hundred million bunches of this wholesome fruit on the markets of the North. Fifty years ago, Queen Victoria offered a handsome prize to anyone who would place a bowl of mangosteens upon her table at Buckingham Palace. The prize could not be claimed, because this queen of tropical fruits grew only in far-off Malaya. But twenty years ago, mangosteens were sent from the Hawaiian Islands to Washington and arrived in perfect condition. What further advances will be wrought by airplane transportation we do not know. It is fair to assume that they will be great.

And aside from the attractive possibilities of tropical fruit production for northern markets, there is the limitless field of home consumption. When the plant explorers have marshalled their introductions; when plant breeders have finished their work; and when horticulturists have applied their skill to propagation and culture, remarks regarding the inferiority of tropical fruits will no longer be in order.

It is impossible to point out all those species which in improved form will grace the tropical orchard of a hundred years hence, but it is possible to discuss some of them which experience has shown to possess unusual merit.

THE MANGO, APPLE OF THE TROPICS

More than five hundred years ago the Turkoman poet Amir Khusrau, whose grass-covered tomb is still venerated at Delhi, wrote in Persian verse:

> The mango is the pride of the Garden,
> The choicest fruit of Hindustan.
> Other fruits we are content to eat when ripe,
> But the mango is good in all stages of growth.

Because of its widespread cultivation, the diversity of its forms, its great popularity, and the many ways in which it can be used, the mango can rightly be considered the tropical counterpart of the Northern apple. Yet the American tropics have by no means realized the full measure of its possibilities.

Credit for bringing the mango (botanically *Mangifera indica*) to this hemisphere probably belongs to the Portuguese, who had become familiar with its merits in their East Indian colonies, and who are believed to have planted it at Bahia, Brazil, about the year 1700. Some fifty years later it was carried from Rio de Janeiro to Barbados; and during the succeeding half century it spread to many other regions, in some of which it found conditions so congenial that it rapidly took on the appearance of a wild or native tree. But all this was accomplished by means of seeds. The fine grafted varieties of the Orient were slow to reach this part of the world, due to difficulties of transportation in the days of sailing ships, and to the ease with which seedlings could be grown—or grew them-selves—as compared with grafted trees.

No northern horticulturist of today would think of planting an orchard of seedling apples, or peaches, or pears; he goes to the nursery-man and buys grafted trees of varieties which will produce fruit not only of superior, but of uniform, quality. Most cultivated fruits, especially the highly improved forms, do not come true from seed. An occasional indi-vidual may turn out well; it may even be superior to its parent. But to be sure of good results, and especially to be sure of a uniform product which will meet the exacting demands of an educated market, grafted trees must be planted.

It is not surprising, therefore, that mango culture in tropical America has lagged. For it is safe to say that more than ninety-nine percent of the mango trees now growing in this hemisphere are seedlings.

With the introduction and propagation of fine grafted varieties from the Orient the situation is changing. Asiatic horticulturists have for cen-turies devoted solicitous care to their mangos, and have produced and propagated many superior forms. Due largely to the efforts of the British and French in the West Indies, and the United States Department of Agriculture at Washington, many of these have lately become available to us. Eating them, we can at last understand the enthusiasm of early writers who became familiar with this fruit in the Orient. Fryer, writing of Indian mangos in 1673, said "The Apples of the Hesperides are but Fables to them; for Taste, the Nectarine, the Peach and Apricot fall short." And half a century later Hamilton went even further when he said: "The Goa mango is reckoned the largest and most delicious to the taste of any in the world, and I may add, the wholesomest and best tasted of any Fruit in the World."

Fine mangos do not come from India alone. True, that country pos-sesses the greatest number of fine varieties; but the mangos of Indo-China, of the Philippines, and of Java have their own peculiar merits and are preferred by some to those of India. For beautiful coloring, enticing aroma, and delicious taste, however, such Indian mangos as Pairi and Amini have few if any equals. Perhaps it is this wide range in size, in shape, in coloring, and in flavor which makes the mango one of the most attractive of all tropical fruits, just as wide range in these same characteristics lends added interest to northern apples and peaches.

It could not be expected that commercial mango cultivation, utilizing the finest oriental varieties, could be developed in the American tropics without encountering obstacles. Jersey cows require better environmental conditions and more care than scrubs. The finer mangos are more exacting in their requirements than the average run of seedlings.

Most mangos will withstand temperatures down to or even a little below the freezing point. Thus their cultivation is practicable in southern Florida, where small commercial orchards have been developed in recent years. But the major possibilities of mango culture are in the tropics proper. Even here there are limitations, particularly that of climate. In regions of heavy and continuous rainfall, the mango keeps on growing from one year's end to the next, and produces little fruit. It is therefore important to limit plantings of the finer varieties to regions with the right sort of climate; and even there the soil should not be too rich, else again the tree will devote most of its energies to vegetative growth.

Also there is a fungous disease which attacks the flowers and young fruits, and if favored by moist weather, may destroy them. And there are fruit flies, whose maggots infest the ripe fruits and render them worthless. Horticulturists are gradually mastering these difficulties.

Propagation by various kinds of grafting presents few problems, though it requires rather more than usual skill, which is precisely the reason it has been slow in coming into widespread use.

Because of its relatively perishable nature, it is probably too much to expect that the mango, as an export fruit for northern markets, can ever vie with such products as the pineapple and the banana. But the day will surely come when it will be possible to purchase fancy mangos, grown in the American tropics, in all the larger cities of the United States. And perhaps even more important, mangos of superior quality will add to the pleasure and healthfulness of life in many tropical regions.

THE AVOCADO, SALAD-FRUIT

The mango is a welcome immigrant; the avocado is the native son who made good. Fifty years ago avocados were practically unknown in the markets of the North; and the few people who grew them in Florida, and the fewer still in California, usually called them alligator pears. Down in the American tropics the situation was very, very different. The Indians were growing avocados in their diminutive gardens, all the way from Mexico to Peru, when the Spaniards arrived.

The avocado was first brought to the attention of Europeans when the Bachelor Fernández de Enciso, who was coasting along the Spanish Main with one of the first expeditions, wrote that he had found a fruit near what is now Santa Marta, Colombia, which looked like an orange, and when it was ready for eating turned yellowish, and "that which it contains is like butter and is of marvelous flavor, so good and pleasing to the palate that it is a wonderful thing."

That was in 1519. A few years later the great naturalist-historian Oviedo saw avocados in Nicaragua, where the only gardener (he remarked) was God; but the people esteemed the fruits so highly that they turned out at the ripening season to guard them jealously.

But it was not until they reached Mexico and Guatemala that the Spaniards really learned to appreciate this fruit. Here it was, and still is, one of the staples; and here it was that the Spaniards adopted the Aztec name, *ahuacatl*, which became *ahuacate* and has come down to us as *avocado*, a corruption formed in Jamaica by the British shortly after they took over that island in 1657. The British went even further; they coined the objectionable misnomer "alligator pear." It is interesting to see how this came about. The Spaniards, who had introduced the avocado into the West Indies from the mainland, brought with it the Aztec name *ahuacate* instead of the South American *palta*, which the Incas were using in Peru. The British struggled with this word manfully, but in vain; it became *albecato*, *abacado*, *avocado*, and finally "alligator." Then, because they had the habit of likening every tropical fruit to something with which they were familiar at home, they added pear.

Sometime in the last century, the avocado (*Persea americano*) crept into southern Florida from Cuba, and into southern California from Mexico. About 1900, North Americans woke up to an appreciation of the remarkable qualities of this fruit—qualities which are well-nigh unique in the pomological world. For the avocado is not a fruit in the popular sense of that term; it cannot be cooked, canned, or preserved. It is eaten as a salad; but unlike most salads, its food value is so high that it ranks alongside bread and rice as a source of human energy.

Horticulturists in California vied with those in Florida in searching out the best local seedlings and propagating them by grafting, so as to establish orchards which would produce fruit of uniform character and quality, suitable for presentation in the most exacting markets. The Californians went further; they sent horticultural explorers to the great avocado-producing centers of Mexico, where they brought to light an excellent sort which was named Fuerte, because it was such a strong grower. This has since become the leading commercial avocado. The

United States Department of Agriculture took up the search, and kept an explorer in tropical America from Mexico to Chile for the better part of ten years, hunting for avocados which might extend the ripening season in the United States or otherwise contribute to the successful development of the industry. California now ships something like twenty million pounds of avocados annually, and Florida also has done well.

The countries around the Caribbean are awakening to the possibilities of this crop. Cuba has long been in the business; shipments to the United States have been made from Colombia and a few other regions. There is much work still to be done. The presence of three horticultural races—Mexican, Guatemalan, and West Indian, differing in climatic requirements, in character of fruit, and in season of ripening—means that there are avocados for almost any situation, from the lowlands of the littoral to mountain valleys at 8000 feet. There is one limiting factor: the avocado does not tolerate wet feet. It has to be grown on well-drained soils, which means that many of the heavy clays extensively used for such crops as sugar cane, are not suitable. Many failures have resulted from attempting to grow avocados on these lands.

The seedling trees present in most tropical American countries provide a sufficient range of material from which to select superior sorts. Nevertheless, tropical horticulturists have leaned heavily upon varieties from California and Florida, where the selecting has already been done, and where many natural crosses have originated between the horticultural races.

Because of its unique position as a salad-fruit, because of its high food value, and because it withstands shipment better than many other tropical fruits, the avocado can reasonably be expected to play a major role in the future of tropical pomology. There are people who have predicted that it will take its place alongside the orange in volume of production. This is perhaps expecting too much; but it is, at least, an indication of potential value. And here, as in the case of the mango, one should not overlook the increased importance which the avocado can assume in the dietary of tropical peoples, when its cultivation is placed upon the sound basis of modern horticultural science.

THE LYCHEE, FAVORITE FRUIT OF CHINA

In these days of rapid transportation, it is hard for us to appreciate the difficulties experienced in bygone years when attempts were made to bring some of the crop plants of the Old World to the tropics of the New. In the case of cereals, propagated by means of non-perishable seeds, the job was easy. Even the banana came at an early date, because its huge pseudo-bulbs can be kept for weeks, only to break into vigorous growth the moment they feel the stimulus of warm, moist soil around them.

In other instances, much time elapsed before success was attained, and then it was only through well-organized effort that it was possible. After Captain Cook had reported upon the usefulness of the breadfruit, its importance was considered to be so great, as a potential foodstuff for negro slaves in the West Indies, that the British government sent out the recently well-publicized expedition under Captain Bligh to bring the tree from Tahiti to their tropical American plantations.

In southern China there grows, and has been grown for centuries, a fruit so excellent that neither the orange nor the peach is held to equal it. This is the lychee or litchi (botanically *Litchi chinensis*), so delicious that the poet Su Tung-po declared, while living in exile at Canton, that lychees would reconcile one to eternal banishment.

But lychee seeds do not keep well, and lychee trees are difficult to transport. It took a long time for the tree to gain a foothold in the American tropics; in fact, it has scarcely done so yet. Perhaps we should say that it has nothing more than a toehold; but it is here, and it is here to stay.

Readers may scoff. They may say, "I have eaten the lychee nuts which the Chinese in the United States distribute to their friends at Christmastime. They are nothing to write home about." But dried lychees—the only kind known to most people in the United States who know lychees at all—no more resemble fresh lychees than a dried apple resembles a well-ripened Gravenstein. And just as there are few more beautiful sights than a lychee tree, with its dense crown of glossy foliage, bending under the weight of many clusters of fruits which resemble large strawberries in appearance, so are there few fruits more satisfactory to the palate than the ripe lychee with its glistening white pulp surrounding a single seed the size of a bean. The flavor is not easy to describe, but is perhaps best likened to that of a Muscat grape.

In recent years, largely through the efforts of the United States Department of Agriculture, lychees have been planted in Florida. They are doing well in several parts of that state. They have not been so successful in California; they do not stand much frost. They have been planted in Cuba, where good crops have been produced and gobbled up by Chinese residents of Havana at fancy prices. And they have been planted elsewhere, here and there, in Honduras, in Panama, in Jamaica, in Brazil. But in general, if you mention the word lychee to a resident of tropical America, he will stare at you blankly.

Expansion of lychee culture will perhaps be slow, for the tree is somewhat exacting in its requirements. It needs the stimulus of a cool season or dry weather to make it fruit abundantly. Its propagation is by no means as simple as that of the mango, for example; the seeds do not keep long, as has already been mentioned, nor can the best varieties be reproduced in this way.

In the greenhouses at Washington, experts have shown that cuttings can be rooted satisfactorily. But conditions must be just right. In time, tropical horticulturists will doubtless develop simple methods of grafting or budding. Up to the present, most of the trees which have been distributed to experimenters in the tropics have been propagated by the ancient oriental method of air-layering—simple, effective, but laborious. A ring of bark is removed from a limb about as thick as one's finger. Around this a ball of moss and soil, and in the Orient cow manure, is formed and tied in place securely. This ball is watered daily for several months (unless rainfall is regular and adequate), by which time roots have formed at the point where the ring of bark was removed. The branch is then cut from the parent tree, ball of moss and all, and started on its independent existence.

As an addition to tropical orchards, in all those regions where climate and soil are favorable, the lychee has a future. It is not too delicate for shipment to distant markets, and it may some day rank among the export crops of several Caribbean countries.

THE KAKI, OR JAPANESE PERSIMMON

Though not purely tropical in character, and perhaps not likely to attain great commercial importance in the tropics, the kaki (*Diospyros kaki*) is such an excellent fruit that it deserves at least passing notice.

The Japanese cultivate some 800 varieties, which means that the kaki is of more than ordinary merit or they would not bother to grow so many of them. In northern China also it is highly popular. It was introduced into the southern United States at about the time of Commodore Perry's visit to Japan, and is now cultivated commercially along the Gulf coast, in Florida, and in California. It is a half-hardy tree, better suited to climates like that of California than to the wet tropics, but recent experience has shown that it is quite successful in the tropical highlands, and fairly so on the coast.

Little has been done to study the possibilities of this fruit in tropical America. The presence of many varieties in the orchards of the United States and the Orient means that we have abundant material from which to select those best adapted to our conditions. At Canton, China, which is just about equal in latitude to Havana, Cuba, excellent kakis are produced. North American horticulturists have not been interested in the more tropical forms of this fruit—rather the opposite.

Seedlings of good parentage sometimes turn out satisfactorily, but choice varieties must be propagated by grafting, and the question of suitable stock plants is of importance. In the United States, the hardy American persimmon (*Diospyros virginiana*), is often used, but this is not suited to the tropics. Seedling kakis are preferable here.

One way to develop good kakis for tropical America would be to plant large numbers of seedlings and then to select from the resulting trees those most satisfactory in quality of fruit and best adapted to our conditions. This would be a worthwhile undertaking, and highly interesting besides. Many choice fruit varieties of the North have been produced in precisely this manner.

During the past half century, the kaki has become a familiar sight upon fruit-stands of the United States. It has a future in the tropics also— a future made more fascinating by the fact that scarcely anything has been done to plumb its possibilities.

THE CHERIMOYA AND ITS RELATIVES

"The pineapple, the mangosteen, and the cherimoya," wrote the botanist Seemann, "are considered the finest fruits in the world. I have tasted them in those localities where they are supposed to attain their highest perfection,—the pineapple in Guayaquil, the mangosteen in the Indian Archipelago, and the cherimoya on the slopes of the Andes,—and if I were called upon to act the part of a Paris I would without hesitation assign the apple to the cherimoya. Its taste, indeed, surpasses that of every other fruit, and Haenke was quite right when he called it the masterpiece of Nature."

Such lavish praise perhaps invites skepticism; one's first reaction is to ask, "Is the cherimoya really so good as all that?" It is; but only when grown in precisely the right climate. It definitely is not a fruit to be grown in the wet lowlands of the tropics. Its native home is in southern Ecuador and northern Peru, at moderate elevations, where the climate is cool and rather dry. For this reason those who have attempted to grow this excellent fruit in other climates have often been disappointed.

When produced in the tropical highlands, as it is in Mexico and Central America, the cherimoya (*Annona cherimola*) merits the eulogies of Dr. Seemann. It is a fruit of irregular form, commonly heart-shaped, sometimes up to three or four pounds in weight. Within its rough exterior is firm white flesh in which hard brown seeds are embedded. When chilled, it is remarkably suggestive of ice cream with the combined flavors of pineapple and banana. The British, who lean more to custards than ice creams, early gave the generic name "custard apple" to the fruits of this family.

Years ago, fine cherimoyas were occasionally shipped from Mexico to the United States, but the plant quarantine business put a stop to all that. California has gone in for cherimoyas, with a certain degree of success. The tree is not very frost-resistant and must be grown in the mildest locations in that state, but where it succeeds, as in the vicinity of Los Angeles, it succeeds very well. Selection of superior seedlings and their propagation by grafting has, as usual, wrought miracles; but there is a problem of pollination which has given trouble and will continue to do so until it is solved by horticultural skill. This difficulty exists also in the tropics.

Because of its rather perishable nature, the cherimoya may not become a commercial fruit of great importance so far as northern markets are concerned. But sooner or later it is likely to appear upon fruit-stands in northern cities where such things as winter strawberries, Chilean melons, and Florida mangos are now displayed.

One of its congeners, the tropical guanábana, has perhaps an even better future. For the guanábana makes one of the most distinctive sherbets known to the tropics, and a delicious refresco or fruit drink called *champola* in Cuba. More than once, plans have been made for placing guanábana concentrate on the soda fountains of the United States—plans more than likely, some day, to be carried out. Visitors to the tropics rarely fail to enthuse over guanábana sherbet, especially when prepared as it is in Havana or in Rio de Janeiro. The Brazilians vie with the Cubans in knowing how to utilize tropical fruits.

British settlers in the West Indies, who early displayed a regrettable penchant for applying unattractive names to tropical fruits (witness, alligator pear), dubbed the guanábana "soursop," which was easier to say, but added nothing to the prestige of a really noble creation.

Two or three other members of the genus Annona, all of them American in origin, are cultivated from Mexico to Peru. One of the best is the ilama (*A. diversifolia*), which is a lowland counterpart of the highland cherimoya. It grows in southern Mexico and Central America, and has recently been the recipient of horticultural attention in southern Florida. Another excellent species is *A. squamosa*, called in the British West Indies "sugar-apple," presumably because it is not an apple and is not made of sugar. This has long been grown in the Orient, where it is perhaps appreciated more than in the American tropics. The guanábana also has spread around the world.

Few other genera of tropical fruits offer such possibilities at the hands of the plant breeder as the Annonas. The fact that there is a considerable number of edible species differing widely in climatic requirements, means that hybridization, which has already received attention in Florida, may develop new forms of great interest; propagation by grafting is simple, and brings up the problem of which species to use as stock-plants.

THE MANGOSTEEN, QUEEN OF FRUITS

David Fairchild, who has probably done more than any other man to advance the cause of tropical American fruit growing, early chose the establishment of commercial mangosteen culture in this hemisphere as his particular hobby. He had learned to appreciate the fruit during a sojourn in Malaya back in the 1890's. Everyone who has heard of the mangosteen, and has not tasted it, is consumed with curiosity regarding the character of this oriental product which the early botanist Jacobus Bontius compared to nectar and ambrosia, declaring that it surpassed the golden apples of the Hesperides, whatever these are. For this reason Fairchild's description of the mangosteen is worthy of reproduction here:

"This delicious fruit is about the size of a mandarin orange, round and slightly flattened at each end, with a smooth, thick rind, rich purple-red in color, with here and there a bright, hardened drop of the yellow juice which marks some injury to the rind when it was young. As these mangosteens are sold in the Dutch East Indies—heaped up on fruit baskets, or made into long, regular bundles with thin strips of braided bamboo— they are as strikingly handsome as anything of the kind could well be; but it is only when the fruit is opened that its real beauty is seen. The rind is thick and tough, and in order to get at the pulp inside it requires a circular cut with a knife to lift the top half off like a cap, exposing the white segments, five, six or seven in number, lying loose in the cup. The cut surface of the rind is of a delicate pink color and is studded with small yellow points formed by the drops of exuding juice. As one lifts out of this cup, one by one, the delicate segments, which are the size and shape of those of a mandarin orange, the light pink sides of the cup and the veins of white and yellow embedded in it are visible. The separate segments are between snow white and ivory in color, and are covered with a delicate network of fibers, and the side of each segment where it presses against its neighbor tinged with green. The texture of the mango-steen pulp much resembles that of a well-ripened plum, only it is so delicate that it melts in the mouth like a bit of ice cream. The flavor is quite indescribably delicious."

Many years ago, the British made attempts to introduce the mangosteen (*Garcinia mangostana*) into their West Indian colonies. These attempts often failed because the seeds retain their viability only a short time, and it was (in those days) a long way from Rangoon or Bangkok to the Antilles. But a few specimens were established in Trinidad and in Jamaica. There, during the 1890's, others were propagated and distributed, one or two getting as far afield as the shores of Lake Izabal in Guatemala.

Aside from being hard to propagate, the mangosteen is rather difficult to grow, though not so difficult as was thought forty years ago. It is highly sensitive to cold,—resenting temperatures lower than 40 degrees F., —which has effectively prevented its establishment in southern Florida. Nevertheless, Doctor Fairchild and his colleagues in the United States Department of Agriculture at Washington succeeded in fostering the development of several small plantations in the Caribbean region, and a resident of the British island of Dominica made another. Today the largest mangosteen orchard in the western hemisphere is undoubtedly that which was established by the United Fruit Company at its Lancetilla Experiment Station in Honduras, planted in the late 1920's and now in full bearing.

Efforts have been made to impart greater vigor and hardiness to the mangosteen by grafting it onto other species of its genus. To date these have met with little or no success. The problem of seedling variation is of little importance, for the mangosteen, unlike most other fruit trees, comes true when grown from seed, and there are no superior forms crying for vegetative propagation.

But there are other problems, one of which is the long time it takes an orchard to come into bearing—anywhere from five to ten years, usually nearer the latter than the former.

Mangosteens have done well in the Canal Zone. There are several trees near Guayaquil, Ecuador, which have been in bearing for more than twenty years. Individual trees and small plantings now scattered throughout the West Indies and on the mainland from Guatemala to Ecuador provide the material on which an industry can be built, once satisfactory arrangements are made for importing the fruit into the United States. Shipment in cold storage presents no difficulties, but the fruit spoils quickly once it is removed to higher temperatures.

In any event, we have this consolation: mangosteens at last are growing in the Americas, where residents and visitors can have opportunity to taste the fruit which has been the recipient of more praise than any other pomological product of the tropics.

THE UBIQUITOUS GUAVA

This is the ugly duckling of its tribe. The bush is so common throughout tropical America as to be a weed in many places, and it takes a very courageous soul to go into ecstasies over the merits of the fruit. "It contains many seeds," wrote Oviedo in 1526, "or more properly speaking, it is full of small hard stones, and to those who are not used to eating the fruit these stones are sometimes troublesome." The odor of ripe guavas is so pungent as to have given rise to misconceptions, such as the one which occurred in New Jersey, where a box was shipped from Florida marked "Guavas; Perishable; No Delay." The agent of the express company waited several days for the consignee to show up; he then became alarmed and sent a postcard: "Please call for your guavas; I think he is dead."

Of course, there are many who like the guava (*Psidium guajava*), and might even agree with Oviedo, who wrote "to those familiar with it, the fruit is beautiful and appetizing." But its reputation as a desirable horticultural product is based on guava jelly, the *facile princeps* of its kind. Guava jelly is, in fact, unique in the jelly world, and is likely to meet with increasing consumption in northern countries. It is already the basis of an industry in Cuba, and might easily become so elsewhere, if the tropics can meet the competition of south Florida.

It need not be said that the guava, like some people in this world, must depend upon the reputation of its family for its position; but it has some very respectable relatives. There is, for example, the pitanga of Brazil (*Eugenia uniflora*), a small shrub which produces crimson fruits having somewhat the appearance of diminutive tomatoes. Instead of containing small hard stones, like the guava, each pitanga contains only one, and the flavor of the juicy pulp is spicy and aromatic. This last-named characteristic seems to be typical of most members of the family Myrtaceæ.

The pitanga is much used in its native country for jelly making. Still better, it is the basis of one of the most beautiful and delicious sherbets or water ices imaginable, orange-red in color, with a well-marked spicy flavor liked by everyone. The shrub is so widely adaptable and of such easy culture that it is likely to meet with increasing appreciation in tropical countries, few of which now grow it.

The jaboticaba (Myrciaria) is another of the myrtles native to Brazil, which country seems to have something of a monopoly on fruit-bearing species of this family. It is a beautiful tree, round-topped and spreading, with the peculiar habit of producing its fruits all along the trunk and

larger limbs instead of at the ends of the branches. Brazilians are extremely
fond of jaboticabas, which look and taste like grapes but do not come
in bunches.

Still another popular member of the tribe is the grumichama, sometimes called Brazilian cherry. The glossy-leaved tree, an ornament to any
garden, produces an abundance of dark red fruits strikingly suggestive
of the sweet cherries grown so extensively in the westen United States.
Botanically this plant is known as *Eugenia brasiliensis*.

With the exception of the lowly guava, the myrtles may not possess
attractive commercial possibilities, but their wider cultivation in tropical
gardens is strongly to be recommended, and certain to take place.

THE PAPAYA, BREAKFAST MELON OF THE TROPICS

Residents of the tropics have long since learned that good melons
cannot be produced in many places, but they have found a highly satisfactory substitute in the papaya. Residents of the United States have heard
of this fruit in recent years as the source of papain, an enzyme similar to
pepsin in its action. But there are not many dyspeptics in tropical
America; and the papaya (*Carica papaya*) will therefore continue to be
looked upon as one of the most popular breakfast fruits rather than the
answer to an invalid's prayer.

It grows, or can be grown, almost everywhere, but attains its highest
perfection only in rather dry climates. It has the great advantage of
coming into production within a year from the time the seed is sown,
and it bears prodigiously. It has only one disadvantage: It does not withstand shipment to great distances, which accounts for the fact that it has
never been placed on northern markets in profusion. Papayas grow well
in southern Florida, where a respectable little industry has developed in
recent years. But even from this nearby region, papayas cannot be shipped
to New York with much success. When ripe, the large hollow-centered
fruit breaks down rapidly with handling in the market; and if picked
green, in order to withstand shipment, it does not develop its best
flavor.

The health-faddists of California have attempted to furnish papayas,
for a consideration, to suffering Californian humanity; but the plant withstands very little frost, and rarely develops satisfactory flavor in that
climate. American residents of Hawaii are among the world's greatest
consumers of this fruit. The plant is well adapted to climatic and soil
conditions in that part of the world.

The native home of this peculiar species is not known with certainty.
There are botanists who hold that it is a hybrid whose parents still grow

wild in middle America. Certainly the behavior of the plant in cultivation is such as to suggest hybrid origin. Typically it is dioecious; that is, pistillate flowers, which are the only ones which develop into fruits, are borne upon one individual and staminate flowers upon another. The presence of both in the garden is necessary to insure fruit. But it is not unusual to see plants with flowers of both sexes, or even both sexes in the same flower; while it is reliably reported that a male plant, if cut back severely, may sprout up again as a female.

Because of these irregularities, perhaps the development of superior varieties through modern methods of plant breeding has been no simple task, though it has been attempted in Hawaii and elsewhere in recent years. Good strains seem to "run out" when grown from seed, and when grafted behave in a most peculiar manner.

GRAPES FOR THE TROPICS

To slake their honest Spanish thirst, the first colonists in the New World planned to grow grapes and make wine just as they had done at home. Something went wrong with the program. European vines did not prosper any more than they did when planted by the British, with a view to slaking their honest British thirst, in Virginia, the Carolinas, and Georgia. But the British had more imagination, in this instance, than the Spaniards. When they found they could not grow European grapes, they planted the native American species by which they were abundantly surrounded. In time there were developed, through hybridization and the selection of seedlings, the excellent grapes of our eastern states.

The Spanish went on trying to grow European grapes, or viniferas as they are known to horticulturists, and through a process of elimination eventually found that the possibilities of wine making were pretty definitely limited to Argentina, Chile, and Peru at one end of the hemisphere and to California and northern Mexico at the other.

Throughout the tropics proper, fungous diseases made the growing of viniferas difficult, and still do; but it has been discovered in relatively recent years that some of the American grapes can be grown here quite successfully. This is more than passing strange, when one remembers that the American grapes originated farther north than the viniferas; but it is true nevertheless.

A variety known as Isabella, believed to be a hybrid between vinifera and one of the American species, was the pioneer in the tropical field, and has served to demonstrate the possibilities of grape culture around the Caribbean. Isabella is a grape much like the well-known Concord. Europeans, who do not like American grapes in general because they are not so sweet as viniferas, and Latin Americans, who lean strongly in the same direction, do not take readily to the tartness of Isabella, but eventually learn to like it. Thus, in central Brazil and in the far-famed Cauca valley of Colombia, Isabella grapes are grown commercially on quite a respectable scale. Isabella is doing the pioneering in a field which holds great promise. Think what American grapes have done for our eastern states; think of Concord and Catawba, think of the wines of Lake Cayuga, think of Virginia Dare.

Attracted by the possibilities of grape culture in southern Florida once suitable varieties could be produced, an enthusiastic young horticulturist, Joseph L. Fennell of Miami, went to work a few years ago and has been producing hybrids which bid fair to place tropical grape culture on a sound basis. All around the Caribbean there grows a wild species, *Vitis tiliæfolia*, which is as much at home in the tropics as a sunflower is on the Kansas prairies; and this, when crossed with fine European varieties, is giving rise to new sorts of excellent quality and tropical habits. Florida and Mexico have furnished other wild forms for the breeding program which Fennell is now carrying out at the Instituto Interamericano de Ciencias Agrícolas in Costa Rica.

TWO FAVORITES OF THE AZTECS

When Cortés made his famous march from Mexico City to the Gulf of Honduras, to find that other Spaniards had already taken over the conquering business and were making a pretty good job of it, he and his companions were able to survive hard months in the trackless jungles of Petén only because there was an abundance of the wild fruit known to the Aztecs as *tzapotl*, and most probably, the *tzicotzapotl*, or gum-producing tzapotl. They simplified the names to zapote and chico-zapote, and did not realize that the latter would eventually become known to every American stenographer as the source of chewing gum.

The importance of chewing gum must not be allowed to detract from the importance of the chico-zapote (or sapodilla, as it is called in Florida) as a fruit. It is definitely good—the best of its family, which is a group of tropical American trees of which five or more are cultivated in various countries.

Thomas Firminger, a great British horticulturist who lived in India and wrote a standard textbook on tropical horticulture, said of the sapodilla (*Achras Sapota*), "A more luscious, cool, and agreeable fruit is not to be met with in this or perhaps any country in the world." This is a sound, sensible, carefully worded statement, interesting to compare with the more poetic French outlook of Michel Etienne Descourtilz, who said it

PLATE 1. Two native markets in Highland Guatemala

PLATE 2. Upper left—Sapodilla, a foremost tropical fruit
Upper right—Mango, a new fruit for the Americas
Lower left—Kaki, another new fruit
Lower right—Bacába, a fruit of the deep tropics

has "the sweet perfumes of honey, jasmine, and lily of the valley." After all, one might not care to eat lilies-of-the-valley indefinitely.

If one still remains skeptical regarding the merits of the sapodilla, he has only to talk with residents of the Florida Keys. There is perhaps no other place in which finer specimens are produced—fine large round or oblate fruits, up to four inches in diameter, rusty brown on the outside, with melting sugary pulp and few seeds. The tree is handsome, is easy to grow, and has the advantage that it withstands the force of hurricanes better than many others, which may account in part for its popularity on the Keys.

Twenty-five years ago, P. J. Wester and Edward Simmonds found at Miami that the sapodilla can be propagated readily by grafting. Perpetuation of choice seedling forms thus became a simple matter, but it has not yet been practiced to any great extent. It is something which will come.

The zapote (*Calocarpum mammosum*), big brother of the sapodilla, is perhaps not quite so delicious, though here as in most other cases, much depends upon the variety. Though it is native to Mexico and central America, Cuba is the country where it has met with the greatest popular approval, and those inimitable artists, the proprietors of Havana cafés, have learned to prepare a zapote sherbet which is excellent.

THE PEJIBAYE OR PEACH PALM

The classic conception of the past century—that the tropics are lands where the indolent native, reclining comfortably in his hammock, has only to reach out his hand at dinner-time and pluck a ripe banana from an overhanging stem—has required revision in recent years. In the first place, tree-ripened bananas are not much good; they have to be picked when green and ripened in the shade. And in the second place, we eat our bread by the sweat of our brows in pretty nearly all parts of the modern world.

But there are crops which, without much effort on the part of man, add to the food supply of the tropics: an avocado tree in the dooryard; a breadfruit tree or two (if one likes his carbohydrates in that form); some plantains and bananas; and the pejibaye or peach palm, solice of the aboriginal inhabitants of Costa Rica, of the Orinoco, and the Amazon since time immemorial.

Just why the pejibaye should have remained in relative obscurity is hard to understand. For here is a species which is easily propagated from seed, which requires practically no cultural attention, and which produces annually a hundred pounds or more of fruits which when boiled in salted water taste like chestnuts. These fruits contain quite a good amount of fat, which is one of the scarcest elements in the tropical dietary, as well as some thirty-five per cent of carbohydrates to give the farmer strength to go out and plant more pejibayes.

It required a considerable flight of the imagination to dub this plant "peach palm." Its fruit may look somewhat like a peach—a very small peach—but there the resemblance begins and ends. It is the size of an apricot, and contains a single stone like the latter, but the flesh is farinaceous instead of juicy and subacid.

Countries like Puerto Rico, where there are more people than land, would do well to think of the pejibaye. Four or five palms in the dooryard of every inhabitant would do much to relieve the pressure on wheat flour, imported butter, and canned peas. When the Spaniards colonized Costa Rica, they found the aboriginal inhabitants living largely on pejibayes during part of each year, and it did not seem to affect their fighting qualities in the slightest.

Botanically this palm is known as *Guilielma utilis*. There are seedless varieties in Costa Rica, though their seedlessness may be the result of some environmental influence. Little or nothing has been done to search for the best pejibayes and propagate them by suckers, as was done with the date palm.

2

Maize in the New World

By *EDGAR ANDERSON*
GENETICIST, MISSOURI BOTANICAL GARDEN AND
PROFESSOR OF BOTANY AT WASHINGTON UNIVERSITY

THE subject of tropical fruits is enormous. So is the subject of maize, or corn. The two subjects have several other basic features in common and in continuity. Both are pioneer fields about which Americans generally are only now beginning to realize how little we know. Both are pioneering realms of great significance to the development and improvement of other crops, and to the health and good lives of some quarter-billion residents of this hemisphere. And like the resources of fruits, the maizes are also highly malleable in the skilled hands of horticulturists and geneticists.

Edgar Anderson, Guggenheim fellow, geneticist to the Missouri Botanical Garden and Englemann professor of botany at Washington University, is an internationally respected authority on corn. He insists with almost passionate modesty that he probably knows as much as anybody else in the world about what is not known about corn. To this we insistently add that probably he knows as much as anybody else in the world of what is known about corn, and that he helps effectively in finding out more.

The Americas gave the maizes to ourselves and the world. The various corn strains developed by pre-Columbus Americans now provide the foremost field crop of the United States and the foremost food crop of the Americas south of the Rio Grande. In the United States the greater part of our gigantic corn crop goes for feeding livestock and factories, and thus reaches the every-day consumer as beef, pork, lamb, poultry, eggs, butter, milk, and hundreds of industrial products. In the neighboring Americas corn goes principally and directly as the life-maintaining food for tens of millions of our fellows. As Dr. Anderson explains, corn is a comparatively old American crop which is now impressively and decisively new. But let the authority speak!

2

As a world crop, maize [1] is a prenomenon so enormous that it is almost impossible to see it in perspective. No other crop is so manifold and so uncharted. Its very pre-eminence has kept the facts about it from being recorded and collected. The job is too big for any one man; there is too much maize used in too many ways by too many people. Wheat, too, is a great world crop. It has three main races and numerous sub-races, but these entities have all been given names and their distribution has been recorded. The sorghums of the world belong to a whole group of species and hybrids between them, but there are books which describe the resulting confusion in some detail and even a modern monograph which brings all the outstanding facts together. Maize defies such codification. It grows in the tropics along with the sugar canes and bamboos. It is found doing well in the temperate zone with wheat and other small grains. For the crop as a whole, we have only a few general figures on world production and scattered papers and books on such subjects as "Maize Growing in South Africa," "Maize in the American Cornbelt," "The Sweet Corns of New York State." As yet, no one has attempted to give even a brief description of the maize of the world and what the main kinds are and where they grow.

So it is that one may spend his life studying *Zea Mays*, the giant and ineredible grass which we Americans refer to as corn, and yet know very little about the world crop as a whole—where it is grown or what is done

[1] The maize plant is the subject of a dual terminology, that of the laboratory and that of the farm. Maize is a grass; therefore for scientific precision we must sometimes use the technical words invented for grass descriptions. But maize is also a familiar plant to the American farmer, and he has evolved a set of his own terms. In the following description technical terms are italicized and the commonly used words of the American corn belt are in bold face. Maize always has a jointed, upright, main stem or **stalk**. This may give rise at the base to side branches (**tillers**). At the top of the stalk the *male inflorescence*, the **tassel**, forms a large branched *panicle*. The *female flowers* which ripen eventually into the **kernels** (*grains*) are borne in a compact *inflorescence*, the **ear**. It is actually at the summit of a short-stalked side branch but the protective leaves which cover it (the **husks**) usually conceal that fact. When a maize plant flowers, the **tassels** shed their *pollen*, which is caught upon the **silks** (*styles*) which protrude from the husks. Each silk leads back to a single kernel on the ear.

with the grain and the plant after it is harvested. He most certainly will not even know what in general the plant looks like in the various countries where it is an important crop. Maize plants in the corn belt are one thing, in Mexico quite another or rather a whole set of other things, and still quite another set in the highlands of Peru or in the mountains of Maylasia. You, by chance, may have spent years growing or studying this plant. Did you know that on the mountainous island of Madura, just off the coast of Java, a small-grained popcorn is the main food of the aboriginal population? Or that in the mountains around Mexico City maize is a coarse and hairy plant with sloppy leaves and only a few branches to the tassels; that along the west coast of Mexico it is prevailingly a tough slender plant with a big, wiry tassel; or that in parts of Mexico it is grown for the fungi which live upon it and that these are pulled off and sold in the market?

Perhaps one reason why no one has taken up the difficult task of classifying all the maize of the world, is that many authorities assume it has been done. In the late 1880's, E. Lewis Sturtevant, the director of the first American Agricultural Experiment Station, published a series of papers in which all the maize then at his disposal was put in five main pigeonholes, each of which was provided with a Latin name. A careful reading of Sturtevant's papers will show that he was under no illusion about the system he set up. It was a purely artificial catalog, based upon whether the kernels were hard starch (flinty), soft starch (floury), hard starch capped by soft starch (dent), or sweet or waxy, or whether they had little separate coverings on each grain (pod corn), or whether they were popcorns. This system served as a useful way of indexing a collection of maize, but in many Mexican granaries it would separate the kernels on any single ear into two or three different categories and put them alongside corn from the United States, with which they had little in common aside from the texture of their kernels. It was in fact, something like an attempt to classify the peoples of Europe on nothing but eye color, ignoring differences in stature, in head shape, in hair texture, and in skin color.

This is particularly true of the classes based upon floury vs. flint, and either of these vs. pod corn or sweet corn. We now know that all of these are single unit hereditary differences, that there is a strong possibility of their originating many times and in many places, and that they are not of fundamental importance in setting up a world classification. Good old Dr. Sturtevant realized these facts himself, but since he dignified his pigeonholes with Latin names like Zea everta and Zea amyplacea, many uncritical students of maize were led astray. Popcorns and dent corns, however, are somewhat more important in distinguishing fundamental differences between different races of maize. Popcorns are hard, small-kerneled, very flinty corns which explode when heated. Unfortunately, they do not constitute a good unit for classification, since there are different kinds of popcorn and about the only thing which some of them have in common is their ability to pop. In Mexico, for instance, the two most extreme types of maize in the entire country are popcorns. One is the white rice pointed popcorn, common in Toluca and in other regions near Mexico City. The other is the ancient *Maíz Reventador* of western Jalisco. All that these two sorts have in common is that they are small grained and that they will pop when heat is applied. The rice pops have wide weak leaves which break in the wind. They have shallow roots and lodge badly; *Maíz Reventador* has stiff narrow leaves and deep, tough roots. The rice pops have short, sharply tapering ears, with a very high number of rows of kernels; *Maíz Reventador* has a long, narrow, cigar-shaped ear which tapers gradually to both ends, and only a medium number of rows.

The dent corns, however, are all evidently related, or at least those in North America are. We do not yet know how and when dent corn originated, but in its most extreme form denting is today particularly characteristic of the central Mexican plateau, and it seems to radiate from it in all directions. A dent kernel has hard starch around the sides and soft starch at the tip, so that as the kernel matures, the tip collapses, leaving a little depression. The size and shape of this depression will vary with different kinds of dent corns; it may be a smooth little bowl, or it may be deep or shallow. Its surface may be wrinkled and rough and the bowl edges may have collapsed against one another, leaving a protruding tip. Whatever their origin, the dent corns are of particular interest because they are associated with productivity. Not all dent corns are highly productive, but nearly all of the world's highly productive varieties are dent corns. In the great American corn belt, a field corn which is not a dent is a curiosity.

One of the greatest achievements in modern plant breeding is the development of these golden yellow dent corns of the American corn belt. There was nothing like them a century ago—the cylindrical ear, well filled out at butt and tip, with golden yellow kernels high in food value, soft enough to feed directly to livestock if need be but hard enough to discourage insect attack. This new type did not spring into being at any one time or any one place; it was gradually and painfully evolved during the westward agricultural expansion of the nineteenth century. Farmers moving westward brought along the varieties they had been cultivating in New York State or Massachusetts or Virginia or North Carolina. In the new Midwest they found still other types of maize which the earliest white settlers had picked up from the Indians of that region. Sometimes these varied sorts were planted together on purpose, with the hope that they might cross; more frequently the old eastern variety did not take kindly to the new environment and only part of the seedlings pulled through. Then the settler planted the blank spaces with local corn obtained from his neighbors, and the different kinds grew together in the same field and crossed back and forth. This is more than mere speculation; we know that James Reid's famous yellow dent originated in just this fashion, and the same general process must have happened again and again as the corn belt was settled. Gradually the new type evolved out of the various mixtures.

As the rich black-soiled region developed, more and more of the corn was used for stock feeding; and by trial and error as each farmer saved the seeds for his next year's crop, a more or less definite ideal came into being and was deliberately bred for. It had the denting and the high row number of the dent corns, which have been spreading northward from the central Mexican plateau since some nearly prehistoric time. It had the long cob and the straight rows and the big kernels which apparently trace back to somewhere in Guatemala and which were already to be found in the flint corns of the eastern states. Not every farmer had the same notion as to just how the corn should look. Some bred for a rough-surfaced dent, some for a smooth. Some desired a red cob, some a white, and there were many minor differences of opinion about the best kernel shape and whether the ears should be low or high in the stalk. Every farmer had his own hunches, but when one was right (or perhaps just plain lucky) he produced a superior strain; and some of his neighbors recognized the fact and started buying their seed corn from him. Just as soon as the real worth of the new variety was recognized, it would be tried out very widely and then new sub-strains would begin to appear on the market. Reid's yellow dent, for instance, traveled to Iowa and Kansas and Indiana, and was even sent back to the eastern seaboard; and selections from it became Black Yellow Dent, McCulloch's Yellow Dent, and many other varieties.

This whole pattern of maize improvement with its national corn shows and its world's prize ears of corn and its local corn breeders in nearly every community vanished almost overnight when hybrid corn finally demonstrated its worth in the corn belt. Like most radical changes, hybrid corn had to make its way against incredulity and indifference and ridicule. From the early 1900's, when East and Shull suggested a new way of breeding maize, a quarter of a century and the work of hundreds of investigators had to go into the project before the new idea became popular.

Edward M. East was a cocky young investigator at the Illinois Experiment Station when he first suggested to Director Hopkins that the corn breeding program was being prosecuted "wrong end to." East had been trained as a chemist and he admittedly knew relatively little about corn at that time, but he had a keen analytical mind, brilliant in its capacity for common sense. He grasped the way in which the precise techniques worked out for breeding the small grains such as wheat and oats would have to be modified if we were to have standardized, productive fields of maize. Unlike most of the small grains, maize is almost completely cross-pollinated. Even the most highly selected varieties of that day were highly variable, and any attempts to standardize them cut down productivity. It was already abundantly clear that maize did not seem to thrive when it was inbred. East's revolutionary solution of this dilemma was to go right on inbreeding nevertheless, to establish as many inbred lines as possible, and then to restore their productivity by crossing them back together again.

It sounded like a fool idea, and most experts laughed openly at the determined young chemist and at mild-mannered Dr. Shull, who advanced similar theories at the same time. Even when the two young men backed up their theories with data, practical men were not convinced that hybrid corn could be made to pay in dollars and cents. So Dr. Shull went on to study other matters, and Dr. East and his colleagues and students, Jones, Emerson, Hayes, and Mangelsdorf, worked out the kinks in the method. Hybrid corn "caught on" slowly year by year until its great advantages for modern standardized, mechanized farming were adequately demonstrated, and then the whole corn belt switched to hybrid corn almost overnight.

It is a weird method of crop improvement, looked at from the sidelines. No wonder practical men thought it a college professor's pipe dream. The young tassels of the parent stock are confined in big paper bags to catch the pollen; the young silks are protected in other bags, and each plant is pollinated with its own pollen. Next year's crop is grown from this incestuous mating, and the line is carried on year after year. Sterile plants, freaks, and dwarfs turn up and are discarded. Few of the inbreds are kept for any time, but from the lot by trial and error, by careful planning and good luck a set of inbreds is at length built up with the capacity for combining well when planted with each other. Four-way crosses are the commonest commercial method at the present time, which means that for every hybrid variety sold to the farmer, the breeder must have a quartet of four inbred varieties.

The actual hybrid seed is two years in the making, even after the inbred varieties are established. Let us refer to the four inbreds in each quartet, as A, B, C, and D. The first year A and B are grown together in one isolated plot, and C and D in another. Crossing them is carried out wholesale by the whole field and is done in a very simple fashion. Let us suppose that in the first field inbred A is the better pollen producer and inbred B makes the better seed parent. Variety A is planted regularly every other row, or every few rows with variety B in between. Then when the tassels begin to develop, the tassels are pulled out of all the B plants. This means that a little later when the tassels blossom and the golden pollen sifts down across the field every morning, it is all A pollen, and the crop from the B plants is all hybrid, B × A. In a similar fashion C is crossed with D in another isolated plot. The second year A × B and C × D are grown together. Since they are both hybrids, they make splendid growth and set fine big ears. The seedsman gets a big crop of double hybrid seed to sell, A × B and C × D, though by the time it gets on the market it usually has lost its pedigree and is presented to the world as Pioneer 836, or Funk's 91, as the case may be.

It has the vigor of a hybrid; and if it has been properly selected for the region where it is grown, it makes a fine crop. The actual yield is not phenomenally higher, or at least not higher than that previously achieved by the best farmers in the locality, though like many hybrids it is more independent of opportunity and stands up better in years that are too dry or too wet. Its greatest advantage perhaps is that remarkable uniformity which so impressed young Edward East when he first experimented with crossed corn. The tremendous variability which has always characterized maize is masked by this system of breeding, and a field of hybrid maize is as uniform as a field of wheat. In these days of power machinery and mass production and scarcity of farm labor, that counts as much as the yield. It is a standardized crop giving a standardized harvest, ripening uniformly, bearing its ears at the same height, and ears of the same size, moreover. And the one disadvantage, the fact that it will not breed true, has been a blessing in disguise. The inbreds remain in the hands of the breeder; he can create the hybrid anew year after year, and every year the farmer must come to him for his seed. At last we have a system by which a clever plant breeder is well paid for his trouble, and the hybrid corn business now is a Big Business in the American corn belt. A whole group of corn breeding corporations is improving the American corn crop and raising American corn productivity, and is making an honest profit in doing so.

In the United States maize is grown on a gigantic scale. We are now producing two to three billions of bushels each year, and the maize crop is our greatest natural resource. We lead the world in maize production, but as a people we ignore it pretty completely. This is because the bulk of the American crop is transformed into other products, and when maize comes within the orbit of our lives (as it does many times each day) it is no longer labeled as maize. Only a selected few have the information and the imagination really to understand the major role it plays in our national life. The cows eat maize ensilage, and we have cream for our coffee and butter for our bread; the hog eats corn, and we are served with bacon. Milk, meat, and eggs take the bulk of the American crop. Only a fraction is left over for the industry, but that fraction serves us in a variety of ways. When you lick a postage stamp, the adhesive most likely came from a corn plant. If you buy a candy bar, it is probably from one-third to ninety percent corn. If you take a vitamin tablet, the yeast whose dried extract gives the tablet its potency was cultured in corn steep water. The packaged powder which the cook whipped up into a caramel pudding was elaborated in its entirely from various corn by-products. The plastic comb in your hair, the very tires on your automobile may be made in part from atoms yoked together in the maize plant. For that is what maize is in the modern world—our most efficient single source of useful molecules.

A good cornfield in the American corn belt is putting together more useful molecules per man-hour per acre than can be obtained in any other way. As modern technology advances, we will have more and more new uses for the maize plant, since it is such an efficient source of organic molecules. There are only three possible sources: coal, petroleum, and plant products. Of plant products two are outstanding: maize and molasses. The latter products cannot be used for as many processes as maize, and owe their pre-eminence not to their efficiency but to cheap labor in the regions where they are produced.

Useful though we find the maize plant in modern technology, it is difficult to predict in what new ways we shall be trying it out tomorrow. World War II, for instance, cut off our sources of commercial tapioca almost overnight. One of the few substances which can be substituted for it is a gummy kind of maize, technically known as waxy maize, and previously known only as a curiosity. One of the most fascinating stories in modern plant breeding is the way in which Dr. Merle Jenkins and a group of associates in the United States Department of Agriculture built up this freak corn to a productive field crop which was actually grown on a commercial scale by 1943. Whether or not it actually will be able to compete economically with tapioca (or with the new waxy sorghums) in peace-times, it has given us a breathtaking view of what maize breeding may well become. Waxy maize, the chemists now tell us, differs from normal maize in the molecular structure of its carbohydrates. It seems highly possible, therefore, that in the food chemistry or the industrial chemistry of day after tomorrow when a particular kind of carbohydrate molecule may be desired, waxy maize may play a unique role.

With the industrial chemists able to break down and spin out their molecules in new kinds of ways, and with plant breeders able to present different kinds of maize molecules as raw products to the chemists, it is hard to predict in what ways we may be using the bulk of the world's maize crop in 1950 or 1960. As Henry Wallace said most prophetically in 1934, "Most farmers still look on corn as corn. But those who have worked with corn and studied it in all its intimate details for many years realize that corn is not merely corn. It is a composite of many things and can be molded in many directions. The possibilities with corn are almost as infinite as with humanity itself. The past 60 years are a mere beginning. The future is limitless as long as our desires are keen and our minds are open."

In the southwestern United States maize reverts to its rightful place as the traditional crop of the Indians. Indian cornfields are small for the most part, and they are fearfully far between by comparison with the corn belt, but the corn grown in them is no less remarkable.

But before discussing the corn grown by the Indians, we must first insert a word of caution. Finding out what kind of maize is being grown is a very different proposition in the Indian Southwest from what it is in the corn belt. In some tribes, for instance, it is taboo to discuss maize at all at certain times of the year. If an ignorant investigator does not know this fact, he may come away with the notion that the Indians have very little corn and that they know very little about corn growing. And even if the Indians whom he questions have broken away from the old tribal customs, enough of the taboo will have persisted so that they feel it is bad manners to ask such questions at such times of the year, and they will be loathe to give very much information.

That is not the only source of error in the white man's notion of what Indian corn is like. The Indians have long since learned that their discards can be palmed off upon him, and much of the corn that is sold at Indian pueblos is from the actual discard piles. While it is true that some tribes take little pride in their corn, many of those in the Southwest are very careful to keep their stocks pure. After the harvest, the corn is sorted over and ears which show different-colored grains are laid aside and not saved for next year's crop. The Indians soon learned that these parti-colored ears took the tourist's eye and that he would even pay extra for them. So in more than one pueblo now the good unmixed ears go into the storage rooms for use during the year and for seed for next year's crop, while the gaily speckled discards are solemnly sold to tourists as genuine Indian corn. So commonly is this done that even intelligent travelers who take more than a passing interest in the maize of the Indians are too often misled.

Speaking very broadly, there are two main Indian cultures in the Southwest, and each has its own race of maize. There are the Indians of the plateaus who live in apartment-house villages or pueblos, and there are the Papago and their relatives who live (or recently lived) in more or less scattered single-family houses on the desert. The Navajo and other professional war-makers who have taken to agriculture only since the Conquest, have borrowed corn from their neighbors, and this blurs the picture somewhat, as do various commercial strains brought in by Spanish-American communities and by Yankee farmers. But by and large, the corn picture in the Southwest is not greatly different today from what it was in 1500. The pueblo Indians grow maize of many colors and of distinctly different flavors, but it is prevailingly large cobbed and many rowed, and a majority of the ears show a perceptible dent in some or all of the kernels. The maize of the Papago is more uniform and belongs to another race of corn. It is usually white or yellow and is generally small cobbed; the husks are so tight that the ear tapers nearly as much to the base as to the tip, and the wrinkles in the cobs make fine striations along the surface of the kernels as they develop.

In the better pueblos several different varieties of maize are recognized, and they are used for special purposes. Among the Hopi, for instance, a good farmer would have at least four or five varieties all carefully kept separate, each known by a special name and generally used for a special purpose. He would certainly be growing a broad-eared, soft white flour corn which forms the main food of the people. He might have dye corn with kernels the color of a black sweet cherry set on a reddish purple cob. It is not preferred for eating since it stains the mouth, but it is used as a dye for baskets and textiles and is made into a body paint used in ceremonial dances. He would certainly be growing one or more varieties of the blue corn used in making the famous *piki* bread, the most beautiful aboriginal food in the New World. A very thin dough is spattered against a hot stone griddle and then pulled off almost immediately. It forms a cake or wafer larger than a large pancake, but thin as parchment paper. It smells like popcorn and is crisp and toothsome. It can be made directly from the blue corn, or a pinch of alkali may have been added as well. While the *piki* is still hot it is rolled up into a convenient size for eating. A plateful of these rolls looks more like a display of pastel-tinted tissue papers than it does like a plate of corn wafers.

While some of their relatives, such as the Pima, no longer live right out on the desert, the modern Papago are to be found living almost as their ancestors did. They use the desert crops of mesquite pods and cactus fruits and cultivate their drought-resisting crops in the midst of the desert heat. If possible they build long low ridges of earth so that when the scattered showers of midsummer come—if they do come—the water will be brought and held at a central point. When it finally sinks into the ground, they plant their corn and beans and squashes in the mud while it is still wet and hope for another rain in the same area. If they are unlucky, there may be no other rain before the crop matures; but even under these conditions some of the corn may give a usable return. Or even worse, they may have a cloudburst which will drown out the crop and wash away the earthworks. But if they are lucky and at least one more good rain falls after the crop has been planted, then early October will find the slender corn plants growing thriftily in a field of handsome squash vines.

In Mexico, as in the United States, maize is the most important crop. But in Mexico the bulk of the crop is eaten directly and there is not a Mexican who does not understand that his country's prosperity depends upon the corn crop. In the all too frequent years when the crop is not big enough to meet the country's needs, part of the people must go hungry, and even the big metropolitan newspapers carry news of the corn crop on the first page, day after day and month after month. In buses, on trains, in the marketplace, along the streets, and in the fields and homes, it is for the country as a whole the commonest topic of conversation—what the harvest is like, what the price is here and in the next village and in the big cities, what the prospects are for next year, and where the best place is to buy it or sell it.

The student of maize finds Mexico a wonderful land in which to travel. Literally everyone is interested in maize, and nearly everyone has useful information to contribute. Farmers, as might be expected, are full of data on what kinds of corn are grown in their district (no mean accomplishment in Mexico, where a single village can have more main types of corn than are found in all of the United States), and housewives can list the seemingly endless variety of dishes made from maize. More surprising is that elegant city bankers, with degrees from the Sorbonne, should be quite as much interested, and that even foppish students from the University should galvanize into conversational activity at the first mention of maize, and discourse learnedly and at great length on its history and its impact upon Mexican life.

The following list is the result of one such conversation. It was dictated by a woman from the state of Jalisco and it represents the foods made with maize which came immediately to mind. They are all well known in her part of Jalisco (the region around Tapalpa).

Esquite—salted, toasted kernels of corn.

Roscas—popcorn balls made with brown sugar syrup and *Maíz Reventador*.

Sopitas de elotes—sweet cakes made with a meal obtained from ripening green corn.

atole—maize gruel flavored in various ways.

pinole—parched corn ground to a fine powder, and sweetened and flavored.

gorditas—cornmeal cakes cooked in fat.

tamales—cakes of cornmeal rolled in a corn husk and boiled. May be flavored with sweets for use as a dessert. May be mixed with meat, or may be very hot with chile.

posole—a rich, nourishing stew made with hominy, usually with meat.

tortilla—the universal wafer-thin pancake, made with a special meal (*masa*—freshly prepared every day).

Any part of Mexico would seemingly yield a list just as long, or even longer, but many of the maize dishes prepared in one part of the country would be very different or completely unknown in another. In maize as in many other matters, Mexico is in truth as in name the United States of Mexico, and the maize of one state may be quite different from that of another.

There are innumerable varieties of maize in Mexico, but most of them fall into four main races. One of these four is centered around Mexico City. In the field it looks unkempt because it is shallow rooted and is readily blown over by the wind. Its broadish leaves are not very tough, and by the end of the season they are badly broken and hang in disconsolate tatters. The leaves are usually hairy, are often flushed with purple or red, and the tassel is made up of a few coarse branches. The ears are short and many rowed, and often taper sharply to the tip. The kernels are of many colors, though white is the commonest, and they are dented or pointed or both. Whatever its origin, it seems to be the center from which all the dent corns of North America have been ultimately derived.

On the west coast of Mexico a very different race of maize is to be found. It is tall, slender, and tough, with stems which stand up well in spite of wind and rain. The leaves do not break readily and the slender tassels are made up of many wiry branches. The ears are prevailingly fewer rowed. Many are undented; a deeply dented grain is very unusual, and pointed ones are almost unknown. In Chiapas a third type is found with ears having large kernels and with a strong heavy ear stalk nearly as wide as the ear itself. The fourth type is found only in mountainous regions and is often more or less hybridized with Mexican dents or popcorns. In its purest form it is a quickly maturing plant with small ears of bright yellow kernels. Like yellow corn generally, it is high in nutritional value and in parts of Mexico this is so commonly recognized that the knobby little ears of mountain yellow corn sell at a premium for use in fattening livestock.

Some Mexican varieties show these four basic types in almost pure form; many others are more or less mongrelized as is generally true of races, whether they be of maize or of man. Mexico's most important corn-growing district, the Bajio (literally the low place), is a series of low plateaus surrounded by higher ones and centered on the state of Guanajuato. It grows a series of varieties which are almost exactly intermediate between the maize of western Mexico and that of the high plateaus around Mexico City. They are white dent corns, but not so deeply dented or with such pointed grains as those near the capital city. The ears taper, but on the average not so sharply, and the plants are tougher and more deeply rooted.

The dent corns certainly seem to have originated in central Mexico and to have spread from there in all directions, though there is another clustering of them way to the south in Bolivia. But maize itself—where did it come from? Certainly a giant and peculiar grass like *Zea Mays* could not just spring into being without leaving behind any traces of its creation! Yet search as we will, there is even yet little evidence on that subject, and some of it is conflicting. Maize is found only in cultivation. Left to itself, it may volunteer for a year or so in a forest clearing before it is at length blotted out by more aggressive plants. Though a truly wild Zea may be discovered day after tomorrow, all that have been reported up to the present have turned out to be nothing more than cultivated maize persisting for a few seasons in the wild. If it is true that man cannot live without maize, it seems to be quite as true that maize cannot live without man.

When we look for close relatives among the indigenous floras of the world, the evidence is again disappointingly meager. There is a group of bony-seeded grasses in the Burma-Indochina area, most of them at least occasionally cultivated and none of them looking at all like maize, though apparently the technical evidences of their relationship are indisputable. In the New World there is a genus known as Tripsacum with one highly variable species in the valley of the Mississippi, another in the valley of the Amazon, and various species in between. Then there is teosinte, *Euchlæna mexicana*, whose relationship to maize is unquestioned by scientist and native American alike (the name comes from the two Aztec words *teo* and *zintle*, and means "Maize of the Gods").

But teosinte is quite as much a mystery as maize itself. A common weed in maize fields in certain parts of Central America, it has never been found as an unquestioned component of the native flora. To be sure, it does indeed exist in extensive areas in Guatemala in places where there are no fields of maize, but where there were very certainly plenty of maize fields in the not too remote past. Teosinte is a giant grass, very much like a more slender, bushier, tougher maize until it ripens its ear. The ears are small and very much branched, with little pearl-like grains, and they are vastly inferior to the big, productive ear of maize. Because teosinte is so much like maize and can cross with it so readily, more than one person has hazarded a guess that it might be one of corn's primitive ancestors.

Two Texas investigators, Mangelsdorf and Reeves, threw a bombshell into this theory in 1941, when they advanced the novel theory that the relationship was the other way around, that maize came first and that teosinte was a secondary phenomenon. Though their theory has not been universally accepted by maize experts, it has won increasing respect, particularly as more and more data of various kinds are shown to be more readily explained by it than by any other theory. To account for teosinte they pointed to their own success in hybridizing maize and Tripsacum, the other American relative of maize. Could Tripsacum possibly have played a role in the origin of teosinte and have contributed indirectly to the phenomenal variability of modern maize? It would hardly seem possible from the looks of the plant. Aside from the fact that Tripsacums are likewise a grass, they do not look like corn, and the minute technical differences are quite as great as those in general habit and superficial appearance. It seems incredible that they could even be artificially hybridized with maize, but Mangelsdorf and Reeves did so and also succeeded in crossing this nearly sterile hybrid back to maize.

Since several species of giant Tripsacums are known from Central

America and since they often grow in the vicinity of maize fields, these Texas investigators imagined that among the millions of pollen grains blown about for hundreds of growing seasons, at least once a Tripsacum pollen grain might have landed upon the silk of a maize ear, fertilized it, and produced a hybrid plant. The hybrid would have been a strong weed, a perennial with creeping rootstocks, and quite capable of shifting for itself along the border of a maize field for a good many seasons. During all the years it persisted there its pollen grains would have blown across the nearby maize fields season after season, and among them there might well have been one which produced a new kind of maize—a maize of hybrid origin, approximately eighty percent maize and twenty percent Tripsacum—in other words, teosinte.

This startling theory has not yet been proved, but more evidence in its favor accumulates every year. However, it tells us relatively little about the origin of *Zea Mays;* it merely directs us away from the blind alley labeled "teosinte." If teosinte arose from corn, rather than corn from teosinte, where then are we to look for the origin of maize itself? Mangelsdorf and Reeves suggested the Amazon basin, and there are certainly some very primitive types of maize growing in that region. Other experts have revived the claims of the Andean highlands and the Guatemalan region. It is true that maize is highly variable in each of these places. Mangelsdorf himself has shown that there is as much variability in one state in Guatemala as in all of North America put together.

Yet in all this variability there is nothing approaching some of the peculiar sorts which are known only from the highlands of South America. More recently Anderson has even revived the suggestion of a pre-Columbian transfer across the Pacific. He has found strong resemblances between a primitive type of maize from Peru and Chile and a strange sort introduced into China from the hills of Upper Burma, and concludes that before we can discuss the question intelligently we shall have to make a careful survey of oriental as well as occidental varieties. Maize crosses so readily with any new varieties which are brought in from the outside that a determination of pre-Columbian transfer date would be difficult indeed, and determining the direction in which the transfer took place might be quite impossible.

So for the present we must accept the fact that the origin of maize remains a puzzle. Maize might even have come from the Old World at a very remote time; it may quite possibly have mixed with Tripsacum in the New World and bred a new weed, teosinte, into being. Nobody can answer these questions for certain today, but much new work is being done, and tomorrow we shall be able to answer at least some of them.

3

The Fashioning of Livestock Breeds

By *ALBERT O. RHOAD*

DIRECTOR, IBERIA LIVESTOCK EXPERIMENT FARM,
UNITED STATES DEPARTMENT OF AGRICULTURE

NO discussion or exposition of new crops for the New World would be complete or even well started without mention of the new livestock crops. For livestock is a gyroscope and assurance of valid agriculture and replenishment of soil fertility. It is a more or less endearing expedience for changing casual, bulky vegetation into invaluable concentrations of meat, milk, wool, leather, and scores of other animal products that are indispensable to a good life. In a sense good livestock is valuable conversion machinery. But it is much more than machinery; it is ever-interesting and challenging life which stimulates the creative urge of man to develop from the mysteries of blood and the magic of chromosomes a more perfect living animal than ever walked before.

Corn and other grasses are agronomic indispensables to livestock for the Americas. In the following chapter Albert O. Rhoad, director of the United States Department of Agriculture's Iberia Livestock Experiment Farm, and one of our most distinguished authorities on animal husbandry, discusses challengingly the current progress in shaping breeds of livestock to fit the varying domestic and environmental needs of the Americas. The age of the roaming herd is past. Today productive and indispensable livestock must be anchored to the many locales which it serves.

Here are vitally inmportant new crops for the New World—the first distinctly American breeds patterned to facilitate a better life for all Americans.

3

UNLIKE the numerous contributions of wild and cultivated plans of the New World that have added to man's industrial development, physical well-being, and pleasure, the livestock of the Americas has, with the exception of the llama and its cousin the alpaca of the high Andes and the turkey of our barnyards, been introduced from the Old World. These introductions from across the seas have been going on from Colonial time to the present. Some species and breeds have prospered in the New World, others have been greatly improved, and a number of new breeds have been developed in the Americas.

Over the centuries and unawares a vast trial-and-error experiment has been going on with these introductions in a search to find that combination of soil, climate, and economic structure where the animals would thrive and serve man best. It is not surprising that many failures occurred. Breeds from the northern climates have been introduced into the humid tropics, large breeds have been placed in regions of scanty vegetation, lowland breeds have been placed in the highlands, and vice versa.

Many species and breeds have been tried in almost every major livestock region of the Americas. Experience has taught us which fit best into given localities, and there is now discernible over the Americas a sort of stratification of types and breeds as they have found their areas of greatest usefulness to man. In the northern part of the United States the European breeds have prospered; in the warm southern states the heat-tolerant mule and Jersey cow predominate. In the regions of medium rainfall, cool climate, and good pastures mutton-type sheep prosper, and in the drier regions the wool producers. In the semi-arid regions goats thrive. Farther South the crossbred Brahman (Zebu)[1] appears, and in the true tropics of Central and South America the purebred and high-grade Zebu and Criollo cattle are the chief work and meat animals. Farther South into the cooler regions of South America the European breeds again as found in large numbers.

[1] *Bos indicus* or Indian cattle, referred to in the United States as Brahman cattle and in Latin America as Zebu cattle.

45

It is in the tropical and subtropical regions of the Americas that the major livestock improvement problem exists, for the highly specialized European breeds do not thrive as well in hot climates as native cattle do. The present type of farm animals found there are, for the most part, not highly specialized in production, although they do possess high adaptability to the severe climatic conditions.

Only recently has the husbandman become aware that climate affects livestock in much the same way that it does plants. That this fact was not appreciated earlier is not strange, for animals move about. When they have the choice, they seek the nutritious, palatable herbage and leave the less nutritious and the less palatable; they go to water when thirsty or to high ground in time of flood; they seek shade from the scorching sun and the warmth of the sheltered knoll when cold winds blow. Plants fixed to the soil, on the other hand, must grow on what is within reach of their roots. They must accept drought or flood, hot sun or dense shade, excessively high or low temperatures or whatever other element of the climate is characteristic of the locality where they are growing. No little wonder that in the development of new crops for the New World scientists endeavor to determine the nutritional, water, light, and temperature requirements of the new crop, and then go to great pains to find localities where the combination of soil and climate is such as to offer the most favorable prospect of success. When the right combination—that is, the optimum condition—is not found, plant breeders frequently modify the genetic structure of the plant to make it better suited to the environment.

The same scientific procedure is required with livestock in order that the most efficient use may be made of the excellent animal material on hand in the Americas. Livestock breeders have demonstrated marked skill in molding breeds to fit market requirements. It remains for them to fashion breeds to fit more closely the factors of the natural environment that cannot economically be corrected by management practices.

HOW CLIMATE AFFECTS LIVESTOCK

The most obvious effects of climate on livestock are seen in the influence of the seasons of the year on production and growth. In the United States and in South Africa it has been shown with beef cattle on the range that the rate of growth from birth to about thirty months of age is directly influenced by seasonal changes in weather. With dairy cows in the wet-dry tropics milk production falls off as the dry season advances and increases with the return of the rains. The records of Rhoad on Brazilian dairy cattle showed an average drop in production of twenty-seven percent, but there may be total cessation of production when the normal dry season is prolonged. Toward the end of the normal dry season when breeding stock on the range is in poor condition, the rate of conception is likewise materially lowered. These facts are illustrative of the marked influence of weather on the plane of nutrition of animals and the consequent effects on growth, production, and reproduction.

Under conditions of year-round adequate nutrition the effects of climate on production are still evident. That dairy cows produce less during the heat of the summer is a common observation of the dairyman. This would be influenced by the stage of lactation, but Gowan's work indicates that cows whose calves are born in March gave about sixteen percent more milk than those whose calves were born in summer. Regan and Richardson have found, under controlled conditions, that as the atmospheric temperature is increased from 40 to 95 degrees F. milk production gradually dropped from twenty-nine to seventeen pounds per day. This bears out observations reported by Rhoad in Brazil that dairy cows imported into the tropics produced on balanced rations only fifty-six percent of their apparent capacity. From work reported by Kelly and Rupel it appears that the optimum temperature for dairy animals is about 50 degrees F. That high-quality dairy cows of European origin produce best under relatively cool conditions is well illustrated in the results reported by Villegas with Holstein cows in Singapore in an air-conditioned barn kept at 70 degrees F. Cows in this barn produced an average of twenty-four pounds of milk per day compared with the production of nine pounds for a similar group in an open ventilated barn exposed to tropical temperatures.

Atmospheric temperatures, especially high ones, have a profound effect on the reproductive as well as the productive efficiency of livestock. Villegas, in the work cited above, reports that fifty-eight percent of the cows in the air-conditioned barn conceived within five months, as compared with only twenty-five percent in the ventilated barn. The breeding efficiency of males in particular is affected by high temperatures. Dawson, studying the breeding efficiency of proved (aged) sires, found that those used in the southern experiment stations of the United States Department of Agriculture had an average fertility of thirty-six percent, while those in the western and northern stations averaged forty-nine percent. Bonsma attributes the sterility during hot months of the year of a large percentage of bulls of exotic (imported) breeds in South Africa to the high temperature. Phillips and McKenzie have experimentally demonstrated that high summer temperatures materially lowered the vitality of the spermatozoa in the ram, and if continued for periods of several weeks caused degeneration of the reproductive organs and resulted in sterility.

That sunlight is an important factor affecting the adaptability of farm animals to the climatic environment has been demonstrated by Rhoad with beef cattle. When cattle were moved from the shade and exposed to strong sunlight on a summer day, their respiration and body temperature rose, indicating increased difficulty in disposing of body heat. Animals that are made uncomfortable by high atmospheric temperatures do not spend as much time grazing during a bright summer day as animals that are unaffected by high temperatures and strong sunlight.

Rainfall is an important climatic factor in the case of sheep. It is generally recognized that the Merino as a breed is not naturally adapted to moist conditions. On the other hand, British mutton breeds thrive best in a moist cool climate. Nichols has shown that, apart from their effects on pasturage, temperature and rainfall have a pronounced influence on the distribution and development of the British breeds of sheep. In England the denser sheep populations are found in areas with twenty to forty inches of rainfall annually. In South Africa the best wool-growing areas have less than twenty inches of rainfall, and the production of fat lambs is possible only in areas with more than thirty inches.

With poultry the same principles are evidenced as with the larger farm animals. Summer eggs are smaller than winter eggs from the same birds, and larger eggs are produced in the northern than in the southern latitudes. Ellsworth Huntington, however, has shown that egg production as well as milk production and slaughter weight of steers in the United States follows more closely the isothermic lines of the climatic map than latitudinal lines.

On the other hand, within the geographic tropics, altitude has a pronounced effect on animal life. This is primarily through modifying climate. For every 400 feet of elevation there is approximately 1 degree F. change in atmospheric temperature, producing, in mountainous regions, what is termed "vertical zoning"—that is, progressive changes in plant and animal forms from the typical tropical at sea level to subtropical at 3000 to 5000 feet and typical temperate forms at about 8000 feet. The height of the zoning effect varies with latitude, being lower as the distance from the equator is increased and higher as the equator is approached. In Mexico and in Colombia large concentrations of people are found at the high altitudes where temperate climatic conditions prevail. The yearly average temperature at Mexico City is 60.1 degrees F. and at Bogota 58.1 degrees F., with only minor changes from season to season.

It was pointed out above that these temperatures approach the optimum for European dairy cattle. It is little wonder then that in the districts surrounding these two capital cities large numbers of high-quality purebred European dairy cattle are found. Under these conditions there is no need to modify the breeds, as capacity production may be obtained following well-known management practices. It is at the lower altitudes where the effects of a tropical environment come into play that increasing attention must be given to finding or developing types of cattle to fit the environment.

OVERCOMING CLIMATIC DISADVANTAGES BY BREEDING

Farm animals are kept in an environment that in many ways is artificial, or man-created. Much of the success of the livestock industry depends upon our ability to furnish adequate nutrition, proper housing, and care in order that farm animals can develop and produce to the limit of their inherent capacity. To the extent that this cannot be done economically with existing types or strains, it is necessary to select and modify breeds to fit the natural environment. It has been clearly demonstrated in recent years that the lack of adaptability of certain types of animals to tropical climatic conditions, as evidenced by discomfort, low production, and frequently degeneration in type, can best be overcome by breeding. That there are distinct differences between species and breeds in ability to withstand climatic conditions has been amply demonstrated. It is easily notable that as the amount of Brahman (Zebu) breeding is increased there is an accompanying increase in heat tolerance. The purebred Brahman is not materially affected or inconvenienced by the heat and intensive sun.

The superior adaptability of the Brahman (Zebu) types of cattle to tropical climatic conditions has been verified in many parts of the tropical world and is being utilized in various ways. Edwards has shown in Jamaica that when the relatively low-producing but highly adaptable Montgomery (Sahiwal) type of Zebu was crossed with European cattle, the heifer offspring were frequently much better milk producers than their dams. Crossbreeding had given them a constitution capable of permitting them to express high productive capacity in a tropical environment. Comparable results have been obtained with crossbred beef cattle in South Africa, Australia, and the Gulf coast region of the United States.

Crossbreeding of Brahman with the standard beef breeds for resistance to subtropical climatic conditions has been the general practice in the Gulf coast region for more than a generation. From one of these crosses, the Shorthorn × Brahman, there has evolved the first strictly American breed of beef cattle—the Santa Gertrudis, developed by the Klebergs of the King Ranch, Kingsville, Texas. In an experimental way the United States Department of Agriculture is developing a new type at the Iberia Livestock Experiment Farm, Jeanerette, Louisiana, by crossbreeding the Aberdeen Angus with the Brahman.

Improved dairy types of cattle adaptable to the tropical and subtropical conditions are being developed in India with the purebred Brahman (Zebu) stock, while in Brazil, Jamaica, and the Philippines new European Brahman crossbred types are appearing.

THE BASIS OF IMPROVEMENT

Before improvement of farm animals in the tropics is attempted, there are two fundamental points to consider. The first is indicated above, namely, that breeds differ in their ability to thrive in a warm or tropical environment. The second is that the improvement sought should be within the limitations of the environment to support the improved types. The first point emphasizes the necessity that improvement must be within or through the breeds of proved adaptability. The second emphasizes the necessity of maintaining a balance between the degree of improvement sought and the level of the environment in which the breeds must produce and reproduce.

It is common knowledge that the present breeds of cattle found in tropical America have not been highly selected or improved for milk or meat production. They are, on the other hand, eminently suited by heredity to withstand the severities of a tropical environment. From the point of view of the animal breeder, the superior qualities of adaptability are as important in improving a breed as high milk production or desirable beef conformation. A method of measuring adaptability is, therefore, important.

The hitherto time-consuming, hit-and-miss method of determining adaptability of breeds to a tropical environment is disappearing with the development of scientific methods of measuring the fitness of animals to survive in warm climates. The Iberia Heat Tolerance Test developed by Rhoad at the Iberia Livestock Experiment Farm is based on the capacity of cattle to maintain normal body temperature, 101.0 degrees F., in a tropical environment. This is a physiological process referred to as the "efficiency of heat disposal." Animals with low efficiency have difficulty in dissipating normal body heat, and as a result develop a febrile condition when placed in a tropical environment. By measuring the degree of fever under standard conditions, a measure of their adaptability is obtained. Based on 100 as perfect heat tolerance under standard conditions, tests at the Iberia station gave the following results, 1944: purebred Brahman,

89; 1/2 Brahman 1/2 Angus, 84; 3/8 Brahman 5/8 Angus, 84; purebred Santa Gertrudis, 82; 1/2 Africaner 1/2 Angus, 80; purebred Jersey, 79; 1/4 Brahman 3/4 Angus, 77; grade Hereford, 73; 1/4 Africaner 3/4 Angus, 72; and purebred Aberdeen Angus, 59. Using a modified test, Villares in Brazil rated the following breeds in descending order: Zebu, Caracú (Criollo of Brazil), Brown Swiss, Guernsey, Holstein, and Aberdeen Angus. The latter two breeds had about equal heat tolerance. What previously took several generations of cattle to determine may now be accomplished through these tests in a few weeks.

Although the capacity to withstand considerable heat is primarily a physiological function, certain morphological characters as coat color, color of skin, and length and thickness of hair coat contribute to the capacity to thrive in a tropical environment. Cattle with the lighter coat colors, as the white of the Brahman or the fawn of the Jersey, throw off a much larger proportion of the intense solar heat than cattle with deep-colored or black coats. Short hair and pigmented skin are also important. Short hair facilitates body heat elimination. Bonsma has shown with cattle in South Africa that the Africaner has only 0.1 by weight as much hair as the exotic Shorthorn. A deeply pigmented skin beneath the hair coat impedes the penetration of strong solar rays that cause skin burns in animals with non-pigmented skins. Breeds native to the tropics, as the Brahman, and the Criollo, that have through the centuries become acclimated to warm climates, have short hair coats, pigmented skins, usually are gray or cream colored, and most important, are physiologically adjusted to warm climates. All these add up to demonstrated heat tolerance and adaptability to a tropical environment.

The established native breeds and those carrying Brahman blood are genetically adjusted to warm climates but many are low producers of the products for which they are kept. The problem of the animal breeder is to develop in these breeds greater specialization in meat or milk production without materially reducing their superior adaptability. The amount of heat tolerance to retain or to breed into cattle depends upon the severity of the climatic conditions. In the subtropical Gulf coast region of the United States one-fourth Brahman and three-fourths European breeding is sufficient. As the climate approaches true tropical conditions a greater proportion of Brahman breeding, or native breeding carrying equivalent heat tolerance, would be necessary to insure satisfactory adjustment. To have animals genetically adjusted to the environment is a primary prerequisite to any successful cattle breeding program directed toward increasing production.

BREEDING FOR BEEF

With meat animals the problem is not so difficult as with dairy animals, for within certain of the tropical breeds the variation in type is sufficiently wide to permit selection toward the ideal beef animal without introducing, through crossbreeding, beef blood from exotic breeds. That specialized beef-type animals approaching the ideal can be developed within the pure tropical breeds is demonstrated in the improvement made in the Zebu in Brazil and in the United States. The Caracú of Brazil and the Blanco-Orejinegro of Colombia are examples of similar improvement through selection within the pure Criollo breeds.

Crossbreeding the Criollo or the Brahman with the specialized European beef-type breeds is carried on in many parts of the Americas where the tropical breeds show only limited specialization as beef animals. In other words, these breeds are inefficient producers because their inherent capacity to produce is below what the environment can support, and specialized exotic breeds are imported to increase the potential level of production. In the Gulf coast region cattle are bred up so close to the purebred European type that Brahman cattle are used to incorporate heat tolerance into the former. Here the environmental and the potential level of production are in reverse relationship to the above, for along the Gulf coast inherent capacity to produce is above what the environment can support, and consequently growth, production, and reproduction suffer. Whether the crossbreeding is carried on under the severe conditions of the tropics or under the milder conditions of the Gulf coast, a proper balance between heat tolerance and beef type must be maintained for best results. Once the proper adjustment is obtained in the crossbreds, progress toward fixing new strains may be made through the systematic application of known genetic principles. In this manner the Santa Gertrudis breed of beef cattle of southeast Texas was evolved.

Developed by crossbreeding the Brahman with the Shorthorn, the Santa Gertrudis is the first American breed of predominantly European blood which possesses high productive efficiency and high tolerance for heat. Considerable numbers of Santa Gertrudis bulls are being used in Central and South America in grading up native cattle. The results are being watched with interest. Aside from this very practical phase, the Santa Gertrudis has made two significant contributions which are of interest to the breeder of cattle in the tropics. They are, first, that starting with good foundation stock, new and improved breeds can be evolved through judicious crossbreeding, skilful selection, and intelligent mating; and, second, that the beef production of tropical cattle can be improved through grading up to a breed of predominantly European blood without materially reducing the heat tolerance or the adaptability of the progeny.

Crossbreeding the heat-tolerant Zebu or the Criollo cattle with the highly specialized European breeds is one of the methods through which new and improved breeds may be evolved. It is, however, the most precarious method at the disposal of the breeder. It is hazardous, for it necessitates the mating of crossbred sires with crossbred dams. If this is not systematically done, it will more often result in the creation of nondescript herds of low market value than the establishment of new improved types. The possibility of establishing new and improved types through crossbreeding is one of the important contributions of the Santa Gertrudis to livestock improvement in the tropics.

The establishment of new breeds through crossbreeding is a long process, which usually requires many years of continuous effort. It has often been debated whether new breeds of our larger farm animals can be evolved within the lifetime of an individual breeder. The Santa Gertrudis proves the possibility, for twenty-two years after the crossing in 1918 of Brahman bulls on purebred Shorthorn cows, the descendants were recognized as a distinct breed.

A quarter of a century is about as short a period as can reasonably be expected in which to develop new breeds of cattle. Considering that some of our modern breeds have taken centuries to develop into their present well-balanced form and high productive efficiency, this is a very short time. Science and the practical breeder have been largely responsible for the more speedy arrival at the goal set. With the aid of our present knowledge of the science of animal genetics the livestock breeder can follow proved procedures and avoid some of the costly pitfalls in his breeding operations.

The development of superior new breeds of larger farm animals through crossbreeding is not a task recommended for the breeder with a small herd and limited time and capital, for it takes considerable equipment, experience, and technical knowledge to achieve success. It is, however, proper field of endeavor for the government experiment stations or large ranches where material is available and continuity of effort is assured. For these reasons not many breeders and only some agricultural experiment stations will undertake the task of developing, for the tropics, superior new breeds through crossbreeding.

In the development of new beef-type strains at experiment stations, the Brahman × Angus crossbreeding project at the Iberia Livestock Experiment Station at Jeanerette, Louisiana, is well advanced. This work by the

United States Department of Agriculture carried on at the Iberia Livestock Experiment Farm was started in 1931 by breeding Brahman bulls to Aberdeen Angus cows. By 1942, eleven systems of mating had been employed, and to the end of the same year 439 calves had been born. The first ten years of this project were devoted to determining the most desirable percentage, based on tests for heat tolerance and production performance, of Brahman and Angus breeding to incorporate into the new strain or strains, and to determining the system of mating that produced the most satisfactory results. At the present writing the strains with a desirable combination of characters are being increased, and progress toward fixation of type has started. When finally established, the new breed will resemble the Aberdeen Angus in type and color but will have sufficient Brahman breeding to make it better adapted to warm climates.

In east Texas a number of breeders are crossbreeding the Brahman with the Hereford, the progeny of which are commonly referred to as Braford cattle, from which a new beef breed may eventually develop. In Minas Gerais, Brazil, some crossbreeding of Zebu with the Cherolez, a French breed, has been carried on for some years, and recently an effort has been started to develop this cross into a new beef breed.

Because the developing of new improved breeds of cattle is a long process entailing considerable financial and technical risks, it is not likely that many such undertakings will be made by private breeders. On the other hand, most breeders are concerned with improving the productive capacity of their herds for immediate commercial purposes. The time-honored system of attaining this end has been the practical method of grading up the herds to an improved type by the use of purebred sires. This method has been very successful in many parts of the world. The generally high quality of farm animals in the United States is the result of long grading up of common herds by the use of purebred sires. It is the recommended practice where the purebred sire is of a breed adapted to the environment in which it is placed.

In the tropics the method has not proved successful with cattle when purebred sires of European origin have been used. Grading up to the improved type of Zebu or the Criollo, on the other hand, is successful and is being done on a large scale in many parts of the American tropics. The failure, in the tropics, of grading up to the European type is due to the fact that they reduce the heat tolerance of the progeny in each succeeding generation. As a result, the progeny of the second and latter generations decrease in size, vigor, and productiveness.

Before a continuous grading up program can be effective in the tropics with breeds carrying a large proportion of European blood, it is necessary to have breeds of high productive efficiency possessing high tolerance for heat. When continuously crossed on low-producing cattle, these breeds will progressively improve the production of the progeny without materially lowering their heat tolerance. This will be the principal use to be made of the new tropical breeds now in the process of development. For the present only the Santa Gertrudis is available for a continuous grading up program.

BREEDING FOR DAIRY PURPOSES

While the principle of maintaining a balance between the capacity of the animal to produce and the capacity of the environment to support is equally applicable to dairy cattle, the solution is more difficult because the level of milk production of native tropical cattle is generally low. There are, however, several breeds of Zebu cattle such as the Sahiwal and the Scindi that show considerable capacity to produce milk. Individual production records of 11,721 pounds of milk in a year have been reported from India for the Sahiwal and 8573 pounds for the Scindi. Only the Sahiwal, also known as the Montgomery breed, has been imported into the New World. This breed has been used in Trinidad and Costa Rica in a limited way in developing the dairy industries of these countries. On the other hand, the Gir breed of Zebu, although not quite so productive (6000 pounds), is very numerous in Brazil and is extensively used as a dairy animal. For the most part, however, the native cattle of the Americas are poor producers. Working with a group of animals whose proved production under the best of feeding and care does not exceed 2000 pounds, it is quite impossible genetically to develop a tropical dairy breed with an average production of 5000 pounds. If the group does not carry the genes for an average production of more than 2000 pounds. there are no genetic means of increasing production without incorporating genes for high production through crossbreeding with an exotic breed possessing the necessary genes.

This fact is generally recognized throughout tropical America. As a result, recourse to crossbreeding to increase milk production is more generally carried on than crossbreeding to increase beef production. The solution of the dairy problem is made more difficult because, for the present, there is no improved dairy breed of European-Zebu or European-Criollo breeding possessing high heat tolerance and high production, as does the Santa Gertrudis beef breed, that could be used for grading-up purposes. The creation of such a breed awaits the skill of some master breeder.

The foundation material from which a tropical dairy breed or breeds may be created is already available in the Americas. Reference is made to the large numbers of European Zebu and European Criollo crossbreds, *mesticos*, that are to be found in many parts of Latin America. Through the process of several generations of inter-se crossbred matings and the elimination through natural causes of the less adaptable progeny, there are within these large populations many individuals in which the superior qualities of both parental stocks are harmoniously combined. Although they are quite heterogeneous and therefore uncertain in their transmitting abilities, they are good basic stock from which new types and breeds may be evolved through the application of known genetic principles.

Fortunately sufficient experimental work has been done with the *mestico* dairy animal that some knowledge of their capacity as milk producers is available. As early as 1932 Edwards reported with cattle in Jamaica that high-grade cows, with no Zebu blood, when bred to pure-bred dairy bulls of European breeds, produced daughters that averaged 400 pounds less milk than their dams, while cows of similar breeding bred to a Sahiwal bull had daughters that averaged 970 pounds more milk than their dams. Although the inherent milk-producing capacity of the Zebu was less than that of the purebred European sire, the daughters of the former produced more milk than their dams because the Zebu sire transmitted to his progeny greater resistance to tropical climatic conditions, thus permitting the daughters to produce in accordance with their inherent capacity.

Working with the same type of cattle in Trinidad, Harrison in 1944 reported average production per lactation of purebred Friesian to be 2979 pounds; 7/8 Friesian 1/8 Zebu, 3616 pounds; 3/4 Friesian 1/4 Zebu, 4486 pounds; 1/2 Friesian 1/2 Zebu, 4316 pounds; and 1/4 Friesian 3/4 Zebu, 3287 pounds. These records were made at the Government Stock Farm, St. Joseph, and were made, therefore, under good conditions of feeding and management. Rhoad studied the production of similar cross-bred cattle in Brazil under the common practice of one milking per day, on pasture the year round, without any supplementary feeding, and the cow nursing her calf until the age of weaning. Under these conditions an average production of 1156 liters, approximately 2500 pounds, was obtained. But even under these conditions of management the better cows produced upward of 2000 liters or approximately 4400 pounds. That cows of this type are good basic stock from which new breeds may be developed was shown by Rhoad, who reported that, when removed from the common system of management, fed balanced rations, milked twice daily, and the calves reared separately, the herd average may be increased by as much as 280 percent.

PLATE 3. Upper—Mangosteens, one of the most delicious tropical fruits

Lower left—Seedless pejibaye, another fruit of the American tropics

Lower right—Guanabana or soursop, another renowned tropical fruit

PLATE 4. Upper left—Grapefruit in the Rio Grande valley
Upper right—The American papaya
Lower—Loading spinach into a refrigerator car

PLATE 5. Irrigated banana cultivation

PLATE 6. Upper left—Loading bananas with conveyor
Upper right—Truckload of grapefruit
Lower—Looking down on the Riventazon River, Costa Rica

There remain many details to be studied, but our present knowledge is sufficient upon which to base action programs directed toward the establishment of improved breeds of dairy cattle adapted to tropical America.

OTHER CLASSES OF LIVESTOCK

Efforts to improve such other classes of livestock as sheep, goats, swine, and horses in the American tropics have been made from early times. Considerable progress has been made especially where the imported breeds found soil and climatic conditions favorable. Where this has not been the case, degeneration in type has occurred. This is particularly evident with sheep. Dominques has pointed out the modification of type that has occurred since the Colonial period with sheep imported into the dry northeastern states of Brazil. The completely wooled breeds originally imported have progressively lost their covering of wool until the present-day "native" sheep, as the Morada Nova, are completely without wool or have only a narrow band extending along the topline. Athanassof, as well as Dominques, has initiated efforts to develop within these sheep, showing adaptive modification, improved strains for meat purposes. Efforts are also underway to improve the highly adapted *lombo preto* strain of goats for milk as well as for meat.

With these smaller farm animals, including swine, there are many local types, which up to the present have received little attention by the livestock improver. These local types, however, offer an opportunity for improvement that would materially benefit the livestock industry.

HORSES

Of more than local importance is the improvement of the horse. Horses are very important in the life and work of the rural population of all the Americas. Because of the lack of improved highways and the remoteness of many habitations, the saddle horse is still the only means of transportation for many people in tropical America. The horse is likewise essential to the operation of the large plantations and cattle ranches. Although not used for traction purposes since its place is taken by the more suitable ox, it does serve as parental stock for the hardy mule, also of considerable economic importance.

The horse has been held in such high esteem in the Americas that considerable attention, skill, and pride has gone into its improvement. As a result there are excellent types to be found in all the Americas. Only recently a movement was started to draw together the breeders of the Quarter Horse of North America with the breeders of the Criollo Horse of the Argentine, Uruguay, Chile, Peru, and the Crioulo of Brazil into a united organization called the Pan American Horse Association, with the object of furthering the development of this most useful animal.

Livestock improvement at best is a slow process, but as our knowledge is applied to the problems of tropical America there will continue to emerge out of the mass of animal material on hand new types and breeds of farm animals as closely identified with the New World as many of our present breeds are identified with the Old World.

4

Palm Oils and Waxes

By MIRIAM L. BOMHARD

ECOLOGIST, UNITED STATES FOREST SERVICE

PALMS and waxes are traditional backlog crops important in war or peace, to all humanity. Second only to corn and the other life-making grasses, the palms are the most provident of crops. As Dr. Miriam Bomhard, distinguished ecologist of the United States Forest Service, points out, the palm crops, at least a great many of them, are not new to the Americas botanically. For centuries this enormously diverse and "second most important" of the crops of mankind has ranked among the pre-eminent potential resources of the Americas—with the unfortunate necessity of italicizing potential. Brazil alone has native stands of about half the known palm species.

But the world-wide commerce in palm crops is relatively new to the Americas, which are only now beginning to appraise the international possibilities and the even more impressive subsistence importance of this most picturesque and versatile of crop families. Dr. Bomhard here outlines the highly newsworthy role of palms and wax crops as inter-American staples spotlighted with new and impressive significance in future world trade. Her chapter also describes many of the non-food uses of palm oils and waxes.

4

THE PALM family numbers among its members the most majestic and beautiful trees in the entire plant kingdom. It stands second in usefulness; the grass family with its cereal-grains, bamboos, forage, and hay plants ranks first. Native populations of the warmer regions of the world have from remotest time depended upon palms for practically all the necessities of life—food, drink, shelter, clothing, illumination, fuel, cooking, medicine, and ointment. They have fashioned from the various parts of palms most of the requisites of a primitive economy, such as nets, baskets, bags, ropes, string, poles, cleansing materials, screens, mats, cooking and eating utensils, furniture, brooms, paper, blowguns, bows, bridges, rafts, pilings, pipes, boats, and numerous other items. Palm nuts have even served as money.

An ancient proverb of India refers to the 999 uses of the coconut palm, conceded even in this day to be the most useful tree in the world. A Tamil poem extols the 801 uses of the palmyra palm. Every part of these trees is put to some useful purpose. The coconut, date, African oilpalm, palmyra, buri, doum, raffia, murity, carnaúba and babassú [1] may be listed as outstanding among the all-purpose palms of the world.

The modern inhabitant of a tropical or subtropical area where palms grow is ordinarily at least aware of the value of palms to his primitive neighbors. He may indeed have financial interests in some palm of the region that furnishes raw materials—oils, waxes, fibers, starches, nut shells— entering into civilized economy or international trade. The dweller of temperate zones, however, unless his business demands that he know about such things, is usually woefully ignorant of the part these raw materials play in his every-day life.

THE OILS

The impact of the war upon rubber supplies from the East is known to everyone. That it has had the same effect upon sources of palm oils

[1] Date: *Phœnix dactylifera* L.; palmyra: *Borassus flabellifer* L.; buri: *Corypha utan* Lam.; doum: *Hyphæne thebaica* Mart.; raffia: *Raphia pedunculata* Beauv. and other Raphia species. The scientific names of the other palms listed will be found in the species discussions at the end of the chapter.

has not been so well publicized. Our former dependence upon tires made from natural rubber requires no explanation. But how many of us are aware that the sudden cutting off of palm oils supplies from the Far East and Africa has upset the normal balance, especially in the United States and Europe, in the production of oleomargarine, shortening, soap of various kinds, shampoos, shaving cream, cosmetics, toothpaste, confectionery, candles, lubricating oils and greases, livestock feed, terne plate, tin cans, and glycerine?

Many of the world's 2500 to 3000 species of palms have oil-yielding fruits, yet commerce and industry have become, in the course of more than a hundred years, almost entirely dependent for their palm oils supplies upon but two species—the coconut palm and the African oilpalm. Coconut oil and copra (from which this oil is derived) have come principally from the tropical area extending from India and Ceylon to the Pacific islands. The Philippines in particular, the Marianas, Carolines, Solomons, and other island groups had extensive coconut plantations that contributed substantially to world trade. Supplies of palm oil or kernels from the African oil palm have been exported mainly from West Africa, Sumatra, and British Malaya. Enemy occupation of these areas and, until recently, the impossibility of shipping materials from unoccupied territory cut off these supplies. It became necessary to look to the New World for palm oils as well as for numerous other raw materials.

It is a strange paradox that the United States has been importing most of its palm oils or kernels from halfway round the globe, when coconut palms and African oilpalms have been growing in this hemisphere for centuries. The former now number several millions, and the latter total at least one and one-half million trees. Not only these two top-flight oil producers but some twenty-five other palm species that are strictly indigenous to the New World are known at the present time to be worth commercial exploitation. In fact, there is a larger concentration of oil-yielding palms in this hemisphere than anywhere else.

In his *Index of American Palms*, Dahlgren lists 1170 species as described from the western hemisphere up to the end of 1935. Of these, 440 species and some 57 varieties are in Brazil, Colombia is second with 201 species, Peru has 127, Venezuela 88, and so on down the line. Certain species have a wide distribution and appear, therefore, in the lists of more than one country. Allowing for a re-evaluation of the species already described and for the addition of new discoveries, it would be reasonable to consider that there are at least 1250 palm species known in the New World up to 1945. Nearly half this number occur in Brazil, which is one of the two world centers of palm distribution, the other being the Indo-

Malayan region of Asia. The vast Amazon valley is teeming with palms, and although some of the oil-yielders in the lower basin are already proving their commercial value, the potentialities of those in the upper reaches—the Oriente region—are still virtually unknown.

The presence of oils or fats in seeds is a common occurrence, representing a type of reserve food material for the germination of the embryo plant. Although the fruit flesh may also be oily, the number of commercial and industrial oils derived therefrom is far fewer than from seeds. The palm family is renowned for the high percentage of species whose fruits contain appreciable amounts of oil. The great majority of these are stone-fruits or drupes, and fundamentally similar to a peach. A peach has a thin skin or peel, soft edible flesh or pulp, and a hard stone. All together these are the pericarp, a term frequently misapplied to mean the skin and pulp. If you take the trouble to crack a peach stone, you will find the seed lying loosely inside. A thin brown membrane (seedcoat or testa) encases the white meat or kernel in which the tiny embryo is embedded. Palm stone-fruits show remarkable modifications of the basically peach-like structure. The flesh varies from slightly fibrous to completely so, as in the coconut where the entire outer portion (husk) down to the nut (stone) is densely fibrous and inedible. There may be more than one seed inside the palm nut, and the nut wall (shell) is so hard and thick in some species that mechanical breaking with cracking machines has been the major goal for steady production of kernels. The nut of babassú is the hardest structure imaginable, and except for the several cavities in which the seeds lie singly, the whole thing is solid wall. A few of the oil-yielding species have a berry type of fruit, which may have only a thin membrane separating the seed from the fruit flesh.

Palm oils are either kernel ("nut") oils—kernel often refers to the whole seed—or pulp ("pericarp") oils. Some palm fruits yield one or the other kind; some have both. The seedcoats also usually contain oil. Coconut oil is obtained from the fresh or the dried kernel; the latter goes under a special name—copra. Both the kernel and the fleshy-fibrous pulp of the African oilpalm yield oils, and these are of different chemical composition. The pulp oil of this species is known simply as "palm oil," probably because it was the first of this type to be used commercially; "palm kernel oil," also without a palm name modifier, refers rather quaintly but specifically to the African oilpalm kernel oil.

The United States has, since the first World War, superseded Germany to take first place in world trade in the utilization of copra and coconut oil. Statistics that begin with 1869 show that the United States has been importing coconut oil and also palm oil in ever-increasing quantities, with some high and low years, of course, for more than eighty-six years; copra and African oilpalm kernel imports are more recent. In 1941, the United States consumed 637,970,000 pounds of coconut oil, 278,487,000 pounds of palm oil, 10,364,000 pounds of palm kernel oil, and 38,975,000 pounds of babassú oil.

Wars always have required increased supplies of fatty foods and, of course, explosives. In this global war, the United States has had to meet the requirements of its civilian population and armed forces as well as those of the United Nations for enormous supplies of fats and oils, not only for food and glycerine (for medicinals as well as explosives) but also for more soap, more tin cans, more sheet steel, and even more candy! Obviously plants offer a more quickly available raw-materials source than do animals. Strenuous efforts have been made in the present emergency to stimulate increased production in New World palm oils to provide truly tremendous exportable surpluses, which had to be built up in a hurry. Babassú, ouricury (licuri), tucum, murúmurú, dendê, and cohune are foremost among the "new" palm oils that have come to the rescue, but supplies are not yet reaching the United States in sufficient quantities to meet all the demands. In addition, bacába, patauá, macaúba (mucajá, mocaya), corozo, and many other palm oils hold promise of increased future production. These oils are "new" only in the sense of modern commercial exploitation; the natives have always used them. In the meantime, the industries that use palm oils have done a marvelous job of "stretching" the available supplies of the old stand-bys and have succeeded in substituting larger quantities of other vegetable or animal fats and oils in the manufacture of their products.

Fortunately, industrialization of certain of the more promising oil-yielders was already well under way in this hemisphere before the present emergency. It was during the 1914-18 period that the New World became increasingly aware of the economic possibilities of its oil-yielding palms. The first World War was not the only cause of this awakening; sometime before 1914, the consumption of vegetable fats and oils by the industrial countries of the world had taken a decided upswing. The acreage of cultivated coconut trees in the East, especially in the Pacific islands, and in Africa was increasing enormously. Precise scientific research was being carried out to obtain maximum fruit yields and better quality copra. A revolutionary palm oil development was also taking place. Sumatra, beginning in 1910, and British Malaya, in 1917, created extensive African oilpalm plantations, almost from scratch, to produce a palm oil so superior to the earlier African product, which with a few exceptions was poorly prepared and rapidly turned rancid, that the United States and certain other nations eventually came to import most of their palm oil needs from the East. To meet this competition, some of the West African palm oil producers also installed first-class methods. On this side of the globe, the vast native palm oils resources of Brazil were being opened up; efforts were begun to commercialize the cohune palm in British Honduras and Mexico, and new coconut developments took place in Central America and the West Indies.

Brazil is today the most important New World source of palm oils. From the very beginning Europe displayed marked interest in the new palm kernels which were being brought to its attention and which were shipped there before they were known in the United States. Nuts of babassú, the biggest name among the "new" crops, were first exported to Europe in 1913 and a factory for babassú oil was established in Rio de Janeiro in 1915. In the latter year, 96,632 pounds of babassú kernels went to the United States; by 1941, the United States was importing 71,504,000 pounds, after a peak of 115,704,431 pounds in 1939! The amounts now being obtained are not available for publication, but an agreement with Brazil assures the United States exclusive rights to all exportable babassú surpluses until 1946. Interestingly, kernels from "piassava" and other related palm species have been intermixed with babassú from the first, the oils being practically identical in chemical composition. Investigations in Pará into the commercial value of tucum and murúmurú, widespread in the Amazon basin, also date from 1914, and a suitable nut-cracking machine for murúmurú was early put into operation. Preparation of ouricury (licuri) oil for local industrial use began in Bahia in 1915, but it was not until 1922 that kernels were shipped abroad. Brazil has the largest acreage of coconut trees in the New World and is the only country in this hemisphere possessing an abundance of African oilpalms (introduced so long ago into Bahia, where they are called "dendê," that they appear to be native) but, surprisingly, no unusual large-scale exploitation of either of these palms occurred during the first World War when Brazil was occupied with revealing its wealth of new native crops. To be sure, exportation of coconut oil and copra was initiated during this period and fresh coconuts were being shipped abroad, mainly to Argentina and Uruguay. Sometime later, however, the precocious dwarf coconut of Malaya was introduced into Bahia and experimental government plantations were set out. Dendê kernels began to be exported, amounting to over 67,000,000 pounds in 1925-26, and industrial use of coconut oil and palm kernel oil was stepped up. But even today, only a small fraction of the tremendous potential oils resources of these two palms in Brazil is being realized.

The cohune palm, native from Mexico to Guatemala and Nicaragua, produces a fine kernel oil that has always been locally important, especially in Mexico and in British Honduras. Like babassú nuts, but in a lesser degree those of cohune are extremely hard to crack and this difficulty has been a major drawback in placing this palm on a firm industrial footing. Ironically, the nuts rather than the kernels of both cohune and babassú came into immediate use during the other World War because the nut shells proved to be as suitable as coconut shells for gasmask filters. However, in the last twenty-five years, hand-cracked cohune kernels have arrived in United States markets from time to time. The cracking problem very recently appears to be solved, and factory-produced oil is being exported.

Certain of the West Indies and Central American countries have been the center of coconut production in the New World since before the turn of the century, and have long supplied United States markets with fresh coconuts. Panama San Blas coconuts from carefully managed plantations have been renowned for their superb quality. Expressing coconut oil for local use has been practiced in the New World for years, and some regions, notably Trinidad and Mexico, produced sufficient amounts of copra or oil for exportation even before 1914. In the 1920's, nearly all the western hemisphere coconut-growing areas were making occasional exportations of coconut oil or copra, in addition to fresh nuts, to the United States, Europe, or various South American countries, and a few were preparing shredded coconut. Jamaica, Panama, and Honduras have been the principal exporters of fresh coconuts to the United States for a number of years.

The increasing use of New World palm oils up to the beginning of the present war is, in part, a reflection of the internal industrial expansion that has been taking place in some of our palm-growing areas. The total exports had not been large, as world statistics go, and the drop in world prices for all vegetable fats and oils in the 1930's discouraged exportation to the big consumers. However, the manufacture of oleomargarine, soaps, salad oils, and other products in improved factories with modern machinery had so advanced, especially in Brazil, that by 1937 most of the countries south of the Rio Grande were utilizing palm oils produced in this hemisphere.

Except for coconut and some African oilpalms, none of the palm oils crops come from systematic plantations. For profitable big-scale yields of oil from palms growing as Nature planted them, much organization and capital is required for quick and expert handling of the fruits from the moment of collection to the bagged dried kernels or finished oil ready for shipment. Inadequate transportation facilities, inaccessibility of some of the densest stands, the sparseness of population in some areas, the recent absorption of native labor in the collection of rubber latex and other war projects, the everlasting struggles to develop foolproof nut-cracking or decorticating machines (different types for the different kinds of fruits), and numerous other difficulties have seriously handicapped accelerated wartime production. Even at that, by the end of 1942 large stocks of palm kernels were accumulating in Brazil, and by the middle of 1943, reduction in the shipping quotas on babassú, ouricury, and tucum kernel oils had to be taken under consideration by the United States because of the lack of ships to pick up all the supplies available.

Thus far, all the new palm oils that are being exploited to an appreciable extent are kernel oils. They are similar to coconut oil and palm kernel oil in chemical composition and utilization. No large pulp oil sources have been developed in the New World to take the place of palm oil that plays an exclusive role in the tin-plating industry. Obviously, the African oilpalm itself, that grows so extensively in Bahia, Brazil, as dendê, is the logical source of supply, but attention has hitherto been focused on the kernels. With the start that has already been made in cultivating dendê, it is not unlikely that the marvelous success achieved in Sumatra and British Malaya may one day be duplicated in Brazil. Moreover, the plantings of African oilpalm that have recently been set out in Honduras, Haiti, and Costa Rica augur well for the future. Then, too, bacába and patauá pulp oils from Amazon valley palms are by no means unknown to world trade but the amounts produced thus far have been comparatively insignificant. The pulp oil of macaúba (mucajá, mocaya) is already being employed on a factory basis in Paraguay and Brazil and experimentation is under way to develop a satisfactory method of separating the pulp from the nut.

Coconut oil and palm oil, and later palm kernel oil, first came into use in Europe and then in the United States in the manufacture of candles and soap. With increased knowledge of the chemical composition of vegetable oils and improved technical methods, especially refining and hydrogenation, their utilization for edible products in temperate regions advanced enormously.

The coconut series of kernel oils have a high saponification value which accounts for the excellent lathering properties, even in cold water, of the soaps that contian one or the other of them. In 1941, the peak year of soap production in the United States, nearly one-half billion pounds of coconut oil and one-fourth as much palm oil were used in soaps. It was estimated that 2,100,000,000 pounds of fats and oils would be needed for 1944 requirements—to make four billion pounds of soap! Under normal circumstances thirty-five percent of the oils and fats used in soap are imported, including twenty-five percent coconut oil. The shortage of palm oils has resulted in increased use of tallow, grease, and lard as basic materials. Coconut oil has always been one of the principal components of shampoos and liquid soaps. An effective shampoo can be achieved with as little as twenty percent coconut oil. However, the prevalence in the United States during part of the war period of virtually non-lathering skin-irritating soap fluids attests that not even the requisite minimum of kernel oils was available for these products.

The fat-salvage campaign in the United States forcibly brought to the attention of everyone that fats are the basis of glycerine for explosives. But most people are not aware that the coconut series of kernel oils gives higher yields (twelve to fourteen percent) of glycerine than does any other vegetable or animal fat. Glycerine is mainly obtained from residual soap lye. Its recovery has been habitual for the larger soap factories in the United States, and of course, in recent years, this has become obligatory for the smaller concerns as well. As the war has progressed some of the soap installations in South America have awakened to the importance of glycerine recovery and have not only been making more for domestic needs but have also been able to contribute some amounts of soap lye directly to the war effort. Glycerine has many uses in medicine, in various industries, and in the arts. It is not likely that this important by-product of the soap factory will be lost sight of in New World palm areas in peace-time.

Just as present-day manufacture of soap is an improvement of the simple process still carried out by primitive or backwoods people, of preparing wood-ash alkali for saponifying palm or other vegetable or animal fats and oils, so the modern preparation of oleomargarine, vegetable butter, shortenings, and confectionery is a refinement of the native use of various palm oils for food, for cooking or frying other foods, or as a sweetmeat.

The manufacture of oleomargarine as a cheap butter substitute began in France in 1870. At first composed predominantly of animal fats, butter substitutes gradually came to contain large proportions of vegetable oils, such as coconut, palm kernel, cottonseed, peanut, and sesame. As better qualities of palm oil became available, it too entered into edible products. In Europe, butter substitutes made entirely of palm oils soon found favor— the so-called "vegetable butters." In the United States, where oleomargarine production has increased by leaps and bounds, cottonseed oil has been the basic oil both in oleomargarine and in vegetable shortenings. By 1930, however, imported fats and oils accounted for forty-five percent of the oleomargarine produced in the United States, but since then the use of foreign oils has been gradually decreasing, amounting to only 16.8 percent in 1939 (including by this time babassú oil), and to 8.4 percent in 1940. Soybean oil has come to play an important role, and both it and neutral lard have been increasingly used in this war period. This trend is partly due to the fact that both cotton and soybeans are domestic temperate zone crops and partly that the use of palm kernel oils was forbidden in the United States in all processing that would not yield glycerine. On the other hand, the manufacture of margarine and vegetable butters composed exclusively of palm oils has advanced remarkably in some of our palm-growing countries since the first World War, and there is every indication that this production will continue. Moreover, it is probable that the consumption of palm oils for edible products will be resumed or even stepped up in Europe after the present war, unless the increased use of hydrogenated whale oil and various vegetable oils other than from palms offers too serious competition.

The north temperate portion of the New World continues to use the oils of olive, cottonseed, corn, peanut, and soybean as salad oils and dressings. The first two are favorites in many other areas as well, but factory production of certain palm oils for salad oils is increasing, particularly in Brazil. It was pointed out during the first World War that South American dependence upon imported alive oil could be alleviated by increased use of such native Brazilian palm oils as bacába and patauá, and during the present war avocado oil has also been brought forward as a substitute. The chemical composition of patauá and bacába pulp oils, used as salad oils and for tinning fish, closely resembles olive oil, but they must stand on their own individual merits as distinctive oils that have characteristics similar to olive oil but do not duplicate it in flavor.

In the so-called "chocolate-fats," coconut oil and palm kernel oil came to be used as substitutes for, and dilutants of, cocoa butter (the expensive fat from the "bean" of the cacao tree) and constitute an important element of the "cream" of chocolate cream candies and the filling of some fancy pastries. In the United States, coconut oil has been looked upon as almost indispensable for many kinds of candy bars and other confectionery. Apparently manufacturers have not been very favorably impressed with the behavior of other vegetable oils (except palm kernel oils), certain animal fats, and similar wartime replacements. Babassú oil was the first of the "new" oils to be taken up by candy-makers, about eight years ago. Tucum and ouricury kernel oils will, no doubt, also be welcomed by confectioners as supplies become available. The splendid keeping quality of coconut oil, as well as of the other palm kernel oils, is a highly valuable characteristic; its sharp melting point has made it the favorite oil for coating candies. Coconut oil was also thought to be indispensable for roasting and frying nuts, but in this case, hydrogenated cottonseed oil has proved to be eminently suitable.

The various palm oils serve primitive populations as lubricants. In modern practice, African oilpalm palm oil is frequently a component of the heavier axle greases. Some of the kernel oils form part of cutting oils and greases, but none of the palm oils are usually used for delicate machinery, except perhaps babassú oil. Palm oils were previously employed to a greater extent than at present in printing inks, especially for cotton textiles. They enter into some types of shaving soaps and creams, cosmetics, perfumes, dentifrices, and numerous other products.

Although African oilpalm oil is used for most of the purposes for which the kernel oils serve, it occupies a unique position in the manufacture of tin plate (mainly tin coating on steel), terne plate (lead and tin coating on iron), and more recently cold reduced sheet steel. Tin cans are made of tin plate—the United States produced 17 billion tin containers in 1937—and terne plate is a roofing material or "tin." In 1941, the total United States consumption of palm oil for tin and terne plate was 42,159,000 pounds; in that year the production of these plates had increased by almost a million tons over that of 1940. In making tin plate, the palm oil serves as a bath to help spread the molten tin uniformly (at the same time precluding its oxidation), gives a shiny appearance by preventing oxidation on the surface of the plate, and the thin film of oil that adheres reduces the possibility of early corrosion. Palm oil superceded tallow, and now hydrogenated cottonseed oil has been found satisfactory in the United States and hydrogenated whale oil has been used in Germany. However, if palm oil is available, it will probably continue to be employed.

Many kinds of palm fruits constitute a highly palatable food, either fresh or cooked, for human consumption; some of them are customarily sold in tropical markets. The juices of certain palm fruits also make fine refreshing drinks. Besides, both wild and domestic animals consume palm fruits throughout the palm-growing areas. In some cattle-raising, palm-inhabited regions, the pulpy fruit flesh forms a substantial part of the subsistence of the cattle. Moreover, after expression of most of the oil, the palm kernel press cakes, as such or ground into meal, are used in northern countries as a livestock feed, but where produced in the tropics, they find utilization mainly as a steam-boiler fuel. Press cakes and meal are also employed as fertilizer. Copra cakes and meal are the only palm source-materials used in large enough quantities to be mentioned by name in United States feed statistics, but those of other palm kernels also definitely enter into the livestock feeding picture.

Palm oils have been used as fuel in internal combustion engines, particularly palm oil in some parts of West Africa. The kernel oils may serve a similar purpose, and very extravagant claims have been made for the future of babassú oil as a Diesel engine fuel in Brazil. Naturally, countries that have ready access to petroleum have no great interest in the fuel value of palm oils, but the latter may help solve the transportation problem where some of these palms are native. The husks and nuts are commonly employed for fuel in the tropics not only for household needs but also for locomotives, boats, and even in modern factories. They may also serve as fertilizer. Destructive distillation of the nut shells yields a high-grade charcoal and also such by-products as acetic acid, methyl alcohol, and crude creosote, from which still other substances of value in industry and the arts may be derived.

It has been said that "the inhabitant of a tropical country who first collected the oil which ran off the broken kernel of the coconut, on exposure to the sun, may be looked upon as the first manufacturer of vegetable oils and fats." The very simplest methods are still employed in many parts of the world, particularly for home use. Softening or breaking up the cells of the fruit pulp or kernel facilitates release of the oil imprisoned in them. This may be accomplished by grinding or crushing, by boiling in water, by letting natural fermenation set in, or by a combination of these methods. Following these preliminary preparations, the oil is then obtained by boiling the crushed mass in water or by some form of pressing or squeezing. The Cochin coconut oil of India made by the age-old method of breaking the nut in pieces, letting the kernels dry in the sun, then boiling them in water, skimming off the oil that rises to the surface, and straining or settling it, is of such fine quality that it early set a standard for excellence in world trade.

Probably one of the earliest methods of releasing oil by pressure consisted in placing the crushed oil-mass in bags covered by a few planks, weighted down by stones. The *tipiti* used in parts of the Amazon region is a cylindrical sievelike device, made of the fibers of the leafstalks or midribs of various local palms, through which the oil is pressed out. Pressing apparatus operated by levers, wedges, or screws, still used in many areas, may be considered as representing developmental stages in the mechanics of oil-pressing that culminated in the invention of the hydraulic press in 1795. The improved hydraulic presses and the continuous-operating expellers or screw-presses used in up-to-date oil mills are relatively complicated machines capable of exerting pressures up to several tons to the square inch. Large quantities of fats and oils are also now prepared by solvent extraction methods.

Pulp oils may be obtained by expression or by centrifugal extraction. Because of the perishable nature of the fruits, pulp oils must obviously be prepared near where the palms grow. Kernel oils may also be expressed in the producing country; in fact, this tendency is increasing. It is still more usual, however, to ship the kernels after they have been suitably cleaned and dried, even though more space is required proportionately than for the oil. The press cakes find wider utilization in the importing countries of northern climes.

Among the New World palm oils, babassú kernel oil now occupies first rank. It is not only the first of the "new" oils to challenge the previous world supremacy of coconut oil and palm kernel oil but it bids fair to outstrip them in importance. The limit in palm oils development in this hemisphere would appear to be set only by the total amount that the world can, or cares to, consume. And if by any chance, the United States, the biggest consumer, chooses to revert completely to the old stand-bys after the war, these could also be developed by its neighbors to the south.

THE WAXES

The commercially valuable palm waxes may well be termed leaf crops, inasmuch as the leaves are harvested to obtain the waxy substance that coats their surfaces. A group of locally important Andean palms, however, produces wax on the trunks. There are only two palm species that play a prominent role in the industries which utilize waxes, and both of these are native to Brazil. The fan-leaved carnaúba palm has long been the outstanding source of palm wax for the entire world; the wax value of the feather-leaved ouricury (licuri) palm has been discovered only within the past decade.

The United States has been suffering from an acute shortage of all waxes. Normal supplies of beeswax, montan wax, and Japan wax (a vegetable fat) have been considerably reduced or are entirely unobtainable. Even though the various waxes do not completely substitute for each other, the war has made it urgently necessary to secure larger quantities of palm waxes than ever before; but the submarine warfare caused the total loss of large consignments of carnaúba wax, shipping facilities have been inadequate to transport the amounts that are available, and erratic wax harvests have only added to the dilemma.

The diversity of products for which carnaúba wax is employed is nothing short of amazing. It was first used for candles and is still so employed in both native and modern practice. Carnaúba wax is the principal ingredient of polishes for floors, automobiles, and furniture; it enters into the manufacture of shoe polish, carbon paper, cable coverings, waterproofing materials, photographic films, dictaphone and phonograph records, and artificial fruits and vegetables. It serves as a luster filler in textiles; it is used to stiffen beeswax foundations for beehives. This wax was first analyzed in 1810, and in 1846, about 64,000 pounds were exported from Ceará. In 1913, Brazil's shipments of carnaúba wax totaled 8,525,426 pounds. By 1919, the quantity had nearly doubled; it then fell off for a time, but in 1941 climbed to 26,000,000 pounds. The United States is the principal buyer, having imported 22,167,000 pounds in 1941.

The carnaúba palm is native to a large section of northeastern Brazil that has prolonged dry seasons. Although it has been introduced into many parts of the world as an ornamental, prospects of cultivating it for commercial wax yields outside its native home are not bright, unless it would be possible to duplicate the unique habitat conditions under which it grows naturally. Systematic cultivation of it in its native home has recently been initiated; such plantations augur well for controlled yields, although it is still too early to draw definite conclusions.

The harvesting of the leaves begins sometime after the dry season has set in—about July or August. The newest leaves have more wax, but the collection of these would be ruinous to the trees; therefore, to insure leaf crops over a long period of years, the medium-aged leaves are the ones that are cut off—about twenty annually per tree in the course of three, or sometimes only two, cuttings in a season. The leaves are dried for a few days to loosen the wax; they are then split, shredded, and finally beaten until as much of the wax as possible has dropped off. The wax-dust is gathered up into buckets, melted over a slow fire (with or without water), filtered to remove foreign matter, and then poured into suitable molds or trays for cooling. It hardens into brittle cakes that are packed into bags for shipment.

The ouricury (licuri) palm has the double value of yielding the fine kernel oil already mentioned and an increasingly important industrial wax. The first commercial sample of wax was prepared in Bahia in 1935. In this instance, the powdery wax is scraped from the undersurface of the leaves with a blunt instrument or else the leaves are crushed and then subjected to heat to obtain the wax. Ouricury wax differs somewhat from carnaúba wax in its chemical constitution, but it can be used for most, if not all, of the same purposes. At least one closely related species that grows in the same area with ouricury yields wax containing a large percentage of gum. Efforts are being made to discontinue the practice of mixing it with ouricury wax, but it may find a separate place in the trade for its distinctive qualities.

The several species of Colombian feather-leaved waxpalms (Ceroxylon) that produce wax on their trunks provide an article of local trade for the making of candles and matches. The wax is usually scraped from living trees but sometimes they are felled first. These, the most renowned and tallest palms in the world, were once thought to have great industrial promise. The wax, however, not only differs from carnaúba wax in its larger resinous content, but commercial exploitation of it is neither profitable nor necessary.

THE MOST PROMISING OIL- AND WAX-YIELDING PALM SPECIES [2]

African oilpalm; dendê or dendê da Bahia, in Brazil. *Elæis guineensis* Jacq. (*E. melanococca* Gaertn. is a later name based on the same palm.) Apparently native to Africa, occurring from Senegal to Angola across the interior to the Nile and Great Lakes region; then, less abundantly, on the eastern coast, in Zanzibar and Madagascar. Western Hemisphere: subspontaneous and cultivated in Brazil (Amazonas to Bahia) and Haiti; also growing in other parts of South America and the West Indies; cultivated in parts of Central America, and elsewhere. Present producing area: Bahia, Brazil. Relatively slender, erect, single-trunked palm, averaging 50 ft. in height, but up to 100 ft., and 1 ft. in diameter. African oilpalms rather resemble datepalms in habit but the feather-like leaves, about 16 ft. long and spiny at the base, have the segments folded downward like an overturned canoe, as in all members of the coconut relationship. Male and female flowers in separate heads in each tree; heads compact, awkward-looking, with spine-tipped branches, wedged in the midst of the leafcrown. Fruits orange-red (often purplish at tip), smooth, oblong but angular, 1 to 1½ in. long and 1 in. in diameter or larger, borne in the axils of spiny-tipped bracts, and containing 1, sometimes 2, seeds. Both the pulp oil ("palm oil") from the fibrous-pulpy flesh and the kernel oil ("palm kernel oil") from the seed are of first-class commercial value.

American oilpalm; cayaué, caiaué, or dendê do Pará, in Brazil; corozo,

[2] Reference may be made to Dahlgren's *Index of American Palms* for more detailed geographic distribution and additional vernacular names. The author's list "Palm Genera," pp. 444-452, in *Standardized Plant Names* (1942), edited by H. P. Kelsey and W. A. Dayton, may be consulted for the common names of many palm species cultivated in the United States or entering into international trade.

in Panama and Colombia; corozo colorado, in Panama and Venezuela; palmiche or coquito, in Costa Rica; nolí, in Colombia. *Corozo oleifera* (HBK) Bailey. (Synonymous names include *Alfonsia oleifera* HBK and *Elæis melanococca,* as used by various authors when it was thought that this palm was an American species of the African oilpalm genus, Elæis.) Colombia through the Amazon region to Panama, Costa Rica, and Nicaragua in wet, mostly shaded areas. Rather similar to the African oilpalm but trunk seldom more than 6 to 8 ft. high and frequently leaning or inclined; leaves with more regularly arranged segments. Fruits in the axils of spineless bracts, somewhat smaller than those of the African oilpalm, reddish brown, oblong but not angular. This palm is not yet exploited commercially but the kernels could be important for oil; the pulp is rather dry and yields less oil than does that of the African oilpalm.

Andean waxpalms. Ceroxylon, with 20 species, is distributed from Venezuela into Peru, mainly at high altitudes. Wax deposits give a shining white appearance to the trunk of some species. The wax of two species of Colombia—the Quindío waxpalm, *Ceroxylon quindiuense* (Karst.) Wendl., and the Salento waxpalm, *C. ferrugineum* André—is known to be utilized in local trade. The Quindío waxpalm, the tallest in the world, attains nearly 200 ft. in height, grows up to 10,000 ft. above sea level, and endures temperatures just above freezing.

Babassú palms. *Orbignya oleifera* Burret, *O. martiana* Barb. Rodr., and probably other species of Orbignya. (The names *Attalea speciosa* Mart., *O. speciosa* (Mart.) Barb. Rodr., and *O. barbosiana* Burret are synonyms of *O. martiana.*) Brazil: Minas Geraes through Goyaz and part of Mato Grosso to Ceará, Piaui, Maranhão, Pará, Amazonas, and even beyond Brazil in the upper Amazon region. Magnificent trees, 60 to 70 ft. high and 2 to 2½ ft. in diameter, with vase-shaped crown of elegant feathery leaves that average 25 ft. in length and curve over gracefully at their tips. Babassú palms grow in low-lying humid areas, often along streams, in true Amazon forest, mostly in pure stands with as many as 100 trees to the acre. The top-shaped beaked fruits, borne in long pendant clusters, average 4 to 6 in. in length and 2 to 3 in. in diameter; the hard nut contains 1 to 8 (usually 3 to 5) elongate seeds, the number differing with the species and also with the individual fruits. The untapped reservoir of babassú palms is truly stupendous, and even in the major producing areas—Maranhão and Piaui, and recently, Minas Geraes—it is estimated that only 10 percent of the available supply of fruits is being utilized.

Bacába palms; comou, in French Guiana. *Oenocarpus distichus* Mart. and *O. bacába* Mart. Middle and eastern Amazon valley: mainly Brazil

(*O. bacába* extends into British Guiana). Tall, handsome, feather-leaved palms, bearing heavy clusters of reddish purple or violet fruits, slightly over an inch long, whose pulp yields an oil chemically similar to olive oil. Principal producing area: Pará, Brazil.

Burity and murity palms. Burity: *Mauritia vinifera* Mart., in Brazil from Pará to Minas Geraes and São Paulo; also called murity. Murity: *M. flexuosa* L.f., widely distributed throughout the Amazon region of Brazil, British and Dutch Guiana, Venezuela, and Peru; also called burity do brejo, in Brazil; moriche, in Venezuela; aguaje, in Peru. Murity often covers extensive low-lying areas subject to floods whereas burity occurs on higher, drier land. Both are striking palms 120 ft. or more in height and 1½ ft. in trunk diameter, with fan-shaped leaves about 16 ft. in length. The 2-in. long fruits are covered with small flat scales; the relatively thin pulp layer yields an edible oil. The oil of burity is recently being used in soap factories of Pará, Brazil.

Carnaúba palm. *Copernicia cerifera* (Arr. Cam.) Mart. Brazil: eastern Pará and Maranhão to Goyaz and Bahia, along streams and in relatively low areas that become dry for prolonged periods. Fan-leaved palms of slow growth, averaging 40 ft. in height but sometimes twice as tall, and very long-lived (about 200 years). The leaf blades, about 3 ft. long and carried on claw-margined leafstalks of equal length, have a heavier coating of powdery wax on the lower surface. The carnaúba palm is the most important yielder of palm wax. Although the kernels contain oil, the percentage is too small for industrialization. Principal production areas: Ceará and Piaui.

Coconut palm. *Cocos nucifera* L. Distribution world-wide on humid tropical shores. Both an Indo-Malayan and American origin have been suggested; evidence seems to point to the former. Western Hemipshere: between 25 degrees latitude north and south of the equator; more abundant on the Atlantic than on the Pacific side, extending from Mexico through the West Indies to northern São Paulo, Brazil, on the east, and to Ecuador in the west. It was estimated in 1930 that the world area of coconut palms from which fruits were harvested totaled at least 7½ million acres and that the New World accounted for one-fifth of this acreage. Beautiful trees, usually 50 to 60 ft. tall but up to 125 ft. and from 1 to 2 ft. in trunk diameter (larger at the swollen base). The soft green feathery leaves average 15 ft. in length. Although Brazil has the greatest number of coconut palms in the New World, the yield per tree is not high, except in some fertile soils and on well-tended plantations. The coconut is called coco da Bahia in some parts of that state. Experimental work with the Malayan dwarf coconut, introduced in 1925, is giving excellent results. Principal producing areas of fresh coconuts: Central America and neighboring islands, and the West Indies.

Cohune palm. *Orbignya cohune* (Mart.) Dahlgren, formerly designated as *Attalea cohune* Mart. Central America: Sinaloa, Mexico, to Guatemala on the Pacific side, and from Quintana Roo, Mexico, to Nicaragua on the Caribbean coast, extending into the interior and often occurring in dense groups. Smooth-trunked trees about 50 ft. (up to 150 ft.) tall, with plume-like leaves at least 23 ft. long; aspect somewhat similar to babassú palms. The fruits, from 2½ to nearly 3 in. long and 1½ in. or more in diameter, contain usually one seed (sometimes 2 or 3). Major producing areas: Mexico, British Honduras, and Guatemala. Semi-clearing of jungle growth around cohune palms in natural stands has been found useful in British Honduras in stimulating fruit production.

Corozo palms. This name is in general use for various palm species that are not necessarily closely related. Although corozo should perhaps be restricted to the American oilpalm, it here refers to a number of species of the genus Scheelea, called corozo in Central America, that have been the subject of special effort to step up kernel production for exportation. (The genus Scheelea is closely related to Orbignya, and also to Attalea and Maximiliana. These four genera total some 90 species, distributed almost throughout the palm-growing areas of the New World. They represent a tremendous potential source of kernel oils; some yield pulp oils as well. The possibility of commercial exploitation of the various species depends upon the percentage of oil in the fruits, the annual fruit crop per tree, and the density and accessibility of the native stands. Thus far, only babassú and cohune palms of this group have attained prominence.

Jupaty palm. *Raphia tædigera* Mart. Jupaty is the Brazilian name for this palm that grows in the marshes and inundated lands that ranges from the Lower Amazon northward into Costa Rica and probably Nicaragua. All the other species of Raphia are native to Africa and Madagascar. The whole group is renowned for the colossal size of the feather-like leaves—up to 60 ft. in length. Like the fruits of burity and murity, those of jupaty, from 2 to 3 in. long, are covered with flat scales. The yellow flesh yields a bitter, red-colored oil; it is used locally in Pará for coloring soap, made mainly of other palm oils. The oily fruit flesh of some of the African species furnishes so-called "Raphia butter" or "piassava oil," used for a variety of purposes. Some of these oils are sweet and edible; others are bitter.

Macaúba, mucajá, coco de catarrho, in Brazil; coco or mocaya, in Paraguay; gru-gru, in British Honduras and parts of the West Indies; corozo or corojo, in other West Indies and in portions of South America;

coyol, in Central America. Various species of Acrocomia, about 25 in all, distributed from Mexico and the West Indies through Central America to Colombia, Bolivia, northern Argentina, Paraguay, and Brazil. Heavy-trunked, spiny, feather-leaved palms that prefer rather dry areas, such as upland woodland savannahs and open scrublands. The fruits are usually globular with stringy, mucilaginous, aromatic, oily pulp, enclosed by a thin eggshell-like outer covering; the spherical nuts have a relatively thin but hard wall, enclosing the single oily seed. Paraguay has long been known for its "Paraguay palm oil" or "mocaya oil," formerly attributed to *Acrocomia sclerocarpa* Mart., but the source appears to be *A. totai* Mart. Several species in Brazil are also being exploited at present, especially in Minas Geraes and Goyaz, also in Pará. Both the pulp and the kernel oil are valuable. The fruit pulp constitutes an important natural livestock feed, particularly in cattle-raising Minas Geraes. Machinery is being de-veloped to separate the pulp from the nut. Oil from some of the West Indian species has long been valued locally. The several species of Acro-comia in Central America are perhaps the commonest palms of the flora but they usually occur scatteringly, whereas those of southern Brazil and Paraguay often grow in thick stands.

Murúmurú palm. *Astrocaryum murumuru* Mart. Amazon valley: mainly Brazil, but also in British and French Guiana, Venezuela, and Peru. Spiny palm, with feather leaves silvery white beneath. At present murúmurú is the most important local source of palm kernels in Pará, Brazil, and among the foremost commercial oil-yielders. Unlike many of the tucum palms (also Astrocaryum species), murúmurú does not yield pulp oil.

Ouricury or licuri palm. *Syagrus coronata* (Mart.) Becc., formerly designated as *Cocos coronata* Mart. Brazil: subtropical and tropical eastern portion (Pernambuco, Bahia, Minas Geraes), mainly in rather dry "caatinga" areas. Although ouricury is the name under which both the kernels and the wax of this palm are known to commerce, licuri is the preferred name in Bahia, the main producing area. (The general adoption of licuri would help to avoid the confusion that now exists because a relatively important Amazon valley palm, *Scheelea martiana* Burret [form-erly *Attalea excelsa* Mart.] also goes under the name of ouricury.) The licuri palm may attain 30 ft. in height, but it is usually shorter, and the trunk is about 8 in. in diameter. The gray-green, waxy, feather-like leaves, about 10 ft. long, show a distinct spiral arrangement. The flower clusters are rather similar to those of the coconut palm, but the fruits, about 1½ in. long, are fleshy with sweet mucilaginous pulp and yellowish when ripe. The nuts look like miniature coconuts. The licuri palm has come to take a prominent place in commerce both for its oily kernels and for the wax of the leaves.

Palma real. *Ynesa colenda* Cook. Ecuador: coastal area. Unfortunately this vernacular name is not very distinctive because "palm real" is widely applied among Spanish-speaking people to the outstanding "royal-looking" palms of their region, whether feather-leaved or fan-leaved. This handsome, heavy, feather-leaved forest species, at least 100 ft. tall, belongs in the general Attalea-Scheelea-Orbignya relationship, but it is not yet well known. The nut wall is not nearly so hard and thick as that of babassú, and there is usually only one avoid seed. Interest in the collection of the kernels for shipment to the United States was aroused with the war.

Patauá palm. *Jessenia bataua* (Mart.) Burret, formerly known as *Oenocarpus bataua* Mart. Amazon valley: Brazil, British and Dutch Guiana, Venezuela, to the foot of the Andes. Tall trees (50 ft. or more), with elegant shining leaves having regularly arranged segments and berry-like violet-purple to almost black fruits, quite similar to those of the bacába palms. The pulp oil is utilized commercially in eastern Brazil and some enters foreign commerce, but there is room for expansion.

Piassava palms. The two Brazilian piassava palms best known to commerce for their fibers are Pará piassava, *Leopoldinia piassaba* Wallace, and Bahia piassava, *Attalea funifera* Mart., that are not closely related botanically. It is the kernels of the latter that have apparently long been intermixed with those of babassú palms. However, there is evidence that the kernels of still other Attalea species have also been exported with babassú kernels. There seems to be no good reason why these various palms should not enter into the trade in their own right as oil-kernel yielders.

Tucum palms. Tucum or tucumá, often with a modifying word, is a name of general application in Brazil to various species of the genera Astrocaryum and Bactris, characterized by spiny trunks, leaves, and sometimes spiny or bristly fruits. Aouara or awarra is a comparable term used in the Guianas; chonta, chambira, and huicungo are similarly applied in Panama, Colombia, and Peru. The fibers from the leaves of some species are commercially important. The tucum kernels or oil now being exported from Brazil come principally from two species: *Astrocaryum tucuma* Mart. and *A. vulgare* Mart. The former extends from Venezuela and Peru through the Upper Amazon region of Brazil to British and Dutch Guiana. The range of the latter includes Venezuela and British Guiana as well as the states of Pará, Maranhão, Piaui, Pernambuco, and Bahia in Brazil. Perhaps kernels of *A. jauari* Mart. that has a wide Amazon valley distribution and other Astrocaryum kernels also enter into the export trade. The pulp oils of many tucum species are used locally.

5

Rubber Returns to Latin America

By *WALTER N. BANGHAM*

DIRECTOR, PLANT RESEARCH DEPARTMENT,
THE GOODYEAR RUBBER PLANTATIONS COMPANY

THE palm crops and rubber crops are close neighbors with much in common. Since the world-wide flowering of the automotive age, natural rubber has been the most coveted and the most publicized of tropical crops. By processes of rapid multiplication the stately Hevea tree, native to the Amazon basin, came to supply practically all the millions of tons of rubber upon which this self-propelling mechanized age is abjectly dependent.

When Japan seized Malaya, Sumatra, and Java the rubber man's perennial nightmare became fact. The preponderant and indispensable supply of rubber was lost to us and our allies. Rubber cultivations in the Americas were pitiably small; native stands of rubber-yielding trees were direly inaccessible. In the American tropics people began working hard to establish high-yielding strains of Hevea trees for cultivation. The manufacture of synthetic rubber opened frantically but in some measure brilliantly, though the facts are still sorely obscured by partisaned politics, the quest of United States Treasury subsidy; the naive incompetency of numerous pseudo-scientific reporters and the staging by pretentious political appointees and certain other individuals, of one of the most audacious publicity field meets in history.

This editor considers the following the most authentic and informative article about rubber yet to appear in print. After years of first-hand work in Central America, its author, Ohio-born Dr. Walter N. Bangham, director of plant research for the Goodyear Rubber Plantations Company, has earned much of the credit for the return of improved, cultivated rubber cultivations to the Americas. His ten years or more of active experience in the establishment and "upgrading" of famed rubber estates in Sumatra, the Philippines, and other Pacific tropics has provided excellent background for the memorable work which he now directs.

Among other challenging facts Dr. Bangham here reminds us that while factories are improving and increasing manufacture of substitute rubbers, botanical and agronomical research, as applied to natural rubber, is not idle. He also describes the highly significant progress in supplementing the new rubber plantings with needed subsistence crops.

5

"How CAN we compete with rubber plantations in Sumatra after the war, with our much higher labor costs?"

"Synthetic rubber can be made for less than it will cost us to grow rubber in the Americas."

"The United States is not going to lose the billions of dollars invested to build up synthetic rubber production."

"Rubber is just another wartime crop. The United States Government helps us while the war lasts, as it did during the past war. When the war is over, plantations will die for lack of a market, as they did after the last war."

These are typical comments of Costa Rican farm managers as we discuss local problems during our trips on the Northern Railway train between San José and our respective farms, in the Atlantic zone of Costa Rica. These men have seen new crops appear, with propaganda and promise; they have also seen them fail. They are not going to accept rubber as a new crop without ample proof that it will become a permanent addition to the local agricultural scene, at a profit to them.

Our reply is that rubber plantations did not come to Latin America as war-emergency efforts. The crop was being planted here long before the war by two of the largest corporations of the United States (The Ford Motor Company and The Goodyear Tire and Rubber Company). These corporations did not start their plantations here because they were jittery about the effects of a potential war. Both companies were large users of rubber. Both had their primary interest of protecting their supply of this raw material from all hazards inherent in having more than ninety-five percent of the world's rubber supply come from one small portion of the globe. When they started the plantations in this new region they faced the necessity of initiating extensive and costly research activities not normally considered to be within the province of a commercial company. The supply of this essential raw material must be assured.

P. W. Litchfield, president of the Goodyear Rubber Plantations Company, had strongly advocated that it was vital to the national welfare and economy to have a considerable portion of the rubber available for export grown in the western hemisphere. J. J. Blandin, vice-president of the plantation company, in 1923 edited a series of publications for the United States Department of Commerce, which reported the results of a survey of the potentialities for rubber production of each of the tropical countries of this hemisphere.

Despite their wish to do so, the officials of the Goodyear Rubber Plantations Company could not recommend rubber planting in this hemisphere at that time for several reasons:

1. The South American leaf-blight (*Dothidella ulei*) had already destroyed plantations in Trinidad and the Guianas. Although it had not reached Central America, where several small plantations of healthy rubber were reported, there was good reason to anticipate that it would reach this zone if large plantations were started there. This disease had not been taken to the Malayan region with Wickham's seedlings, and the strict prohibition of export of plants or seeds from Brazil had offset the possibility of the Indies getting the infestation with later lots of planting materials.

2. Laborers were rather scarce, and wages consequently were high, when compared with the East Indian area. No densely populated area provided a pool of labor which could be recruited to operate large estates.

3. Rubber trees then available for planting gave such low yields that the wage for tapping was the major item of the cost of a pound of rubber. With the high wages of Latin America, this cost would be increased above the value of the rubber obtained, until higher yielding trees enabled the tappers to bring in more rubber for a day's pay.

At the time, these factors appeared to be insurmountable. Rubber planting in Latin America did not then appear to have a commercially sound future in competition with plantations in the Indies.

The desire to plant here when possible was not forgotten. With the impulse of the Stevenson Act, passed in 1922, which restricted natural rubber production, raised costs, and reduced the amount of planting in the possessions of the British Empire, planting outside the Malayan region was again considered. The Firestone Company in 1923 started negotiations for plantation sites in Liberia, West Africa. The Ford Motor Company started their plantations in 1927, along the banks of the Tapajos River in Brazil. There some of their concession was almost directly across the river from the spot near Boim from which Sir Henry Wickham collected the seeds which became the foundation stock for the world's plantations of *Hevea brasiliensis*.

The Goodyear Rubber Plantations Company had been planting rubber on a large scale in Sumatra since 1916. In 1928 this company had 16,000 acres planted and started planting on a new property of 40,000 acres in Sumatra. Simultaneously, planting was begun on the Pathfinder Estate in Mindanao, which was outside the zone of frequent hurricane in the Philippine Islands.

The plantation in Mindanao contained 1000 hectares (2470 acres). This was the maximum area that one individual company was permitted to own or plant, according to the Philippine Land Laws. This estate was considered chiefly as a respository of planting material of improved rubber clones when they were developed in Java, Malaya, or Sumatra. It was also a center in which labor costs were more than double those of Sumatra. Here the company could study the possibility of producing rubber from the new high-yielding trees and practice economies in the use of labor, in order to determine if it were possible to keep costs reasonably close to those on the plantations in Sumatra. Pathfinder Estate provided a long and carefully prepared stride in the direction of rubber planting in Latin America.

PLANTATIONS APPLY RESEARCH TO RUBBER PRODUCTION

The offspring of the original Wickham collection had by this time been planted in millions of acres of estates and native areas. They gave a major portion of the income from agricultural crops to the planters of Sumatra, Malaya, Java, Ceylon, Burma, Borneo, Indo-China, Siam, and elsewhere in this area. Soil requirements, diseases, tapping systems, and methods of manufacture of the rubber from latex had been given the first attention of the scientific workers. There was no time to wait for improved seed. The world wanted rubber, and was willing to pay profitable prices for it. The principal desire was to get more acres planted. Few gave a thought to yields.

When prices fell, plantations suffered. Planters looked searchingly at the trees they had planted. Most of the latex, they found, came from a few trees. About seventy percent of the trees gave only thirty percent of the latex, although they were strong, healthy trees. Immediately there arose a demand for planting stock that would not have in it these worthless drones.

Van Helten, in Java during 1918, had demonstrated that the Hevea rubber tree can be propagated successfully by budding. Heusser, in a lecture to the planters of Sumatra in 1919, outlined a systematic program for selection and breeding to improve the rubber yield from this tree.

Estate managers, scientific men, foremen, and coolies were soon all involved in a frantic search for a "mother tree" that would, after budding, give offspring which would fill larger cups with latex. Approximately 20,000,000 of the rubber trees in estates had their individual yields measured periodically for a year or more. On the Dolok Merangir Estate of the Goodyear Company, one tree from each 10,000 trees in the estate became a mother tree. From the budded offspring of about 100 of these mother trees only one was outstanding enough in yield to reach commercial planting. In other words, the clones that were planted literally represented "one in a million."

First results disappointed those who had visions of having the latex gush in unquenchable streams from the trees of the new clones or strains. One leading research station recommended for several years after having released improved clones for planting, that half of the trees planted in any area should be of ordinary seedlings. Gradually good reports of the new buddings began to arrive. At maturity the ordinary unselected seedlings in the first plantations were considered to be of average productivity if a tapper, in his 320 visits to the tree during each year (160 tappings and 160 collections) could coax from it latex from which the factory could prepare four pounds of dry rubber. New clones were reported among which each tree gave six pounds, then eight pounds, then ten pounds, twelve pounds, fifteen pounds, twenty pounds; and one fabulous tree was reported to have given eighty-five pounds during one year of tapping.

When a tapper, working on one of the new clones that gave twenty pounds from each tree, tapped the same number of trees that he had formerly tapped among ordinary seedlings, he brought five times the quality of rubber into the factory for each day's wage. This greatly reduced the relative proportion of the tapping cost to other costs of estate operation, and eliminated one of the factors which had prevented the return of the plantation industry to the home of the Hevea tree.

The native with a small farm contributed nothing to this research. Neither did he utilize any of the improvements as they were made. He continued to plant his small plots with the seeds that he collected from ordinary low-yielding trees of neighboring estates. The large estates could justify their high development and research costs with the better planting material and more efficient operation of their properties than was present among their competitors with small holdings.

RESTRICTION INCREASED PRODUCTION COST

When prices of rubber fell below three cents a pound (United States currency) for rubber delivered in New York during 1932, many of the estates which had not utilized the new types of planting materials faced ruin. Over ninety percent of the 8,000,000 acres of rubber of the Indies were planted with ordinary low-yielding seedlings. With prices low, reserves used up, and prospects poor, the owners could not face the necessity of planting their properties with better clones. Doom was imminent, in the view of these planters. They could see but one solution to their problems—international restriction. The world clearly had too much rubber, and the cure would be found if exports were reduced and planting stopped, even if this did raise the cost of production for each of the fewer pounds produced.

In spite of the fact that the first British Restriction Scheme (the Stevenson Plan, 1923-28) had failed to stabilize prices effectively, an International Agreement (1934-44) was the result of this clamor from the owners of submarginal plantations. By this agreement, the governments of Great Britain, the Netherlands, France, and Siam endeavored to raise and regulate prices at a level that would prove profitable for all types of plantations, including the least efficient. Replanting was permitted on a carefully controlled basis, new planting was much restricted, and the export of planting materials was prohibited. The agreement assigned to each of the major producing areas under its authority a proportion of total exports. An International Board was set up. The Board met at quarterly or more frequent intervals to determine the total quantity of rubber which was to be permitted to reach the world market for the following period. The agreement achieved the purpose of the planters of the Indies. It did not assure the world of an increasing supply of rubber to meet the increasing demand. It penalized efficiently operated estates to salvage poor, unprogressive properties.

The Government of the Philippine Islands remained outside the International Restriction Agreement, and the plantations in that area could export their full capacity of rubber. On the Goodyear Pathfinder Estate in Mindanao there had already been established the largest number of selected, high-yielding clones outside the area from which they could no longer be exported. The Firestone Plantations had some of these clones in Liberia, and the Ford Company had been able to get some for their plantations in Brazil just a few days before the prohibition became effective. Goodyear had over 1100 of these superior clones on their estate, outside the restricted area.

LATIN AMERICA RECONSIDERED

The time had come when it appeared to be a sound venture for this company to start the long-desired plantations in Latin America. The reduction in the amount of rubber an estate was permitted to export from Sumatra or Malaya was accompanied by a considerable rise in the cost of production. It mattered little that labor was paid low wages if it could not be utilized efficiently. The rise in production costs within this area and the availability of high-grade planting material outside, reopened the possibility that rubber could be grown in Latin America at a competitive price, despite the higher wages of that area.

In the meantime Latin America had developed. Travel and freight were leaving river routes and bullock carts, and were being moved on rubber tires over inland roads or through the air. New roads were opened; more trucks, automobiles, and planes appeared, and more tires were required. Tire factories followed, many of them owned by the companies which had formerly exported tires into these regions.

In Manaos, Brazil, one of these factories turned out rubber articles under the shade of Hevea trees that lined the driveway. Despite this contiguity of factory and raw material, the increase in rubber consumption was not followed by local attempts to establish rubber plantations. Some of the new factories were required to import a major portion of their rubber from the Indies, for lack of a local supply.

The rubber manufacturing industry of Latin America is surely faced with expanding markets. This increased business will bring with it greatly increased demands for raw rubber. It appears unlikely that the rubber plantations which develop in Latin America will be able to supply this increasing factory demand of adjacent areas for many years. Producers supplying this local market will have the advantage of not having to pay freight and export charges to a foreign country, and may also have protection above current world prices equivalent to the import charges on rubber from the regions of surplus rubber production. This latter possibility, being subject to changing political conditions, may not be an important factor in long-range profit estimates.

Production of synthetic rubber, under the stimulus of wartime emergency, has been one of the world's production marvels. Costs of production of this product have rapidly been reduced. Although still at a level which will permit rubber to be grown in Latin America at a handsome profit to the producer, these costs will undoubtedly be progressively reduced and the quality of the product will be improved.

At the same time that these improvements are being made, botanical

PLATE 7. Corn, foremost American crop

PLATE 8. An irrigated field of cotton

PLATE 9. Upper—Cattle, the foremost American livestock
Lower—Cattle feeding in Arizona

PLATE 10. Upper—A Spanish-American farmstead in New Mexico
Lower—A sheep ranch in Arizona

and agronomical research workers are not idle. New planting practices are being devised, higher yields are obtained, and the quality of the natural rubber is improved. Production costs of plantation rubber are being constantly reduced by the efforts of these men. Surely this research will be intensified, rather than reduced, as a result of the competition from synthetic.

Synthetic rubber, at its present early stage of development, is more difficult than natural rubber to work into tires, and tire manufacturing costs are increased when synthetic is largely substituted for natural rubber in tires. There is yet no certainty that this handicap can be overcome.

Authoritative sources feel confident that Latin American natural rubber, developed along scientific and rational lines, should find a welcome market in competition with synthetic rubber when grown in those areas where labor is sufficient and physical conditions are suitable to the growth of Hevea trees.

PANAMA ENTERS THE RUBBER SCENE

In 1934 the Goodyear Company officials made their decision to start plantations in Latin America. A base for all of the valuable clones was to be established in Panama, where they would be assured of protection in case war destroyed other sources. A commercial area was to be planted in Costa Rica. No disease had been reported in either of these areas. Photographs which had been taken several years before showed the foliage of the existing trees in these areas to be luxuriant and healthy.

Preparations for planting involved the staff of the company in Akron, Sumatra, and the Philippines. All worked toward getting agreements with the governments, locating a planting site, preparing the budded trees for transport, and getting shipping space, in the manner that our armed forces prepared for D-day. J. J. Blandin and O. D. Hargis selected land for a plantation, and Goodyear obtained a contract with the government of the Republic of Panama. J. C. Huber and the author prepared 42,000 budded trees of 1100 clones, in cases of earth or sawdust. The author and his wife nursed the trees during their thirty-five-day trip to Panama. In Panama the cargo was discharged into barges on Gatun Lake. It was the first cargo to have this privilege. O. D. Hargis and G. M. Slater, Agricultural Superintendent of All Weather Estate, arrived at the property on which the stumps were to be planted, after the cargo was en route from Zamboanga. They had constructed a dock, built shelters, felled jungle, repaired rail-line and bridges, and dug planting holes during record tropical rains, but were ready for the trees when they came.

About two weeks later all of the living trees were planted and properly labeled, by inexperienced labor. Survival was good, and few of the varieties were not represented by living plants. Growth started in remarkable manner, and a bright future appeared to be ahead of the infant project at the end of 1935.

THE VILLAIN APPEARS—SOUTH AMERICAN LEAF-BLIGHT

At this time J. B. Ingle was arranging with the Costa Rican Government a contract to initiate rubber plantings in that country. During the course of the negotiations the author made a trip to Costa Rica to see a small area of Hevea that the Cia. Bananera de Costa Rica, Costa Rican division of the United Fruit Company, had planted near the town of Cano. The planting had been done between the years 1923 and 1926, and the area was abandoned after the rubber prices fell to low levels.

B. E. Bookout, of United Fruit, and the author were not prepared for the desolate sight that greeted them as they started down the Cairo Branch of the Northern Railway. Many Hevea trees carried more bromeliads than leaves. Branches were dying, bark was white and unhealthy, and the few leaves that were left were shattered and covered with harsh black spore-bearing protuberances. Here it was—the South American leaf-blight; our enemy was emplaced before we had arrived. Within the next few days, visits to Turrialba, Costa Rica, and Almirante, in the northern edge of the Republic of Panama, located the infestation firmly established in both places.

What now? Samples of the diseased leaves were sent by the first plane to John A. Stevenson, senior physiologist of the Bureau of Plant Industry, in the United States Department of Agriculture. Back came the confirmation that it was South American leaf-blight. The contract with Costa Rica was before the deputies for the third reading. It had not yet been signed. Should the company assume the responsibility of fighting the disease, or should it admit that the situation was hopeless, and retire? This question was placed before the officials in Akron by Mr. Ingle. Soon their decision came; Goodyear was willing to undertake the job of licking the disease.

LEAF-BLIGHT STUDY REPLACES COMMERCIAL PLANTING

The contract with the Costa Rica Government was signed, and work began on the old rubber plantation near Cairo. This was purchased from the Cia. Bananera de Costa Rica in order that we might have available a source of seeds and diseased trees for our experimental work. Plans were changed. It was no longer safe to plan for a commercial plantation in Costa Rica until experimental work had shown how the disease could be controlled. The disease had not yet appeared in the plantation or nurseries in

Panama nor was it present in a nursery or a small planting of trees at the Summit Garden, in the Canal Zone. Perhaps the eastern clones there were safe for the present.

The Ford Motor Company plantations in Brazil were in the native home of the disease, as well as in the heart of the domain of the Hevea tree. The staff of these plantations had been working in their location for about nine years. Dr. Georald Stahel, in Paramaribo, Suriname, had spent many years of investigation on this disease. At least one plantation had been reported to have survived in rather good condition in Trinidad. Some possibility of having the Hevea tree live in the presence of the disease must exist. We needed to know what had been done and what factors favored the survival of the Hevea tree in the presence of *Dothidella ulei*, in order to avoid duplication of former work in our experimental program.

The author made a trip to Trinidad, British Guiana, Suriname, and Brazil during May and June of 1936. He saw on the Non-Pareil Estate in Trinidad about 1000 acres of rubber with full crowns of healthy leaves. The nearby Sangre Grande Estate was heavily diseased and of no value. In Suriname the opportunity to talk with Dr. Stahel was welcomed. Here was a man with years of experience in the attempt to combat the disease. He had devoted his life to trying to improve the lot of the planters on a flat, water-logged soil that had defeated every effort to make it support profitable crops. Hevea was no exception. The tree quickly succumbed to disease unless it was planted on the high, well-drained canal banks. Dr. Stahel had tried to control *Dothidella ulei* by means of Bordeaux mixture. He reported slight success in nurseries in which he had cut back the tops and forced all flushes to appear at about the same time. He had not encountered *Hevea brasiliensis* trees with resistance to South American leaf-blight, but was much interested in the possibility that there were such trees.

On the Ford Plantations on the Tapajos River Dr. J. R. Weir had started experiments in which he had budded a top of *Hevea guyanensis* at a height of about six feet on the trunk of a high-yielding, non-resistant clone.

The *Hevea guyanensis* top had considerable resistance and made good growth. At this time no tapping had been done on a high-yielding trunk which had a low-yielding species as a crown. This appeared to be an interesting experimental approach, but for successful large-scale application required.

1. A species or clone of rubber that would be resistant under all conditions, that would make a good union with the high-yielding clones of *H. brasiliensis*, and that would not influence the yield or quality of the rubber obtained from the high-yielding trunk.

2. Clones of high-yielding Hevea that would grow large enough to be top-budded without being seriously damaged by leaf-blight; or a method of protecting the trees until they reached this size.
3. Some method of maintaining the budwood supply of the high-yielding clones in good condition.

Bordeaux mixture had been applied with hand sprayers to the non-resistant, high-yielding trees in the multiplication nurseries of Fordlandia Estate. It had not given satisfactory protection to the trees. The climate of the Ford Estates, particularly the Belterra Estate at the time of this visit in 1936, permitted many of the eastern clones to grow to top-budding size without serious damage by the disease. The dry season protected the trees and gave them an opportunity to form undamaged leaves during a portion of each year. This was not the situation in Central America, in areas with evenly distributed rainfall. Here top-working was not a solution until we had a satisfactory spray procedure, or until we had high-yielding clones that were also resistant enough to make fairly normal growth when subjected to heavy spore deposits.

A second discovery, made at Belterra Estate by A. Johnston and his staff, was of outstanding value to operations in Central America. They found that the seeds gathered from the vicinity of their estates on the banks of the Tapajos River gave little resistance to attacks of South American leaf-blight to their seedlings when they were planted in nurseries. When the nurseries were planted with seeds that came from trees growing near the mouth of the Amazon, growth was almost normal; few of the seedlings were defoliated, and budding success was improved. Here was a family of trees with a high degree of natural resistance. This population should give resistance to high-yielding clones when the two types were combined by crosses. Seedlings from this source on the plantation should have their yields checked, to see if high-yielding resistant selections were immediately available.

The Ford Company at this time had only a few of the clones that had been developed in the Indies. Goodyear had many of these, but desired the seeds from the resistant families in order to get well-grown nurseries for rootstock. A proposal was made to the Brazilian Government that they permit an exchange of planting materials between the two companies. An agreement was reached which would permit the exchange of budwood but not of seeds at that time. In 1937, budwood of some of the highest-yielding clones was shipped to the Ford Estates in return for budwood of resistant seedlings from the Ford Estates. These clones were studied to determine whether the resistance expressed itself under the climatic conditions of Central America as well as it did in Brazil. Observers were not disappointed. When clones that had been selected as being the most resistant among Sumatran clones were defoliated, these resistant clones from Brazil developed only a few spots on their leaves.

Progeny grown from these clones are now producing seeds in Panama and Costa Rica. Seedlings from this source grown in unsprayed nurseries are almost equivalent in growth and vigor to seedlings grown in sprayed nurseries. This permits us to eliminate nursery spraying of our rootstock from the list of our essential estate operations, and reduces planting cost here. These seedlings represent one of Brazil's many important contributions in our progress in the battle with South American leaf-blight.

ASSISTANCE FROM THE UNITED STATES DEPARTMENT OF AGRICULTURE

During the steps that were taken to get rubber plantations initiated in Panama and Costa Rica by the Goodyear Company, the United States Government was consulted and informed of the progress made. The company did not consider that it should carry, with the Ford Company, the full burden of the experimental program that was essential if South American leaf-blight was to be eliminated as a menace to the rubber plantation industry of this hemisphere. Clearly it was in the national interest to have a rubber industry established here, and a portion of the job should become a public responsibility through government agricultural agencies.

Agencies of the executive branches of the government took a sincere interest in the project and gave it all the assistance that they could within their restricted budgets. This assistance was of great value, but it appeared to those who were working on the problem that the urgency for a solution required that the United States Department of Agriculture utilize its extensive research facilities on the spot.

Congress on two occasions refused to find reason for alarm in the rubber supply position and turned down requests for appropriations to support a research station to investigate the problems that kept rubber plantations from developing in Latin America. A third request was made after war was already in progress, and after the rubber supply was menaced. This request was partially granted. It is useless to speculate what a difference in the rubber supply during the war years would have resulted had the first request, made four years earlier, been granted.

After the appropriation became available to the Department of Agriculture, things began to happen. Survey parties quickly spread over the tropical areas of Latin America, looking for areas suitable for plantations, and for new mother trees that would give clones that combined high yield and resistance to South American leaf-blight. Introductions of the high-yielding clones on Pathfinder Estate were again made, this time to places where the South American leaf-blight had not established itself. Seeds of good clones were shipped from the Firestone Plantations in Liberia.

Dr. R. D. Rands, capable pathologist of the Department, who had studied rubber diseases in Java and South America before he confined his attention to the problems of sugar-growing, and who had written an important survey of the South American leaf-blight, came to Central America and Panama to investigate and plan a program of experimental attempts to control the disease with sprays, all of which had been disappointing. He arranged for Dr. M. H. Langford to come at once to the Goodyear All Weather Estate in Panama. He was to check the effectiveness of new spray materials, to be applied with the latest type of equipment, as a control measure.

A young nursery that was set aside for the test was badly damaged by the disease before the equipment arrived. Dr. Langford went to work on it with the selfless devotion of the true scientific worker. He walked for miles through the rain in order to be on the job if an hour of clear weather permitted him to get his sprays applied on schedule. He watched the new leaves of the sprayed plots emerge, unfold, and mature without damage, while the leaves on the unsprayed plots often withered and fell. He watched some of the preparations fail. He practiced variations in his schedules of treatment. When finally it appeared that the spray was working, he sprayed the plants with suspensions of spores to insure that they had an opportunity of becoming infected. The satisfactory treatments still kept the spores from getting a foothold. When the weather interfered with a spray schedule and permitted the disease to produce spores on some of the new leaves, he found that its progress could be arrested by subsequently increasing the frequency of treatments.

RESISTANCE AND YIELD UNITED IN SINGLE TREE

The vital link in the shackles which were prepared for *Dothidella ulei* had been completed. With a successful spray procedure available it was now possible to protect the high-yielding, non-resistant clones from eastern sources in the nursery or field, and to keep them growing rapidly until they were large enough to have a completely resistant top budded on them.

Yield figures had by this time been obtained from the first few top-budded trees on the Ford Plantations. These indicated that the low-yielding resistant top had no apparent influence on the amount of latex that the trunk portion of the tree produced. If the crown was healthy and elaborated quantities of starch, a trunk of high-yielding parentage still filled a large cup with latex, just as it did when it had a full crown of its own leaves. Such trees, once established, should meet any severity of infestation of *Dothidella ulei* without serious damage, and should yield as well as the same clones did in the best plantations of the Indies.

South American leaf-blight had been reduced from a menace to a mere nuisance. Many refinements in the procedure of its control remain to be made before it can be forgotten as a factor which will delay planting and increase costs of planting. As one example, when high-yielding trees are budded at a height of six feet, three or more feet of the top of the tree must be cut off to force new growth to come from the bud. This delays the growth of the tree for approximately six months. The procedure requires the attention of a skilled budder. This limits the use of this planting material of the high-yielding, non-resistant clones to plantations or experimental stations which have trained personnel. Throughout the research program to combat South American leaf-blight, the author has worked toward a final goal of a *Hevea brasiliensis* tree which will have both the resistance of the best Brazilian seedlings and the yield of the best eastern clones. Only material of this quality will find enthusiastic reception among the planters of small farms, who have little knowledge of complicated horticultural procedure. They must be saved from every possible hazard before a new crop will be acclaimed.

When the author made his first trip to the Ford Plantations in 1936, he found J. A. Zilles and Charles Townsend keenly interested in selecting and breeding from the wild Hevea of the Amazon valley clones that may be better adapted to their needs than were the non-resistant clones of the Indies. They had resistant trees that were making outstanding growth. They also had eastern clones with high yield. Could these not be crossed? The author agreed that they could and that they should be crossed, and pointed out the procedure that had been used in the Indies for making such crosses. From 1937, this program was followed assiduously. Hundreds of seedlings of various families were made and were planted in the field. There they were subjected to the disease. Some of these seedlings, which had a high-yielding parent, escaped the heaviest disease ravages in remarkable fashion, and some of the families contained a large percentage of seedlings with strong resistance. L. A. Beery, Jr., who had worked on the rubber breeding and selection program of the Goodyear Plantations in Sumatra, went to Brazil to study the Ford hybrids for the Bureau of Plant

Industry of the United States Department of Agriculture. He was much impressed with the resistance of the seedlings among these crosses and remained for two years to make thousands of new crosses. Many new combinations, recombinations, and back-crosses were made. In the germ-plasm of some of these seedlings probably rests the greatest hope of the owner of a small plot of land in Latin America who wishes to use a part of this land for rubber planting.

At this point the Government of Brazil re-enters the program of development of suitable Hevea planting material for the Americas. Young Brazilian scientific workers assisted Mr. Beery in his work, and the precious seeds that developed from his crosses were flown from the Tapajos to the well-equipped experimental center that is being established at Belem. Dr. Felisberto Camargo, director of the thriving young research center at the Instituto do Norte, Belem, has these seedlings planted and studied by his competent staff until they are approved and become the foundation stock for plantations in Latin America.

INTERNATIONAL COOPERATION PAYS A DIVIDEND

The combat with South American leaf-blight has provided a splendid example of international interdependence and cooperation. Brazil contributed the original *Hevea brasiliensis* trees. These, in the Netherlands Indies and Malaya, were improved in their yields to a level that no known native tree has approached. The improved types were maintained in the Philippines, and were established in Panama and Costa Rica by the Goodyear Company. This company also brought to its plantations the full experience gained from practice and research in the major plantation areas of the world.

Some of the improved clones were returned to Brazil by the Ford Company, but would not grow successfully there in the presence of disease. The Ford Company added a system of protecting the trees by top-budding, and first recognized a population of Hevea trees with a high level of natural resistance to South American leaf-blight. They started to combine the good qualities of the clones from the Indies with the most resistant trees that had been left at home in the Amazon. Brazilian scientists assisted in this.

The Bureau of Plant Industry of the United States Department of Agriculture contributed a satisfactory spray technique which made it possible to utilize clones that would otherwise have been lost. The Costa Rican Government cooperated with them in setting up a research station in which the plant materials developed at all other points could be brought together and tested under uniform conditions of infection. From this station planting material is again distributed to the countries that utilize their capital and labor to build producing plantations. The battle with the left wilt has been conducted with frictionless speed because of the same coordinated international effort in one direction that is now winning battles for the United Nations.

NO PERMANENTLY DISEASE-FREE AREAS IN WESTERN HEMISPHERE

The possibility of establishing successful plantations in Latin America remained solely of academic interest until the conquest of South American leaf-blight had been completed. All rubber-producing plants other than *Hevea brasiliensis* were quickly eliminated as the bases of the new industry. During emergency periods, as the present war, profitable production of rubber has been possible from Castilla, Manihot, Guayule, and other rubber-producing plants. These are almost completely superceded as rubber producers by Hevea plantations at any time of normal world trade. An industry in Latin American countries will not be able to maintain a competitive position unless it is based on the most efficient known producer of rubber. This is *Hevea brasiliensis*.

No one can be certain that any area now free from South American leaf-blight will long remain so. After the introduction of eastern clones to Panama in 1935, the disease reached All Weather Estate in eight months. It had also extended its range to include formerly disease-free sites in the Summit Gardens in the Canal Zone, the Pacific coastal area of Costa Rica, and the Turbo and Acandi areas of Colombia. Any planting that is done in this hemisphere must have the assurance of ample protection throughout its productive life. Otherwise, infestation at the height of production may bring ruin to estates planted in areas that are now free of disease.

SMALL FARMS HOLD KEY TO LARGE-SCALE RUBBER PRODUCTION

Having brought disease under control, the chief problem was one of fitting high-yielding, disease-resistant *Hevea brasiliensis* as a new crop to be grown within the established social and economic structure of the region, without diverting necessary manpower from the production of the essentials of life. Labor rates in this area are generally high, and the diversion of even small numbers of laborers from the production of the customary food or export crops is generally followed by a reduction in the essentials or by a general increase in wages.

What a different situation this is from that in the large population centers of the Indies. There approximately 70,000,000 residents of the Netherlands Indies were crowded into a small portion of the fertile area. Java, with an area approximately twice the area of Costa Rica, had a population of 45,000,000. Costa Rica has an equally fertile soil and favorable climate and yet finds it necessary to import a portion of its essential basic foods to support a population of about 750,000. China and India, each with populations of over 400,000,000, had very largely utilized the fertile soils within their borders and had reduced the amount of land per family to a point that permitted one to obtain the essentials of life during years of good crops. Crop failures brought famine to millions.

Contiguous to this heavy pressure of a population to find new opportunities were tremendous expanses of fertile, remote, unpopulated areas of feral jungle, in Sumatra, Malaya, Borneo, and elsewhere. Enormous expenditures of labor and money were required to establish communications, open jungle, combat diseases of men and plants in order to make from the waste jungle the world's leading area of productivity of tropical products. The situation was ideally suited to the development of large agricultural corporations, and it was this type of organization which gave the initial impetus to opening this area. When the area was opened and facilities established by the new industry, laborers who had been imported into the zone saw their opportunity and planted small adjacent farms for themselves. Over half of the rubber-productive capacity of the Netherlands Indies lies in such small properties.

In 1934, the Government of the Philippine Islands, facing independence from the United States and the establishment of tariffs on certain products which had previously enjoyed duty-free entry into the United States, studied the development of non-dutiable products for export. J. B. Ingle, then Resident Director of the Goodyear Rubber Plantations Company, was called to Manila to advise the government on the suitability of rubber for such a need.

He outlined a plan, based on the successful production of rubber on small farms in Java, Sumatra, and Malaya. He recommended that the government start small plantations or nurseries in each potential rubber-producing locality. The budded trees were to be distributed from these nurseries for general planting in the small areas. He advised that each small grower be permanently established on his own property of approximately ten hectares of land. In the first year one or two hectares should be planted by the man and his family to rice, corn, or other food crop. As the food crop was planted, budded rubber trees from the government nursery should be planted among the rows of grain. The grain would provide support for the family, and give them cash income during the period that the rubber was untappable. This area was to be used for such crops for about two years after the rubber was first planted, and another area was then to be opened for the food crops. The first area would by this time be shaded, and would need only an annual slashing of the woody growth between the rubber trees to keep the rubber growing.

When Mr. Ingle later come to Costa Rica to initiate the development of rubber planting, he brought with him the same ideas which he had advanced to the Government of the Philippines. Here was a land with a similar social structure. It was a matter of local pride that every citizen had the opportunity to own and cultivate his own *finquita*. Agricultural credits were available for the small planters through a strong national bank. The population was primarily agricultural, intelligent, and diligent. The soil and climate factors were favorable, and much of the best land for rubber planting was very sparsely populated.

A highly developed culture of coffee and sugar-cane existed in the same area where food crops were grown by primitive hand-tool culture. Here the situation was typical of that in many regions of Latin America. Conditions were eminently suited to the development of the small-farm production of rubber. They did not favor the establishment of large corporate estate holdings.

The interest of the Goodyear Company was primarily centered upon getting a source of rubber established in the western hemisphere. The company was not concerned in the promotion of any political doctrine or social theory. Its policy was based on a careful analysis of the hazards inherent in having the rubber for the world come almost entirely from one small area. In that area the product was subject to the threat of local disturbances, war, and to control by a small international group, which gave the consumers no vote in its decisions.

The company did not start its estates until it was convinced that the profitable operation of small estates here was reasonably certain. Never in the plans of the company for the plantations was there any desire to be the only producer of rubber in any country. Far from it. The officials anticipated that each plantation should be a center which would demonstrate that the profitable production of rubber is possible, and an example to the local planters of the latest commercial practices of rubber culture. The company has never grown a large portion of the rubber that it uses in its manufacturing operations, and had no wish to do so now. It was prepared to purchase the rubber that was grown by the estates that planted this crop, at a price which was determined by the world market conditions, the same price which it paid to its own estates for their rubber.

VARIETY OF CROPS YIELDS PERPETUAL PROFIT

Rubber has proved to be an almost ideal crop for a portion of the terrain of the owner of a small farm in moist tropical areas. The trees can be grown among cash crops of grain for two or more years. Planting cost of the rubber is low. After the trees shade the ground too much to permit grain crops to be grown among them, little further care is required by them until they become tappable.

When the trees reach the size for tapping, a man and his family can maintain and tap an area of two hectares or more for each working member of the family. Tapping can be done only on rainless mornings, so the family is not required to be in the field during heavy tropical downpours. When rains fall and the trees are not tapped, their capacity to give a full yield during subsequent tappings is only temporarily reduced. A crop is not lost or ruined, as may happen to other crops in long-extended downpours.

If, as is recommended, the small farms have a portion of the area planted with other crops, or in pasture for animals, part of the family's time will be utilized in caring for those crops. During those periods the rubber trees can get the periodic rest from tapping that they require. Rubber is not a seasonal crop which requires that the crop be harvested within a few days lest a year's work be lost. If latex is washed from the tapping cups by a sudden shower, only the crop for that day is lost, and the tree stands ready to give its full crop at the next tapping. The crop can be stored until roads are dry before it is hauled to a shipping point, or it can be dried quickly and sold within a week after the latex is collected. Since tapping continues throughout the year, there are no seasonal peaks or valleys in prices. The product can quickly be turned into cash at any time.

Seldom are the prices of all the products that can be grown as inter-crops for rubber low at the same time. If rubber prices are low, the trees need not be tapped and the family can utilize their full time for other crops. When rubber prices are very high, intensive tapping can greatly increase yields for a period of several months.

The preparation of rubber for marketing from the latex requires only simple, inexpensive equipment which can be operated successfully by each grower. Without exceptional skill each small farmer can turn out rubber sheets equal in market value to those produced on large estates. Sheet rubber, if kept in a relatively dry place, does not absorb sufficient moisture to spoil. It has a high value per pound when compared with transportation costs. For this reason, it can be profitably grown farther from a shipping point than can grains or products with a lower value per pound.

World trade in rubber fixes quality and price limitations within a sufficiently narrow margin to prevent local price speculation from causing loss to the producer. There is an expanding local and world market for the product, and we can anticipate a particularly heavy demand for a number of years while the world replaces the deficit in production during the Japanese occupation of the rubber-producing areas. We cannot expect the extreme fluctuation in rubber prices that we have had in the past. These prices have fluctuated between three cents and three dollars per pound, a behavior that may be expected from such a flexible product as rubber. Future prices will have as their ceiling approximately the cost of production of synthetic. Synthetic producers have shown themselves able to cope with war demands within a few years' time, and certainly will enter the market when it becomes profitable for them to do so. Lower prices will be determined by the cost efficient group of natural rubber producers. This may possibly be the group of owners of small farms in Latin America, each with a few hectares of high-yielding rubber trees that have resistant crowns.

Factors similar to those mentioned above influenced the owners of small properties in the Indies when they planted rubber extensively and for years found this crop to produce their most important source of income. Some government assistance and encouragement was given them in getting the crop established. When the growers once learned the advantages of the crop, its spread exceeded all anticipation. Soon the small growers produced more than did all of the plantations in the Netherlands Indies. They became the major factor in producing the temporary surplus of rubber in the world's markets.

Fortunately for the potential rubber planter in Latin America, these holdings were all planted with ordinary unselected planting material. The small Latin American planter will have available to him some of the world's highest yielding clones and will have a decided advantage in competition with his contemporaries in the Indies.

ADAPTATIONS OF PLANTING PRACTICE AID ADVANCEMENT

The sudden appearance of South American leaf-blight had halted all research or assistance that would have helped the small farmers get their properties planted with rubber until safe planting material was ready for distribution. By this time the United States Department of Agriculture had cooperative work in progress in a number of the tropical Latin

American countries. It had a central experimental station, in cooperation with the Government of Costa Rica, at Turrialba, Costa Rica. This station, under the direction of Dr. T. J. Grant, has become a center of investigation of disease, has ample facilities for the distribution of both resistant and high-yielding planting materials through its cooperating stations in other countries, and aids in the dissemination of innovations in planting practice that are reported from any of the cooperators. The Goodyear Company gladly relinquished all such functions and has confined itself to the problems of its own estate.

Under the management of W. E. Klippert, the staff of the Goodyear Plantations continued selection for resistance. Some of the eastern clones were more resistant than were the majority. Some of these had been known to give excellent yields in Sumatra. In 1940, the best of these were planted in large plots where their reaction to the disease could be studied under plantation conditions. Most of the clones proved unable to withstand increasing infection. One group was outstanding. These trees were budded from a few trees which were the most resistant seedlings among a nursery of 1,000,000 plants. Also undamaged were the buddings from the resistant seedlings that originated in the Belem area of Brazil. Each of these plots contained many trees at four years of age that were eighteen inches in circumference—generally considered a suitable size for tapping to begin.

This rate of growth was compared to the growth of trees of 288 clones in a clone-test area on the Dolok Merangir Estate of the Goodyear Rubber Plantations Company, in Sumatra. That estate was located on one of the soils best suited to rubber that was to be found in Sumatra. It was a very pleasant surprise to learn that the growth of resistant types of rubber trees on the Atlantic coast of Coasta Rica in four years was almost exactly equivalent to the growth in five years on that fertile area of Sumatra.

The rapid growth of the trees in Costa Rica should be duplicated in other equally fertile zones of Latin America. Such growth will result in most important savings in upkeep cost during the immaturity of the trees. It will also reduce the period that it will be necessary to await income from an area. This helps to reduce the differential cost of opening plantations in Latin America and in Sumatra.

The cost of upkeep of planted areas of rubber in Costa Rica was higher in proportion to the cost of this operation in Sumatra than was any other important estate charge. Any reduction of this cost gave vital assistance to plans for new planting. Cover crops, such as *Pueraria javanica, Centrosema pubescens,* and *calopogoniup,* which had so successfully assisted in keeping out the competitive growth in Sumatra, did not grow strongly enough to suppress the growth of wild vegetation in Costa Rica. Mr. Klippert and Sr. Hernan Echeverri, Administrator of Speedway Estate, in Costa Rica, tried many systems of maintaining the cover crop in a dominant condition, but without success. Finally it was generally agreed that only a man with a machete could cope with the growth between the rubber trees and keep those trees dominant over their surrounding vegetation. Monthly cleaning of the rows of young trees was required, and the woody growth between rows was held in check by cutting it back at intervals of about six months. These operations required that one man work for about one day each month on each acre of young rubber. No substitute could be found for the tedious hand work connected with cleaning and slashing, which was limited in out-turn by the strength of a man's arm and his ability to complete his task in the cool hours of the day. A large proportion of the labor on a young rubber estate was occupied on this operation. If labor savings are to be made on the estate, this was a place to make them.

The remarkable vigor of growth of grass and shrubs between the rows of rubber was an excellent indicator of the high fertility of the soil of the Speedway Estate. For some months there had been a chronic shortage of food grains in Costa Rica, and their prices were inflated. This brought with it a demand for an increase in wages. There was no accompanying increase in prices of commodities that entered world commerce, as did coffee and rubber.

CAN MACHINES BE USED?

It became obvious to the author that here was an opportunity to work out a solution for several problems at the same time. Food crops should grow well on the fertile soil between the rubber rows, should help reduce cost of upkeep, and should help provide foods at a reasonable cost, at least within the Goodyear Plantations. Officials of the company had long recommended that small farmers use this mixed culture in order to get stands of rubber at small cost. Was this type of culture not also adapted for use in larger developments on a modified basis?

A study was made of the native cultures in the neighborhood of Speedway Estate, in Costa Rica, to find what problems were of paramount importance in reducing the area of crops planted by the neighbors of this region. It was found that:

1. In the rain-forest climatic zone, where there is no definite dry season during a year, the harvesting period of crops may often

coincide with a period of heavy rains. Large fields of crops cannot be harvested at such a season if facilities for drying the crop depend on the heat of the sun, which is the customary procedure here.

2. Sun-drying in areas of high humidity did not reduce the moisture content of grains sufficiently to permit the dried grain to be stored or shipped with safety. Spoilage of grains en route to market was high, and the grains of this region must be consumed immediately after they reached market.

3. Soil preparation for crops depended on the help of fire to reduce weed growth before a crop was planted. The soil was not stirred, weed competition was high, and crop yields were consequently low. There was a theory that the corn growth in this region would not find sufficient foothold in plowed land and would fall over, permitting the crop to spoil.

4. Transportation of grains from field to shipping point was by pack-horse over roads that were often deep in mud. Distance from the shipping point soon became a limiting factor in eliminating an area from crop use.

5. No central storage of grains was available in the producing areas. Such an area may ship its grains to market and between crops pay freight for having similar articles brought into the area as food. Crops could be marketed only during harvest seasons, when prices were usually low.

6. Grains were badly mixed and had not been selected with care for adaptation to the area or for yield.

7. No fertilizing of producing fields had been practiced. Bush and weed growth was permitted to develop for several years between consecutive crops on the same land. Some ash was deposited on the surface of the ground when this growth was burned in preparation for a new crop. It was not worked into the surface, and probably was only partly available to the crop.

8. The crops that were grown were predominantly starchy in content. There was a shortage of protein foods available for both men and their animals.

Officials of the Goodyear Rubber Plantations Company approved a small experiment in growing food crops between the rubber rows. An attempt was to be made to overcome as many as possible of the problems that had plagued the local farmers. Fire could not be utilized to free the spaces between the rubber rows from weeds, brush, and stumps. These were removed by ax and machete, and were piled along the rubber rows, leaving a clean strip to be plowed with a disc plow. Only by plowing the land before each crop could weeds be controlled and continuous crops grown on the same land. A rubber-tired tractor which was on the farm served the purpose well in pulling plows and the disc harrow. Earth roads were built into the area to provide transportation. A dryer was constructed to dry the grains properly. Fertilizers were applied, new crops were introduced and studied, and the factors that determined seasons for planting were investigated.

Some crop failures resulted when crops of beans and peanuts ripened during periods of heavy rains. Excellent crops of them were harvested when weather was good. Loss came from having a dry season coincide with a newly planted rice crop. Out-of-season corn suffered severely from attacks of southern root-worm and flea beetles. Some of these losses could be eliminated by adjustment of cultural practices, and some could not. The crop that best suited the needs at all seasons was corn, and all efforts were concentrated on it. When the corn was planted during the seasons of low root-worm infestation, excellent crops were obtained. It could be planted and cultivated with horse-drawn equipment and required less hand work than did other crops. The ripe crop was able to remain in the field through several days of continuous rain without serious damage. The crop was easily dried in bulk, with heat for drying provided by the cobs of former crops.

The corn of the region was badly mixed. Each field was a hodge-podge of stalks of varied color, maturity, and productivity. Surely some of the types were better adapted to planting in this zone than were others. Field selection gave seed for immediate planting that brought some improvement in the crop.

Self-pollinated lines were established from the most promising plants as a first step toward obtaining adapted types. Three generations each year were grown. At times the planting season for the lines coincided with the season of heaviest infestation by the root-worm. Most of the lines were lost at these periods, but a few were outstanding in their survival. Perhaps these lines will provide a step toward complete adaptation, and may even yield a variety that can be planted at any time of the year without fear of loss from root-worm. It is yet too early to say.

Seed of foreign varieties of corn was obtained from Merle T. Jenkins, principal agronomist in charge of corn investigations for the United States Department of Agriculture; from Prof. P. C. Mangelsdorf, of the Botanical Museum of Harvard University; from Ing. C. G. del Valle, phytogeneticist of the Agricultural Experiment Station at Santiago de Las

Vegas, Cuba; from Prof. Jay B. Park, of the Department of Agronomy, Ohio State University; and from Atherton Lee, then of the Agricultural Experiment Station, Mayaguez, Puerto Rico. Some odd results were noted in the behavior of these varieties, but some grew well and have been included among the lines that are in the test plots. Some may have a place in a future corn hybrid or variety that will produce more in tropical regions than do some of the present mixed varieties. It is too early to estimate the behavior of these lines, as the first crosses have just been planted in test plots.

RUBBER SHOWS GROWTH INCREASE WHEN INTERCROPPED

The program of growing crops had not continued long until it became evident that an unexpected advantage was being realized from the cultivation. It had been anticipated that the crops would not interfere with the growth of the rubber, but not that the rubber trees would make a more rapid growth when crops replaced the customary undergrowth. After a crop of corn was harvested, it was noted that the rubber trees had an unusually fine appearance, much better than that of neighboring blocks in which crops were not grown. It was not possible to check this observation here, as not all of the blocks had the same history of treatments.

A new experimental area was chosen. One portion was planted according to the customary practice and was kept weeded, as usual, by men with sharp machetes. The experimental portion was plowed with a disc plow, lined in two directions so that it could be plowed or cultivated in each direction.

The plowed portion was planted with cowpeas. These were used instead of soybeans, as there was a local market for them. Excellent crops of soybeans had been grown, but were not in local demand. A second crop of cowpeas fell a victim of root-worms, mosaic, and rains at harvesting time, and was turned into the soil. Corn was then planted.

When the trees in these two areas were seven months of age, the height of the shoots was measured. Trees in the portion that had been weeded with a machete in the usual manner were at this time 18.24 inches tall. Those which had been cultivated on plowed land, and which had two crops of cowpeas planted as inter-crops, had in the same time reached a height of 25.38 inches, an increase of thirty-nine percent above the plots with the usual upkeep. Some plots were cultivated as were the above, and also had 250 grams of forty-eight percent acid phosphate fertilizer mixed with the soil of the planting hole at the time that the rubber trees were planted. Trees in these plots now had a height of 26.12 inches, or an increase of forty-three percent above the growth in the plots that had the customary upkeep.

Both cultivation and the addition of phosphate fertilizer had aided the growth of the young rubber trees, when compared to the growth made by trees that were forced to compete with a heavy inter-growth of grass and weeds. The effect of the cultivation was much greater than was the added effect of the fertilizer. It is not known how much of this early effect will be continued to tapping size, or how much earlier these trees can be top-budded. A saving in time required to reach top-budding size will reduce the time that it is necessary to spray these non-resistant clones in the field.

Experimental costs have still masked possible savings in upkeep charges that may eventually accrue from the use of mechanical power instead of manpower for weeding between the rubber rows. Cost of many operations have been drastically reduced since the start of the experiment, and the investment in this project is now being reduced by income from it.

While the necessary research to determine the extent which inter-planted crops will help to bear planting and upkeep costs of rubber estates will need to be reconsidered in each area in which rubber is planted, the present prospects from this type of cultivation are encouraging. There appears to be a possibility for estate areas, as well as small farms, to utilize cultivation and intercrops to assist them in rapidly establishing stands of high-yielding Hevea rubber. Machines may carry some of the tedious upkeep jobs and permit a few men to extend the area that they can keep free of weeds. Crops may be able to pay for the cultivation and thereby greatly reduce the cost of opening new rubber estates.

SUMMARY AND CONCLUSIONS

Hevea brasiliensis, after having gone from Brazil to the Indies, returned to Latin America improved and refined by its travels. It soon met its old enemy, South American leaf-blight, and required new blood from its native home, horticultural care, and sprays to protect it and bring it into the full productivity that it had obtained in the disease-free areas. When given the required care and attention, the Hevea trees throve in the new location and reached tapping size a year sooner than they had in the best locations in the center of the world's rubber-producing centers.

Small land-owners of Latin America should find that this new Hevea brings to them a culture which they can plant within their areas of food crops. Eventually they will have a permanent crop which can be harvested for immediate cash at any period of the year. Little cost is necessary to maintain the culture, once it is established. Certainly this crop should find a permanent and profitable place in the agricultural scene of many of the tropical Latin American countries.

6

Cinchona, the "Fever Tree"

By *WILSON POPENOE*

DIRECTOR DE LA ESCUELA
AGRÍCOLA PANAMERICANA

THE Hevea is the tree that made the world's elastic era. This chapter is the story of another tree that has saved the lives of peoples and empires. The Cinchona tree, the source of quinine, is one more of South America's priceless gifts to humanity, for quinine is still mankind's surest defense against malaria, the foremost communicable disease.

In origin the fever tree is inter-American. In current and recent times it has stood forth as an old American crop with new and dramatic importance to us and all nations. Dr. Wilson Popenoe is one of the Americas' most experienced and best accredited authorities on sources and cultures of quinine. Here he tells the story impartially and with lively interest.

6

THE PROBLEM

THE FIRST World War focused attention upon the seriousness of our
dependence on the Dutch East Indies for our supplies of quinine. Since
then much thought and effort have been given to the establishment of
Cinchona cultivations in the Western Hemisphere; to the possibility of
using all of the crystallizable Cinchona alkaloids instead of quinine alone;
to the synthesis of quinine and most important of all, to the substitution of
a synthetic product, atabrine, for the Cinchona alkaloids.

With the seizure of Java by the Japanese, the situation became a
matter of grave concern. The dramatic escape of Colonel Arthur Fischer
from the Philippines with a supply of Cinchona seed was widely publicized and helped materially to bring the American people to a realization
of their danger. Recently, the satisfactory results obtained with atabrine
seem to have allayed apprehension to a considerable degree, but it is perhaps too early for us to assume that the problem is solved. Those who
should know, consider that the Cinchona alkaloids will continue to occupy
an important position. The feature of greatest interest in this connection,
especially when we view the matter from an agricultural angle, is the
possible substitution, at least in part, of totaquina for quinine.

Totaquina is an anti-malarial which may contain all crystallizable
Cinchona alkaloids, that is, quinine, quinidine, cinchonine and cinchonidine. These are now believed to be more or less equally useful in the
treatment of malaria. But to make totaquina satisfactory to the medical
profession it will be necessary to supply a standard product. This has
already been attempted under specifications set down in the United States
Pharmacoepia, but there is perhaps need for improvement to reduce the
permissible percentage of toxic, non-crystallizable alkaloids, and to place
less emphasis upon the proportion of quinine.

Totaquina can be produced cheaply because the type of tree from
which it is obtainable is easier to grow and more widely adaptable than
the *Ledgeriana* race which has been cultivated in Java since the 1870's
for the production of quinine. Atabrine can be produced cheaply as

recent experience has demonstrated. But in neither case does this solve the whole problem. What the world needs is an efficient and cheap anti-malarial; and up to now there seems to be little relation between the cost of production and the price at which pills are sold over the counter in many tropical countries where malaria is rife. Most probably this phase cannot be satisfactorily solved without the intervention of interested governments.

THE HISTORY OF CINCHONA TO 1900

The discovery of the therapeutic value of Cinchona bark is involved in a maze of legend and tradition, doubly confusing because the name *quina*, by which it first became known to Europeans, was originally applied to Peruvian balsam (*Myroxylon peruiferum*). In a masterly investigation of the subject, A. W. Haggis has shown that Cinchona bark acquired this name in the early days when it was illicitly being used as a substitute for balsam. This makes some of the early accounts unreliable, since we cannot know to which plant they refer.

So far as is known today, the first authentic description is that of Antonio de la Calancha, an Augustinian monk whose work was published at Lima in 1633. This is of such interest as to merit reproduction here:

"There grows, in the region of Loja, a tree which they call árbol de calenturas (fever tree), the cinnamon-colored bark of which, taken in an amount equivalent to the weight of two *reales*, reduced to powder, and administered in the form of a potion, cures fevers including the tertian; it has produced marvellous results in Lima."

How long the merits of Cinchona had been recognized by the Spaniards before Calancha wrote this account we do not know. Probably not many years. Legend has built up diverse tales regarding its first discovery, most of them obviously unworthy of credence. But one thing seems to be clear. Knowledge of its merits came to the attention of the Spaniards at Loja, in what is now southern Ecuador, the region which throughout the seventeenth and part of the eighteenth centuries was the only known source of supply. Modern writers have argued that the use of Cinchona bark was known to the aboriginal inhabitants. If this is true, it was probably limited to the Loja region, else why did it take so long for the Spaniards to discover that Cinchona trees grew all the way from Colombia to Bolivia?

Sir Clements Markham, who possessed a passionate zeal for everything connected with Cinchona, published in elaborate form the generally accepted legend regarding its introduction into medicine through the cure of the wife of the Viceroy at Lima in 1638. Calancha's story proves that the drug was known to the Spaniards some years before that; and the recent discovery of an early manuscript in the archives at Sevilla shows that the legendary heroine of the tale, the wife of the Viceroy don Luis Geronomo Fernández de Cabrera y Bobadilla probably did *not* suffer from malaria, though the Viceroy himself did, on numerous occasions. It is quite possible that much attention was called to the merits of Cinchona bark by the cure of so illustrious a patient.

First mention of Cinchona in European literature, so far as known today, occurred in Belgium in the year 1643. From that time forward, use of the drug rapidly increased, due in great part to the activities of the Jesuits, whence arose the name "Jesuits Bark" which was widely employed in the early days.

Demand for the bark in Europe was keen, and was supplied by the forests in the vicinity of Loja until about 1775. Exploitation was so devastating that as early as 1735 the French scientist La Condamine, one of the first to make an investigation of the situation, as well as the Spaniard Ulloa, had warned that the supply was in danger of exhaustion. Then the discovery that Cinchona trees grew elsewhere in the Andes brought additional supplies to the fore.

It seems rather remarkable that during all this time—a century and a half—no determined effort was made to bring so valuable a tree into cultivation. Yet this can probably be accounted for by the fact that the best kinds are rather difficult to grow, and trees in the wild were still ample to meet the demand.

A keen interest developed in Java, where the Dutch were busy colonizing, and in India, where the British were building up their empire. In 1813, Dr. Ainslie bemoaned the fact that India did not grow her own supplies, a sentiment reiterated by Dr. Royce in 1835; while in Java the botanists Fritze, Miquel, and others argued for the introduction of the tree into that island. The Dutch were the first to take action. The botanist Weddell, who had made a study of Cinchona trees in the Andes, brought seeds to Europe; and in 1848 a few of the resulting plants reach Java. In 1852 the Dutch Government sent the botanist Hasskarl to Peru for plants and seeds of the best forms he could find.

The British were not far behind. The year that Hasskarl left for the Andes, efforts were made to get the British Government to send out an expedition. These bore fruit in 1859, when Clements R. Markham was instructed to organize an exploration of all important Cinchona-producing regions and bring to India material of as many valuable species as possible. Thus began one of the most dramatic series of events in the entire history of plant introduction. The work, in which Markham had the collaboration of the botanist Richard Spruce and several horticulturists from Kew Gardens, was successful. It remained for Charles Ledger, however, to lay the foundations of the modern Cinchona industry in the Far East, by sending seeds of a very superior strain from Bolivia in 1865. This strain was later named Ledgeriana in his honor.

Markham's program envisaged the cultivation of Cinchona not only in India and Ceylon, but also in the American tropics; and it is for this reason that his work is of particular interest to us. He sent seeds to Mexico, where the resulting plants were lost during the disturbances incident to the downfall of the ill-fated Maximilian; and he sent others to Jamaica, where serious efforts were made to establish Cinchona cultivation, with some success at the start. Later, with the fall in the price of bark in world markets, the cultivation was abandoned, though many trees are still to be found in a semi-wild state at the site of the early plantation in the Blue Mountains.

Probably because they had learned of developments in Jamaica and the Far East, enterprising agriculturists in Guatemala began to take notice. Julio Rossignon planted a few seeds at Cobán in 1860; and in 1878 the Sarg brothers, German settlers in the same region, obtained a supply from Ceylon through the good offices of Prince Nikolaus of Nassau. In this same year the Minister of Agriculture at Guatemala City, don Manuel Herrera, presented a lengthy memorandum to President Justo Rufino Barrios, urging the advantages of Cinchona cultivation.

The interest grew; and in 1883 Barrios contracted the services of W. J. Forsyth, an Englishman who had worked with Cinchona in tropical Asia. He was to bring seeds from Ceylon (which he did) and establish nurseries at several places. A year later extensive plantings had been made. The contract with Forsyth was terminated in 1886, however, and Cinchona culture in Gautemala entered into a period of decline from which it failed to recover. The causes are hard to determine at this late day. Colombia was shipping large quantities of wild bark, much of it superior in quality to that being produced in Guatemala; Java was beginning to enter the field with its high-grade Ledgeriana; bark prices were falling rapidly in world markets; and coffee was King.

THE KINDS OF CINCHONAS

Before proceeding further it is necessary to discuss briefly the species and forms of Cinchona which have in the past been important sources of anti-malarials, and which are now receiving attention in connection with the development of Cinchona culture in the American tropics. The subject is almost hopeless if we adhere to a strictly botanical classification. From the time of Linnæus to the present day, the botany of this genus has baffled every student. In the words of Walter Hodge, it is indeed "a botanical headache." This is due to the tremendous range of variation encountered among trees in the wild as well as in cultivation, and to the abundance of natural hybrids.

Authorities have not even been able to agree regarding the botanical standing of the best-known cultivated form, Ledgeriana. After giving serious thought to the matter, T. A. Sprague and N. Y. Sandwith at the Kew Herbarium summed up their findings: "It may be either a variety or a hybrid of *C. Calisaya*."

Early efforts to split the genus into many species—which later were found not to breed true when grown from seed—proved hopeless from the standpoint of the sound botanist as well as the practical agriculturist. The tendency in recent years has therefore been toward "lumping" the wild forms into a few definitely recognizable specific groups, admitting at the same time that within each of these there are many geographic forms of varying economic value.

We are interested in Cinchona as a source of anti-malarials, either as quinine or as total alkaloids. Viewed broadly the major materials with which we as agriculturists are working, or will work, are the following:

Cinchona Calisaya Wedd. Known to the trade in early days as Yellow Bark, and as Calisaya. This species is native to southern Peru and Ecuador, where it grows usually at elevations of 4000 to 6000 feet. The alkaloid content of wild trees is commonly three to six percent, of which four-fifths is quinine. Calisayas are extremely variable and rather difficult to cultivate, but plantations have existed in Bolivia for many years. Markham records that there were 20,000 trees of this species in Jamaica in 1878, but it has disappeared there. Many thousands have been planted recently in Guatemala, and some in southern Peru.

The Ledger variety of Calisaya must be considered separately. It is sometimes called *Cinchona Ledgeriana*. Its origin is Bolivia; but as a cultivated plant it is known only from the trees grown in the Asiatic tropics, where, as has been mentioned, Charles Ledger sent seed from Bolivia in 1865. It is now so hybridized with other species that it is hard for anyone to say just what is a Ledgeriana, and what is not. In Java it is cultivated principally at altitudes between 3500 and 6000 feet.

Many Ledgerianas were planted in Guatemala during the 1930's, from seed brought from Java. About the same time a planting was made in Peru by the Japanese, with seeds said to have come from Formosa. The United States Department of Agriculture has distributed plants to several tropical American countries in recent years.

Ledgeriana bark is the richest in quinine of all known Cinchonas, running as high as nine percent commercially, with occasional samples considerably higher. Cinchonidine and cinchonine content low; quinidine very low.

Cinchona officinalis L. Now usually termed *officinalis* by agriculturists. The wild product from the Andes was formerly known to the trade as Crown Bark, Loja Bark, and Pale Bark. Native from Colombia to northern Peru, usually at elevations between 6000 and 9000 feet. There are numerous forms, most of which were listed as species by the early botanists. The Uritusinga variety, found near Loja in southern Ecuador, is the classic Cinchona, probably the first to have been used by Europeans, and considered by Howard to have been the one on which Linnæus based his original description of the genus. This was one of the species planted when Cinchona cultivation was first undertaken in Java and India. It was tried also in Jamaica. It has received little attention in recent years.

Some of the wild forms are practically devoid of alkaloids, as is true also of *C. pubescens;* others show as much as six percent, though as Rusby says, "The alkaloidal content rarely exceeds 3.5%, three fifths of it quinine." The hybrid between this species and the Chimborazo form of *C. pubescens* is known in Java as *C. robusta.*

C. pubescens Vahl (*C. succirubra* Pavon ex Klotsch). An extremely variable group, occurring all the way from Costa Rica to Bolivia—the most widely distributed of all the Cinchonas. It has also a great altitudinal range in the wild, some of its forms growing at 2000 feet above the sea, others at 10,000. Many are practically worthless for the production of alkaloids; others (particularly the Red Bark found on the slopes of Chimborazo in Ecuador) are of value. Frequently high in cinchonidine, relatively so in cinchonine; low in quinine, and almost without quinidine. Occasional forms may contain as much as five percent quinine sulfate.

Because of its vigor and its adaptability to more unfavorable conditions of growth than Calisaya and Officinalis, it has attracted much attention ever since the beginnings of Cinchona cultivation; and it has been the species usually considered where anti-malarials other than pure quinine were the objective. It is widely and extensively used as a stock-plant on which to graft the more delicate Ledgeriana.

In the early days plantations of this species were made in Gautemala, in Jamaica, and also in Ecuador. It has persisted wherever established, and has hybridized freely with other species.

C. micrantha R & P. This is the Gray Bark of Peru, exploited commercially at one time, but of inferior quality, as it contains but little quinine and rarely more than four percent of total alkaloids. The botanist Standley suspects that it should be classified as a form of *C. pubescens*, which it resembles in its vigorous growth. It occurs in the wild from Ecuador to Bolivia, ranging from 2000 to 8000 feet in altitude. It was included among the species planted experimentally in Java and India, but its low alkaloid content soon resulted in its being dropped. It may be useful as a stock plant, or in connection with breeding work which is certain to be undertaken in tropical America.

C. pitayensis Wedd. A species native to southern Colombia and northern Ecuador, at elevations of 8500 to 10,000 feet. Its bark, which was formerly known to the trade as Pitayo Bark, now usually referred to simply as *pitayensis*, was in considerable demand during the early days because of its relatively high alkaloid content. It commonly shows about 3 percent of quinine sulfate; 2.5 percent of cinchonine, 0.5 percent of quinidine and a little cinchonidine.

So far as known, this species is not now in cultivation, though Markham stated that it was introduced into India in the 1860's. It is of interest because it grows at higher elevations, and hence is probably more cold-resistant than any other worthwhile Cinchona; and because its alkaloid content sometimes goes as high as eight percent.

If the Cinchona grower had only to select from this brief list of species one or several which seemed best adapted to his needs, the problem would be relatively simple. But in addition to a tremendous range of forms within each, he has also to take into account the hybrids, of which there appear to be many in the wild, and new ones occurring every day in cultivation. And it is precisely in this field that the greatest hope of Cinchona cultivation in tropical America is probably to be found. It is well known that first-generation hybrids often possess greater vigor than their parents. Many of the best Ledgeriana forms cultivated in Java are assumed to be natural hybrids between the original Ledgeriana introductions and other species cultivated in that island.

The future of Cinchona cultivation in this hemisphere not only offers great hope because of the possibilities inherent in the highly variable wild species, as well as through the production of new hybrids; it is at the same time one of the most intriguing, intricate, and highly specialized fields in tropical agriculture.

RECENT DEVELOPMENTS

Throughout the first three decades of the twentieth century, Cinchona cultivation in tropical America was in the doldrums. Aside from a few Calisaya plantations in Bolivia, which produced bark of sufficiently good quality so that the Dutch Kinabureau made regular purchases to keep it off a well-controlled world market, there was no commercial production of plantation bark, and shipments of wild bark from the Andes were negligible in quantity. Jamaica had passed out of the picture. Occasional trial shipments of low-grade bark from Guatemala (the only kind which had survived the vicissitudes of the earlier years) usually brought red-ink returns to the growers, or at best no satisfactory profit.

One factor alone was responsible for the revival which took place in the 1930's. This has already been mentioned—the strategic importance of freeing ourselves from dependence upon the Far East.

At the suggestion of the State Department in Washington, Merck and Company, largest American processors of Cinchona bark, generously offered to organize and finance the experimental work which must precede extensive commercial plantings in the western hemisphere. The task was not an easy one. At least ten years must elapse before it could be expected that the groundwork would be laid.

In 1933, Ledgeriana seed was purchased in Java and brought to Guatemala by Colonel Victor E. Ruehl, who arranged with don Mariano Pacheco H., Director of Agriculture at Guatemala City, and with a few local coffee planters, to establish seed beds and undertake the testing of this valuable stock. These were probably the first Ledgeriana plants to be grown in any quantity in tropical America.

The United Fruit Company cooperated in various ways. The United States Department of Agriculture ably supported the project. Seeds were obtained from the Philippines, from Amani in Africa, where the Germans had started to grow Cinchona before the first World War, and from other sources. Some of these were of the Ledgeriana strain; others were Succirubras, hybrids, and species thought to be of general interest. Some of the seeds were sent to Guatemala; others were propagated in the greenhouses of the Agricultural Department, near Washington, under the able direction of B. Y. Morrison.

Naturally, mistakes were made, and obstacles had to be overcome. Those who had worked with Cinchona in Guatemala during the 1880's were gone; there was no recent local experience on which to lean. But there remained the outstanding fact that Cinchona had been grown in Guatemala, and was still growing there. To gain experience as rapidly as possible, plantings were made at different elevations, and on different soils. Within a few years sturdy young trees were growing at Finca Helvetia, Finca El Zapote, Finca Panama, and one or two other places. Several areas were shortly found to be unsuitable for Ledgerianas; but here the occasional hybrids which come from any batch of Ledgeriana seed grew with encouraging vigor and promise.

By 1939 results were beginning to look hopeful. Merck and Company purchased an old coffee plantation of several thousand acres, where was developed, under the direction of Frederic Rosengarten, Jr., scion of the family which first manufactured quinine in the United States, the first real center of Cinchona investigation to be founded in tropical America in modern times.

Gordon Smith and Company, Lind and Company, Owen Smith and Company, and Overseas Estates Ltd. (managed by L. Lind Pettersen) began to think of commercial plantings. Experimentation showed that propagation by grafting was fairly simple. The time factor was the only obstacle to rapid multiplication of the best seedlings which were appearing in the experimental plantings. For it requires several years, beginning with a single superior tree, to work up thousands of grafted plants for setting out in commercial form.

It was realized that no serious effort had been made to explore the Cinchona-producing regions of the Andes since the early days when the British and Dutch carried out the notable series of investigations which made of Cinchona a cultivated plant, and moved the industry from the New World to the Old. It was felt that South America might hold, locked in the fastnesses of the mountains, strains still more valuable than the one found by Ledger, or better adapted to Central American conditions. Boris A. Krukoff was sent to search for these. He brought to Guatemala a vast amount of seed, from which several hundred thousand sturdy Calisayas were grown and planted in the field. It is yet too early to judge results; but, added to the material brought by Colonel Ruehl, and the many introductions of the United States Department of Agriculture, it was felt that Guatemala had a fair start.

By 1941 the Ledgerianas from Java were large enough to permit bark analyses, and the figures were so gratifying that commercial planting was further stimulated. From several trees, bark samples showed quinine sulfate contents of twelve to fifteen percent, which meant that the percentage, when such trees were harvested commercially, would run only two or three percent lower.

Some of the hybrids ran six to nine percent quinine sulfate, considered even more promising; for it must be remembered that the commercial value of a Cinchona tree lies not alone in quinine content, but in *quinine content* $\times$ *bark volume*. These hybrids, being of more rapid growth than Ledgerianas, would produce at a given age—perhaps eight years, which is about the time quinine content reaches its highest point—much more bark than the slower growing, more slender Ledgerianas.

Interest spread to other countries, and then jumped overnight when

Java fell into the hands of the Japanese. It was immediately realized that our quinine from that source was cut off for an indefinite period.

Mexico established a Cinchona experiment station in southern Chiapas, just across the border from Guatemala. This was placed in charge of an unusually able young man, Jesús Patiño N. The United States Department of Agriculture increased shipments of experimental material to tropical American countries. Merck and Company distributed plants to experimenters all the way from Salvador to Peru.

The United States Government expanded its activities. Since the 1930's, careful investigation of many problems of Cinchona culture had been conducted at the experiment station in Puerto Rico, under the direction of Atherton Lee. Arrangements were now made with the Guatemalan Government to take over the huge property known as El Porvenir, where President Justo Rufino Barrios had planted Cinchona trees on a large scale in the 1880's. While the primary object of this move was to utilize the available supply of bark, the project soon took on the aspects of a modern experiment station. William Pennock was brought from Puerto Rico to take charge of propagation. In one year's time Pennock, with the able collaboration of A. L. Bump, developed the world's largest Cinchona nursery—sixty miles of seed beds in which were grown some fifty million young plants, mostly Succirubras and hybrids. Though definitely a war measure, the effect of this project on Cinchona planting generally will be widely felt. Chemical investigations have been conducted on a large scale; propagation by cuttings has been studied exhaustively; and much information has been accumulated regarding the techniques of harvesting and drying bark.

In 1921, Alberto Brenes of Costa Rica had discovered that *Cinchona pubescens* grows in that country as a wild tree, abundant in the vicinity of San Ramón, northwest of the capital. Juvenal Valerio R., Director of the National Museum, had planted seedlings from these trees, and they were coming along well. Merck and Company bought property near Zarcero, and sent down Jorge Benítez, a young Ecuadorean who had been very successful in handling their nurseries in Guatemala. Trees of the most promising varieties were shipped from the latter country, and thousands of seedlings were grown locally—Ledgerianas and Succirubras.

In 1943 work in Costa Rica was greatly expanded through the establishment, by Defense Supplies Corporation, of extensive nurseries stocked with plants grown from the seeds which Colonel Fischer had brought out of the Philippines after the Japanese invasion. These were placed under the skilful care of Claude Hope, who had been trained under B. Y. Morrison at Washington. A contract was entered into, between the gov-

PLATE 11. Upper—A nursery planting of African oilpalm
Lower—Oil nuts of African oilpalm

PLATE 12. Upper left—Coconut palm in Honduras
Upper right—African oilpalm
Lower—A Philippines type of tung nut tree in Honduras

PLATE 13. Upper—Harvesting citronella grass in Honduras
Lower—Cutting tropical grasses for distillation

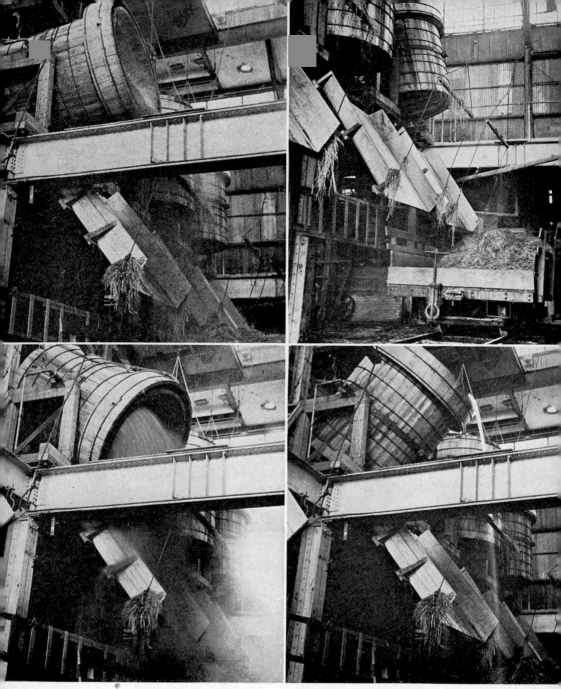

PLATE 14. Upper left—Distilling volatile oils in Honduras
Upper right—Refuse from volatile oil distillation
Lower left and right—Final stages of grass oil distillation

ernments of Costa Rica and the United States, by the terms of which we undertook to develop large plantations, to become the property of the Costa Rica people at the end of twenty-five years.

Ecuador also started a large planting program, sponsored by Defense Supplies Corporation as part of an agreement made with the government of that country. Nurseries were established at two places, under the technical supervision of William E. Martin and Paul Shank. Many thousands of seedlings were grown for distribution among local planters. Already a good beginning had been made. Numerous small farmers in the region of Telimbela, where Spruce obtained his Succirubra seeds eighty years ago, had been growing plants from cuttings for many years. From their small farms they had shipped bark to Europe.

Through its Office of Foreign Agricultural Relations, the United States Department of Agriculture organized an agricultural experiment station at Tingo María, Peru, in cooperation with the government of that country. Advantage was taken of a nearby site where the Japanese had started a Ledgeriana plantation some years earlier. Here notable work has been and is being done, under the general direction of B. J. Birdsall. Plants in large numbers have been distributed to local agriculturists, and much has been learned regarding soil requirements and methods of propagation.

Momentary discouragement was felt in some quarters early in 1944, when the North American press carried announcements of the successful synthesis of quinine. Many questions were asked; doubts and fears were expressed. These were allayed in large part when the directors of Merck and Company, who should after all know more about the prospects of synthetic quinine than any tropical agriculturist, voted to approve a long-term commercial planting program in Central America, to be continued up to 1950. At a later meeting the Board made this reassuring declaration: "The recent completion of the synthesis of quinine has in no way altered the above decision of Merck and Company, with respect to Cinchona cultivation in the Western Hemisphere."

CULTURAL REQUIREMENTS AND PRACTICES

For three-quarters of a century, Cinchona growers in the Asiatic tropics have concentrated on the Ledgeriana form of Calisaya; on the Chimborazo form of Pubescens or Succirubra; and on hybrids. What we have learned from them regarding the propagation and care of Cinchona trees has been based on this material, therefore; and is not too much at that, for the Dutch, in recent years especially, have published very little regarding the cultivation of Cinchona in Java. We have, in addition, the information accumulated in the Philippines, where Colonel Arthur Fischer and his colleagues carried out experimental plantings on a rather extensive scale; we have the information which has accumulated in Guatemala during the past ten years; and we have the observations which have been made recently among the wild Cinchonas of the Andes and the few commercial plantings which exist in that part of the world.

Much remains to be learned, and much remains to be done. We shall not rest until all the interesting possibilities have been fully explored. We have started with the best material available from Old World plantings; our job now is further to develop this, to meet the particular conditions and requirements of our situation. Undoubtedly modern techniques of plant breeding will be brought into play. Some of the little-known wild forms of the Andes may possess characteristics which, when combined with those of Ledgeriana, will produce new strains of greater value, or adapted to a wider range of conditions. For example, there is the possibility of developing a form as hardy as Pitayensis, with a higher alkaloid content. Calisayas may be found which have the high quinine content of Ledgeriana, but are much stronger in growth and produce more bark. Succirubras may be developed which will produce bark with a higher percentage of quinine, less of the other alkaloids.

All these and many other things remain to be done, and in their doing, tropical agriculturists and plant breeders will be working in one of the most fascinating fields imaginable, for the immense range of variation in the genus Cinchona provides materials and opportunities rarely equaled.

Soils. The Dutch have told us that Ledgeriana needs rich, friable loams, with plenty of organic matter. They have not told us what seems to be still more important, namely, that this tree needs soil definitely acid in reaction. Experiments have shown that the upper limit, for good results, is a soil acidity of pH 5.5. At 6.0 growth is poor, and at 6.5 a virtual failure. And at Tingo María in Peru, Birdsall and Martin have found that Ledgeriana promises to grow satisfactorily not only on loams, but on heavy friable clays, provided the acidity is right.

Succirubras are less exacting than Ledgerianas. Experiments in Guatemala indicate that this may also be true of some of the Calisayas. In the Andes, the finer forms of Cinchona, such as Calisaya and Officinalis, usually grow in forests where there is a deep accumulation of leaf mold, through which their delicate feeding roots can ramify without limit, finding in this well-drained stratum ideal conditions for their development. Often the basic soil below this surface layer is hard, almost sterile, and of little use to the tree, which lives out its life in the surface layer blissfully ignorant of what lies below.

On the other hand, Succirubras can be seen in open places, on hill-sides where there has been no opportunity for the accumulation of leaf mold. They thrive on clays and loams alike; and it is precisely this greater adaptability, plus its vigorous growth, which has led to its widespread use as a stock-plant on which to graft the more exacting Ledgeriana.

Climate. The fact that the finer Cinchonas grow in what is known as the cloud-zone—the upper slopes of the Andes where mists and light drizzling rains are prevalent almost throughout the year—early led to the belief that this was the only sort of climate in which the trees would flourish. Experience has shown this assumption to be correct only in part. Ledgerianas have been successful in cultivation where the climate is marked by a well-defined dry season; and Succirubras are still more resistant. So far, however, no good Cinchonas have been successful at low eleva-tions. This has been pointed out in Java, where yields of quinine are said to be poor when Ledgerianas are planted at 2000 to 3000 feet. There is a form in Colombia, *C. barbacoensis,* which is the only Cinchona known to grow in the wild at sea level; but its alkaloid content is negligible.

The upper limit of satisfactory Ledgeriana cultivation has been placed at about 6000 feet in Java. This corresponds roughly to its upper limit in the wild state, in Peru and Bolivia. As has already been mentioned, there are species—notably Officinalis and Pitayensis—the habitat of which extends far above this altitude. Obviously, growth will be slower at high elevations; but at the same time there may be a place for varieties which are suited to them, especially in the coffee-growing regions of such coun-tries as Guatemala, where many planters own large tracts of land, extend-ing far up the mountainsides. Since coffee is not commercially satisfactory at elevations much above 5000 feet, a crop which would profitably occupy the belt immediately above this would meet with a popular reception.

It is to be noted that attempts to cultivate Cinchona in the southern-most parts of the United States have so far met with no success. Even the hardiest forms withstand but little frost.

Propagation. Three methods are in use, (a) by seed, (b) by cuttings, and (c) by various forms of grafting.

Cinchona seeds are so small that it takes 50,000 to 75,000 of them to weigh an ounce. This means, of course, that they are delicate, and require special care if they are to be grown successfully. But it is the sort of care which any good horticulturist can give, once he knows the broad prin-ciples underlying the requirements of this particular genus. It is essential that seeds be kept uniformly moist from the time they are planted until they germinate—two or three weeks. Thus they are sown on seed beds protected from the weather by roofing of some sort, and watered at frequent intervals, not heavily but enough to keep the moisture of the bed just right.

When the young plants appear they have to be protected from heavy rains and from too much light, for their natural home is under the forest cover of the Andes, where light filters through the treetops but the direct rays of the tropical sun never touch them, and where their bed of leaf mold, kept moist by the mists and drizzling rains, provides suitable conditions for growth. When they are a few months old, the young plants are transferred to nursery beds—again with shade (at least, in the case of delicate species)—where they remain for a year or more. When ready for transplanting to their permanent places in the field, they must be a foot or more in height.

Cuttings. In the early days of Cinchona culture in tropical Asia, this method of propagation was widely used. In recent times it has been abandoned in favor of seeds and grafting. Attempts to grow cuttings were not successful in Guatemala during the 1930's, but the fault probably lay in lack of experience. Wholly satisfactory results have been the rule in the greenhouses of the United States Department of Agriculture near Washington, while the Cinchona planters of the region of Telimbela, Ecuador, habitually propagate their Succirubras by sticking short branches into the ground and forgetting about them. If done at the right time of year, a good percentage of the cuttings develop into sturdy trees.

The Dutch have reported that the root system of trees grown in this way is not strong. This may be true of some Cinchonas; perhaps it is not true of all.

Grafting. Taking as the basis of their experiments the published reports of grafting technique in Java, Jorge Benítez and Hans Franke undertook in 1936 to propagate Ledgerianas in Guatemala by this means. From the start, results were sufficiently good to indicate that no particular difficulties would be experienced. With a sufficient volume of material available, cion wood of just the right type could be chosen, and stock-plants would be used only when in just the right condition.

The method known as veneer grafting was finally adopted by Benítez. More recently, Ralph Pinkus has had better success with side-grafting. Others have taken up bud-grafting (which is more economical of propagating material, hence permits more rapid multiplication of newly discovered seedlings of superior character), and this method is rapidly gaining favor. It remains to be determined by experience just which form of grafting will be the most desirable; possibly several will be used, depending upon conditions.

The outstanding facts are these: Cinchona is not difficult to propagate by seed. Vegetative propagation is feasible, both by means of cuttings and by various types of grafting. The multiplication of superior varieties therefore offers no serious problem.

Field Culture. Here we come up against a happy circumstance. Cinchona is a close relative of coffee, and requires very similar cultural treatment. In tropical America there are thousands of agriculturists who know how to grow coffee and who have grown it successfully all their lives. These, in the main, are the men who will grow Cinchona, and they are prepared by experience to do a good job of it.

Some of these men are the big coffee growers, men who have hundreds of acres planted to this crop, and who have unusual agricultural skill. They are probably the ones who will go in for the high-grade Cinchonas— the forms which are most delicate, and which will be utilized for the production of bark to be shipped to northern processors who will extract pure quinine from it. Others are small farmers, such as the coffee growers of the Department of Antioquia in Colombia. In time, it may be feasible to provide them with trees of improved strains which will be easily grown, and which also will provide highgrade barks. Naturally, that should be our ultimate objective.

7

Drug and Medicinal Crops

By E. C. HIGBEE

BUREAU OF PLANT INDUSTRY,
UNITED STATES DEPARTMENT OF AGRICULTURE

By ATHERTON LEE

DIRECTOR OF NEW CROPS,
UNITED FRUIT COMPANY

IN the previous chapter, Dr. Wilson Popenoe discusses quinine, the most renowned of all the American drug crops. But other drug plants call for comparable attention because they, too, are comparatively indispensable to good lives for the Americas. In medicine, pharmacy, chemical engineering, and many other commercial enterprises drug plants continue to play notable, in some instances decisive, roles. As the following chapter points out, drug crops were perennial work trails used by the many and talented Indians in pioneering the still incomplete appraisal of hemisphere resources in plant life.

In terms of botanical knowledge and specialized uses, the drug plants are far more important than their somewhat limited commercial values suggest. Among the drug plants here discussed are several noteworthy new crops for the New World, and several old crops now gaining an increased measure of importance.

The authors are ideally qualified to tell this story. Mr. Higbee, of the United States Department of Agriculture's Office of Foreign Agricultural Relations, is a veteran student of drug crops, as is his collaborator, Atherton Lee, who is a career agronomist with the Department of Agriculture and Philippine plantation groups, former director of our Department of Agriculture's Tropical Experiment Station, and now director of United Fruit's department of new crops. With becoming modesty Mr. Lee cherishes, but usually declines to air, the many medals and citations presented him by several American governments.

7

THE WESTERN HEMISPHERE is already a major producer of several important botanical drugs. Soil and climatic conditions will permit the growing of others not now on the list, although in normal times it apparently has not been economically worthwhile to do so. In the case of crude medicinals obtained from wild sources such as the seed of *Strychnos nux-vomica*, the market price has been so low that plantation culture could hardly have been feasible. On the other hand, some profitable plantation crops such as Cinchona are difficult to handle successfully. So much money must first be expended on horticultural research that interest in the western hemisphere has been discouraged by this fact until recent years.

The distinction between the medicinal products obtained from wild sources and those produced on plantations is an important one economically. For instance, the fact that plantations yielding gum tragacanth do not exist is probably due to the fact that the world market is sufficiently well supplied by the amounts of this product gathered from wild sources. Plantations yielding senna leaves, however, are necessary to meet world demands since there are not enough wild plants.

If a western hemisphere land-owner is interested in establishing either one of these two types of products on his property, he must consider with realism the problems with which he is faced or his profit possibilities will be minimized. Any product gathered from the wild need only be harvested. If prices are not high enough to make gathering it worth a man's time, there is no loss of time or money since no upkeep is involved. But a plantation product requires maintenance. Sometimes when diseases and insect pests are involved or the plant is a particularly difficult one to raise, this may be a costly proposition.

Should land-owners of governments in the western hemisphere wish to introduce and establish those wild growing plants whose products are cheap, they will probably be most successful if they introduce them as part of a reforestation or wasteland reclamation project rather than as plantation crops. For a plantation crop to compete with cheap wild sources, it must be produced from selected stock which grows better, yields more, and is of higher quality. These factors are essential because of the increased costs of plantation culture. Even then agricultural methods may not be able to compete satisfactorily with the uncultivated forest or semi-desert wasteland system by which the plants shift for themselves, and care is taken only in the management of harvests so as not to destroy the desired crop's competitive ability.

If there were a demand for great volumes of certain individual crude medicinals, the picture would be different. Plantations would be necessary to meet demand, and prices would be accordingly higher. Many of the items on the crude drug list, however, are needed in small quantities only. Imports of most of these individual drugs into the United States in normal times are valued at less than $100,000 per annum, and their value per pound is surprisingly low in many cases. With such low values, little investment in research seems justified from a horticultural standpoint. Investment in such research based on its value to the practice of medicine, human welfare, and security might, however, be justified in some cases.

Should anyone in the western hemisphere wish to introduce and establish those plants now grown on plantations in other parts of the world, he must be prepared to spend money on research. Field trials will have to be conducted to determine suitable environments and cultural practices, and special highly productive strains of plants will need to be developed. Disease and insect pest control work will be essential. Although the chemistry of drug plants has advanced commendably and their therapeutics has a greater degree of precision now than formerly, from a horticultural viewpoint the production of tropical drug botanicals is one of the least advanced fields of agriculture. Much of this is due, of course, to the fact that the literature is inadequate, and not to the lack of knowledge on the part of certain planters in other parts of the world. These planters probably have learned by experience and privately financed research, but they have not published specific details about many of the crops which might be of interest to land-owners in the western hemisphere.

Another matter is seriously considered by certain governments and planters when the subject of introducing new medicinal crops is explored. The introduction of narcotic plants, such as the opium poppy, can create a social problem. For instance, in Peru and Bolivia the native coca plant is grown more for popular sale of its narcotic leaves than it is for the extraction of pharmaceutical cocain. Efficiency of labor and the horticultural ability of plantation supervisors is also an important point. Some agricultural areas in the western hemisphere are not favorably equipped in these respects and would be at a disadvantage in competing with certain Far Eastern regions.

Because many of the drug plants are produced by illiterate people in countries with extremely low labor costs, the farming interests of countries with higher wage scales have found it difficult to compete in producing these plants, especially without the advantages of research which was not justified by the value of the crops. A partial solution for this situation would be the financial support of research on these crops in the wealthier countries, based on the necessity for greater efficiency or a better pharmaceutical product. Such research should not be confined to countries of temperate climates alone but should extend into tropical lands in which many of these drug botanicals could best be grown. Education in agricultural techniques will also be necessary to improve both labor and supervisory efficiency.

The production of these drug crops by people lacking the proper education and background has a second disadvantage. In many cases collection or harvesting of these crops is done carelessly, with the result that often detritus and other foreign substances are included with the drug materials. Frequently the drugs are intentionally adulterated with cheaper or more easily obtainable plant products, with a consequent reduction in the therapeutic value of the materials. The crude drug trade is more or less adjusted to this situation. A producer of high-quality product would be faced with this type of competition unless he were protected by contracts calling for a premium on uniformly better quality material. The desirability of a better product from the pharmaceutical point of view can easily be appreciated, but often the highly competitive drug trade cannot afford attractive premiums.

Of considerable interest to some travelers, missionaries, and local observers are the medicinal plant remedies used by Indians. That the Indians of North, South, and Central America were skilful plantsmen we are well aware, since we owe to their observation and selection such every-day staples as potatoes, tomatoes, corn, tobacco, and peanuts. Because of their inquisitiveness and experimentation, they were also the first to recognize the values of the medicinal plants such as ipecac, cinchona, coca, and the tree which yields balsam of Peru.

The plant collectors, Train, Hendricks, and Archer,[1] in their study of the drug plants used by Indian tribes of Nevada, found approximately 300 native plants which those Indians claimed had medicinal properties.

[1] P. Train, J. L. Hendricks, and W. A. Archer: *Medicinal Uses of Plants by Indian Tribes of Nevada*, Division of Plant Exploration and Introduction, Bureau of Plant Industry, Soils & Agricultural Engineering, United States Department of Agriculture. December 1, 1941.

Dr. Alfredo Paredes, professor of botany of the Universidad Central del Ecuador in Quito, has an herbarium collection of scores of medicinal plants used by the Indians of Ecuador. Botanists, professional and amateur, can be found in every western hemisphere country who have made similar studies and collected herbarium specimens.

So far as the great majority of these plants is concerned, little or no chemical research has been done on them. Very likely there are, among the thousands of plants used by primitive peoples for their real or fancied curative values, some which might eventually find their way into the pharmacopœias. The amount of work involved in winnowing out the truly useful from the chaff is necessarily an arduous and expensive proposition. This sorting-out process, however, is going on slowly and steadily all the time.

For those laymen whose interest is aroused by local use of a medicinal plant, there is a definite procedure to be followed if they wish to attract the attention of scientists to the plant and its uses. In the first place, it is not sufficient to report the plant's local name and what it is used for, as such data are themselves of little value. The person whose interest is aroused by a particular plant must himself become an amateur plant collector to the extent of gathering not only sufficient leaves, roots, bark, or whatever is said to contain the active ingredient for chemical analysis, but he should at the same time, and if possible from the same plant, take material to prepare a proper herbarium specimen.

In the case of a small herb such as ipecac, *Cephælis ipecacuanha*, this would require removing the entire plant from the soil. With a tree such as the Cinchona, a small floral branch would be sufficient. Inasmuch as the taxonomic botanist determines a plant's family, genus, and species by its leaves, flowers, and fruits, it is necessary for accurate identification to provide him with an herbarium specimen which is made up of at least flowers and mature leaves attached to a single stem or twig. If the plant does not happen to be in flower but is bearing seed or fruit, then a stem or twig with seed or fruit and mature leaves should be obtained as a second-best reference to provide the taxonomist. Leaves by themselves are of doubtful value. The herbarium specimen should be dried in such a manner that the leaves and flowers are pressed flat.

In providing material for chemical analysis, it is always best to submit a sample of several pounds. Often a few ounces will suffice for certain tests; but if the material is an unknown, many tests for various substances may be necessary. Of course, the sample should always be accompanied by a statement of how the product is locally prepared for medicinal use and of the ailment it is supposed to relieve or cure. The name of the plant as supplied by the taxonomic botanist must be given, and as a matter of courtesy the botanist's name as well. It is doubtful whether a chemist would ever engage in analyzing any miscellaneous plant material if the plant itself had not been properly identified. He would refuse because he would first wish to review the literature, to determine whether any other chemist had ever reported working on that plant. In the second place, his own analyses would be meaningless if he could not associate the results of his work with a specific plant. A local name has no value in realistic scientific procedure.

This business of investigating the medicinal plants used by indigenous people is a fascinating and sometimes fruitful hobby. By carefully following a few simple rules, the curious layman may not only report an interesting observation but he can himself carry out the first steps necessary to a scientific study of the plant.

The following discussion of a few of the more important drug plants and their culture does not pretend to be a planter's guide. Only a few important facts are mentioned to give those unacquainted with the plants a thumbnail sketch of their main peculiarities. Cinchona is not mentioned because it is being considered in another chapter of this book. At the end of the present chapter is a chart summarizing the relative commercial importance of the drug products considered.

ACACIA

Acacia or gum arabic, as defined by the Dispensatory of the United States, is "the dried gummy exudation from the stems and branches of *Acacia senegal*, Willdenow, or of some other African species of *Acacia*, family Leguminosæ." The gum has several important medicinal uses based on its colloidal properties. It is most commonly employed as a demulcent. The Anglo-Egyptian Sudan is the principal source of gum arabic, although considerable quantities are obtained from French West Africa.

Acacia senegal is a small thorny tree which grows to a height of ten to fifteen feet. Though most of the trees are found growing wild in the sandy soils of semi-arid thorn brush desert regions, they are often planted after cultivated crops which have depleted soil fertility. The tree, which possesses a long taproot and extensive laterals, will grow on poor semi-desert lands. In Kordofan province it is established on red sandhill soils, some of which, it is reported, contain no more than eight percent silt and clay. The variable yearly rainfall there is between eight and eighteen inches. Practically all the rainfall comes during the five- to six-month summer period.

Plantations are best established by burning over the land to eliminate grass competition. Seed which has been soaked in water for several hours is then scattered over the burned area; reseeding is often necessary to obtain a full stand. Frequently the tree will grow from naturally dispersed seed if cultivated fields are abandoned. It will even invade poor sod lands and is considered a good plant to stabilize shifting sand-dunes. *Acacia senegal* requires practically no attention after it has grown beyond danger of competition from grass. After five or six years it is ready for exploitation, and if carefully tapped, it will live as long as twenty-five years.

The best gum arabic is produced by wild and plantation-grown trees in the Kordofan region. During the dry season from October to May the trunks and branches of the trees are wounded without injury to the cambium, either by simply cutting the bark or by removing strips of bark two to three feet long and one to three inches wide. For a period of two to four weeks after stripping, a viscous liquid exudes from the wounded tree and slowly hardens into tears of gum arabic. The gum exudes in greatest quantities when the weather is hot. It ceases to form when the rainy season begins. The tears are gathered by picking them from the wounds. Then gum is later spread in the sun to bleach; then it is separated from adhering bark or sand, sorted, bagged, and transported by camel caravans to shipping points.

The annual yield of gum varies greatly. The average for young trees is reported to be about 900 grams, and for old trees about 2000 grams. There are a number of dry-land thorn trees native to the western hemisphere which produce gums resembling gum arabic in some respects. Examples are the mesquite, *Prosopis juliflora*, DC., native to New Mexico, Texas, and Mexico, as well as the algarrobo, another species of Prosopis found in the semi-desert areas of the South American coast. Both of these are legumes which, in addition to their gums, produce pods containing a sweet edible pulp sometimes used not only for livestock feed but for human consumption as well. A dark syrupy liquor prepared by the prolonged boiling of algarrobo bean pulp is used as a tonic in northwestern Peru.

ALOE

Aloe is the dried juice of the leaves of several species of the genus Aloe, which belongs to the Liliaceæ family. There are several commercial types, but the most important ones are Socotrine aloe, derived principally from *A. perryi* and imported from the island of Socotra, the east coast of Africa, and the Arabian coast; Curacao aloe, produced in the West Indies chiefly from *A. barbadensis* and deriving its name from the island of Curacao; and Cape aloe, obtained principally from *A. ferox* in South

Africa. The dried juice of the leaves of most Aloe species has laxative properties.

Cultivated Socotrine and Curacao aloes are said to be capable of growing on poor but well-drained limestone soils in relatively dry regions. It has been recommended, however, as a commercial practice in Barbados to incorporate stable manure in the planting beds at the time of their preparation. Aloes are propagated by offsets separated from mature plants. These may be spaced at intervals of six to twelve inches in rows one and one-half to two feet apart. Transplanting of these offsets may be done at any time the soil is moist enough to adhere to the roots but not so wet as to encourage rot, to which the young transplants are susceptible. With proper weeding and care the plants will produce a commercial crop in one year.

The plants are perennial, growing to a height of about a foot. The leaves are cut with knives and immediately placed in upright positions in wooden troughs so that the juice will flow out of them. The troughs are inclined so that the juice runs to one end and through an oulet into containers. Juice which is expressed mechanically is mucilaginous and has little value medicinally.

After collection from the troughs the juice is boiled until it is the consistency of thick syrup; then it is poured into gourds or skins and allowed to harden. Data from Barbados reported yields per acre in the first year after planting of about 100 pounds of dried aloe; the second year, about 250 pounds; the third and fourth year, 500 pounds. In succeeding years the yields gradually decreased. Plantings fave frequently been maintained from ten to twelve years.

In the seventeenth century, the green leaves were used for burns; and in 1935, applications of green leaves were found to be beneficial in the treatment of X-ray burns. The curative principle for burns is not present in the condensed juice.

BALSAM OF PERU

Balsam of Peru is obtained from the leguminous tree *Myroxylon Pereiræ* (Royle) Klotzoch, which is native to many areas of the South and Central American tropics from Mexico to Peru. Actual commercial production of the balsam is centered in northwestern El Salvador in an area known as the "Balsam Coast," near the village of San Julian. The product itself is used medicinally for the dressing of wounds and in compounding ointments. Large amounts are consumed by the essential oil industry, particularly as a fixative in the manufacture of perfumes.

The Balsam Coast of Salvador has a rough, hilly topography. The soils are generally heavy red clays; much of the area is grassland devoted to grazing. The balsam trees are found in coffee groves and in scattered woodland patches. All grow from naturally disseminated seed. In the coffee groves they provide a suitable shade for that crop. The woodlands of El Salvador where the balsam trees are found are not the dense rain-forest type, although they receive a rainfall of about seventy-five inches annually. The principal producing areas on the Balsam Coast are at approximately 2000 feet elevation, but the tree has been observed to grow well from sea level to 3000 feet.

The balsam itself is obtained both by extracting it from the bark and by forcing a flow of the resinous sap from the trunk and branches by the application of fire. In opening a panel or "window" in a tree, a piece of bark about two to two and one-half inches wide and several inches long is cut from the trunk. These pieces of bark are collected for the extraction of what is called "bark balsam." The wound itself which reaches to the wood is then scorched with a flaming fagot made up of splinters of heartwood of old trees which have been cut down. Most of the heat is applied to the bark surrounding the wound, although the wound itself is heated somewhat. The scorching, which lasts for about five to ten minutes, stimulates the flow of the balsam. As it begins to ooze from under the carbonized bark, the flame is removed and a strip of cotton rag obtained from old clothes is applied over the wound to soak up the balsam. The edges of the cloth are forced under the bark with the point of a broad-nosed knife where they are held pinched in place by the bark.

Over a period of a week to ten days the balsam gradually saturates the rags. These rags are then removed for the extraction of the balsam, which at ordinary temperature cannot be squeezed from them. As the balsam is practically insoluble in water, the rags may be put into caldrons of water boiling over an open fire. After about two to three hours of boiling, the balsam becomes sufficiently fluid so that it can be squeezed out. The rags may be placed either in an hydraulic press or, as is a common practice in El Salvador, in a crude rope press. Under the presses, both the balsam and hot water are squeezed from the cloths. This product is known as "rag" balsam and is the best quality particularly when gathered during the dry season. The balsam settles to the bottom of the receptacles receiving the fluid from the presses. The water is skimmed off the top and the balsam is boiled to remove the last traces of moisture. It is then stored in oil drums until sufficient has been accumulated for shipment.

Upon the removal of the rags, the wound and the bark around it are again scorched with the flaming fagot. This process is usually performed about three times; then a new piece of bark of the same width as the first and about three or four inches long is cut out directly above the old wound. Following this, the whole series of scorchings is repeated. In time, long slender panels are cut in the bark of the tree. Depending upon the tree's diameter, there may be from two to eight around the trunk, giving it a fluted appearance. More area should be left untouched than is cut away, so as not to girdle the tree. Gradually as the panels are extended up the tree and new ones are opened on the main branches, the earlier wounds begin to callous over. To facilitate climbing the trees, the peons either use rope and pulley slings or they bore holes in the trunk and insert pegs made of balsam wood. They climb on these pegs and use them to stand upon while performing the various operations involved in collecting the product.

To obtain balsam from the pieces of bark removed in paneling, this bark is chopped into chips, put into the presses, soaked with boiling water, and squeezed. The balsam flows best during the dry season, which in El Salvador extends from November to May when the rains begin. Harvesting continues the year round, although the yield and quality diminishes during the rainy season.

The experience of balsam producers indicates that a tree should not be exploited until it is at least ten to fifteen years old, preferably twenty-five. Thereafter it may be worked continually for ten to twenty-five years. The value of the product is such that it would probably not pay to grow the tree in plantations. However, as a coffee shade tree or one of a number of valuable trees to be used in a reforestation program, it might be worthy of consideration. This would be particularly true in regions where labor costs are as low as they are in El Salvador's Balsam Coast. There the average daily wage is twenty cents.

BELLADONNA

Belladonna leaves and roots are obtained from the herbaceous *Atropa belladonna* L., a member of the Solanaceæ or night shade family. It is native to central and southern Europe, where much of the commercial supply is gathered from wild plants. It has been cultivated in France, England, and during the war years in the United States. All parts of the plant—leaves, stems, berries, and roots—contain the poisonous alkaloids for which it is valued.

The plant gets its name from the Venetians, who called it *Herba Belladonna* from the fact that an aqueous extract of the leaves was used as a cosmetic to dilate the pupils of the eyes. The chief alkaloid of the leaves is hyoscyamine. Belladonna preparations are used internally as sedatives and to check secretions. The most popularly known use is probably that of dilating the pupil of the eye to permit detailed examination. Scopolamine, a belladonna alkaloid, has been reported as an airsickness preventive.

Belladonna, perhaps more than most drug crops, has had some careful agronomic work done on it. A recent publication by Sievers and Russell [2] is an excellent summary of the best practices to follow in temperate regions such as in the northern United States. In general, its cultivation and preparation for market are strikingly similar to those of tobacco, to which the plant is related. It is best to germinate the tiny seeds, approximately 30,000 of which weigh only one ounce, in coldframes or in greenhouses when market prices justify the expense. There they may be sifted over flats of sterilized soil, pressed firmly into the ground and carefully watered so as to avoid attack by damping-off fungi. The seeds germinate in two to three weeks, and when the seedlings are large enough to handle, they should be pricked out in flats of sterilized soil at a spacing of two by two inches. After the seedlings are about four to five inches tall they may be transplanted to the field.

To obtain maximum yields, the transplants should be ready to go into the field as soon as the danger of frost has passed. These may be set in the ground with a trowel or with a mechanical planter, such as is used in setting out tobacco. The latter is particularly useful when large acreages are to be established or if it is necessary to apply water to each plant on setting. Belladonna is said to grow best on well-drained, fertile loam soils. The fields should be free of weeds, particularly grasses at the time of transplanting. Frequent cultivation thereafter is necessary to obtain favorable development of the crop.

As the result of their experiments with belladonna, Sievers and Russell conclude that the best quality is obtained by cutting the plant stalks near the ground as soon as the flower buds develop. New growth appears after the first harvest, so that a second may be performed later in the season. The plant is a perennial when not killed by frost. When market prices justify, the roots may also be dug, since they too contain the active alkaloids.

When the leaves of belladonna are harvested at the proper stage of maturity, they may contain as much as eighty percent moisture, which obliges the grower to provide some sort of facility for drying the crop. The simplest is a room or shed with good ventilation, where the product

[2] A. F. Sievers and G. A. Russell: *Belladonna as a Domestic Crop*, United States Department of Agriculture, B.P.I.S.A.E., 1942 (mimeograph).

can be spread out on racks or poles or in wire-bottom trays. The drying process can, of course, be hastened by installing a stove or furnace. Temperatures up to 125 degrees F. are not thought to damage the medicinal quality of belladonna. Leaves and roots should be baled separately for market, since they fall into separate market grades. Yields of from 500 to 1000 pounds of dried leaves per acre might be expected from one-year-old plants.

CAMPHOR

Cinnamomum camphora, of the family Lauraceæ, and a close relative of the tree from which the spice cinnamon is obtained, is native to southeastern Asia, Japan, and Formosa. Although there is considerable production of synthetic camphor largely for industrial use in the manufacture of nitrocellulose products, the natural camphor oils and gum are still in demand by the crude drug trade for certain preparations.

Principal sources of the natural product have been the forests of the Far East under Japanese control. There it is obtained by cutting down the whole tree, chipping up the wood, and subjecting wood, leaves, and twigs to distillation. Commercial cultivation of camphor trees was at one time attempted in the United States. While the plants grew well in several southern states, the project was not economically successful. In recent years, some 10,000 young trees have been established on a finca near Gautemala City in Gautemala. There, chiefly because of low labor costs, camphor production promises to succeed.

It is possible to raise the camphor tree in most subtropical regions where the winter temperature does not fall below 15 degree F. and where the annual rainfall is fifty to eighty inches per year. Although it thrives on rich sandy loams, it is often more economically planted on less valuable sandy soils. The tree can be propagated by stem or root cuttings, but freshly picked seed is preferred for large-scale production. This seed should be germinated in soil which is particularly weed-free, since germination may require as long and three months.

When transplanted into the field, the seedlings may be spaced as close as six feet, in rows fifteen feet apart. Such close plantings develop into continuous hedgerows which are convenient to cultivate and to clip. Wider spacing of twenty to twenty-five feet results in normal tree development.

There is a wide range in the crude camphor content of twigs and leaves but the average is between 1.75 and 2.25 percent of the green weight of clippings. The amount of pure camphor gum in the crude product is from seventy-five to eighty percent, the remainder being camphor oil. Camphor hedges have been reported to yield eight tons of green material per acre per year.

CASTOR BEAN

Castor oil, expressed from the seed of *Ricinus communis* L. of the Euphorbiaceæ family, has been used as a cathartic since ancient times. Many fancy recipes have been devised to disguise its disagreeable taste. The Arabs are said to have prepared a hot milk emulsion of the oil and made it palatable by adding a syrup of orange flowers. The bulk of castor oil, however, is used for industrial purposes. It enters into the manufacture of artificial leather, and when properly processed it is used in dyeing cotton fabrics and in the manufacture of paints, varnishes, linoleum, and oilcloth.

Castor beans are widely grown throughout the warmer regions of the world, but India and Brazil are the two most important producers. While the castor bean plant is a perennial if not killed by frost, it is commonly cultivated as an annual. It is a roadside weed in many tropical and sub-tropical areas. To obtain good yields, the plant must be grown on well-drained soil, preferably a silt loam of moderate fertility; excessive nitrogen stimulates growth at the expense of seed production. The ground should be well prepared and the crop grown in much the same way as corn. The seed may be planted by hand or with a corn or cotton planter fitted with special plates. It is spaced at various distances, depending upon the length of the growing season. The range may be from intervals of three feet in rows four feet apart in the cooler areas, to eight feet in rows eight feet apart in frost-free regions. Cultivation is necessary only until the plants have grown sufficiently to suppress weeds by shading.

R. communis does well at altitudes up to 5000 feet above sea level. Regions where it is grown must have a minimum frost-free growing period of about five months and a minimum of about twenty inches of rain for profitable production unless irrigation is possible. Most of the moisture must be available during the early growing period. There are many varieties more or less adapted to a wide range of conditions.

In most places mature bean spikes are cut by hand, since no very satisfactory mechanical harvester has been designed. After the spikes are cut, they are hauled to drying sheds or sun-drying floors until the pods are dry enough to thresh. The beans of some varieties of the castor-oil plant shell out easily when the pod dries. There may even be serious loss in the fields if gathering is not done at the proper time. Non-dehiscent varieties, which are preferred for cultivation, require special machines to remove the beans from the hulls. With favorable conditions in regions where a long frowing season is possible, a yield of twenty-five bushels per acre is considered high. The oil content of the seed ranges between thirty-five and fifty-five percent, depending upon varieties, maturity, and other factors.

COCA

The leaves of the perennial coca shrubs *Erythoxylon coca* Lamarck and *E. truxillense* Rusby are used for the extraction of the narcotic alkaloids cocain and tropacocain. Because of their flavor, leaves from which these alkaloids are removed are also used in the manufacture of certain soft drinks. The plants are native to the eastern slopes of the Andes where there are extensive plantations, particularly in the Yungas region of Bolivia and in the departments of Huanuco and Trujillo in Peru.

The plants have been established on plantations in other tropical regions, particularly in the Netherlands Indies. Large numbers of the population of Bolivia and Peru are addicted to the chewing of these narcotic leaves, and the crop is grown in these countries principally to supply this local market. Those leaves used in the United States in the manufacture of beverages are first treated to remove the narcotic alkaloids.

Leaves imported from Java contain approximately one percent cocain, or about twice as much as the South American leaves. For this reason they are preferred for the extraction of pharmaceutical cocain. The process used for this purpose renders the residue undesirable for beverage purposes. Likewise the method used to obtain beverage flavoring material from crude leaves makes it uneconomical to recover the narcotic alkaloids from the waste material for drug purposes. Inasmuch as experience has shown that the indiscriminate planting of coca may make it possible for large sections of the population to become addicted to the chewing of its narcotic leaves, it is far wiser to discourage the introduction of this plant where it is not known rather than to suggest its cultivation.

In the department of Huanuco in Peru the coca plant flowers and develops seed after every harvest. The dark red, fleshy berries of the plant are stripped and planted in nursery beds, which are usually relatively weed-free patches of ground cleared out of woodlands. The planting season starts in November, which is the beginning of the rainy season. The seeds are sprinkled over the ground and lightly stirred with the hand so as to cover them with a very thin layer of soil. The nursery bed is then shaded with a single layer of palm leaves supported on poles a meter above the bed. The seeds germinate in about three weeks and the plants are left under shade until they are about five inches high, which may be about three months after planting. They are not transplanted from the nursery until they have developed their second branches. They may then be eight to ten months old.

Transplanting is done at most times of the year, but it is better to do it at the beginning of the rainy season. Plants are then set out in holes spaced about two feet apart in rows about four and one-half feet apart. Three or four plants may be set in each hole. About eighteen months later they are usually ready for the first harvest. The leaves of the coca plant are stripped when the tip leaves are matured and the plant is comparatively dormant. Tender immature leaves are undesirable.

The leaves are stripped by hand into baskets which rest on the ground. The pickers are usually women and children. An adult is able to pick between forty and sixty pounds of fresh leaves in a day. This is equivalent to between fifteen and twenty-three pounds of dried leaves. Harvesting takes place only on bright sunny days, since most of the leaves are sundried, although it is sometimes the practice to dessicate them in driers. The typical method followed in the Chinchao Valley in the department of Huanuco is to sweep over the dirt yard about the house and to scatter the leaves lightly over the soil. After about a half day in the sun, they are ready to be picked up and sacked. Yields are said to average about 500 pounds of dried leaves per acre annually.

GAMBIR

Gambir is the dried hot-water extract of the leaves and twigs of the perennial climbing shrub *Uncaria gambir* Roxb., which belongs to the family Guttiferæ. The commercial product is obtained from both wild and cultivated plants. Malaya and the Netherlands Indies produce most of the world's supply. It is employed medicinally because of its astringent properties, principally in the treatment of diarrhea. However, greater quantities are employed in industrial operations where tannic acid is required, such as in the tanning of leather and the prevention of hard-water scale in boilers.

The gambir shrub may be propagated either by seed or by cuttings. When seed is used, it should be sown in comparatively weed-free nursery beds, for it requires about three months to germinate. Most successful growing areas have a well-distributed yearly rainfall of eighty inches or more. Gambir grow rapidly and prefers a warm climate and rich welldrained soils. The young seedlings may be transplanted to the field when they are about nine to ten inches high and should be spaced from eight to twelve feet apart each way. A small crop of leaves may be clipped from the plants at the end of their first year in the field, while at eighteen months larger yields are obtained. By the time they are two years old, the shrubs are mature and produce a heavy foliage for cropping—usually every six months but sometimes as frequently as every three months. While there are reports of gambir producing well for twenty to thirty years, the average becomes unprofitable after about ten years.

When removed from the shrub the leaves and young shoots are cut up, placed in metal caldrons, covered with water, and boiled over an open fire. When the plant material is pretty well extracted, it is removed to a drainboard and the boiling of the water extract is continued. Liquor draining from the material on the drainboard trickles back into the pot. When boiled down to a syrupy thickness, the water extract is poured into shallow wooden tubs. While cooling it is churned until it solidifies into blocks which have a claylike color. Before the second batch of leaves is extracted, those on the drainboard are immersed in fresh water and boiled again to remove the last traces of gambir. The next batch of leaves and twigs is extracted in this rinse water. Annual production of extract is reported to average from 150 to 200 pounds of dried gambir per acre.

GUM TRAGACANTH

Like acacia, gum tragacanth is valued because of its colloidal properties, particularly since it is capable of holding water-insoluble powders in suspension. Considerable quantities are employed for general thickening and emulsifying purposes and in the preparation of torches. It has numerous technical uses, particularly in calico printing.

Gum tragacanth, which is obtained from the leguminous shrub *Astragalus gummifer* Labill., has a considerably higher market value than acacia but smaller quantities are imported by the United States. The plant is native to mountainous areas ranging from eastern Iran westward through Syria. The quality of the gum is said to be distinctly affected by the environment, with the best being obtained from the mountainous region of central Turkey and Kurdistan, where the average yearly rainfall is from ten to fifteen inches.

Commercial gum tragacanth is collected from wild shrubs; frequently, however, the gum gatherers must obtain concessions from local authorities to make their harvests. It is reported to be a practice to burn the leaves off the thorny shrubs in some areas, as the burning is said to stimulate the flow of the gum. To obtain the tragacanth, deep incisions are made in the trunk of the plant just above the root. The gum gradually exudes over a period of days and hardens as it does so. It is reported that if short incisions are made, the gum hardens in the form of threads, whereas, if the cuts are long, the gum runs together into lumps or tears. The roots of *A. gummifer* are also tapped for gum. The soil is removed from around the taproot near the crown, where it is then gashed. In a day or two the gum ceases to flow, and hardens. The gum is harvested during the hottest weather and the cutting process is repeated several times. The collected gum is sorted into three principal commercial grades: white, blond, and yellow. It is said that the gum from the first incisions is white, and that it becomes progressively yellower and of poorer quality upon successive cuttings or if the leaves are burned.

There are many wasteland areas in the western hemisphere where a favorable environment for the tragacanth shrub could be found. Such an introduction would probably be uneconomical as a commercial venture, but it might be included with other useful plants selected for wasteland reclamation in certain high-altitude areas of the tropics.

From the standpoint of supply of gum products themselves, it is possible that there are already gum trees in the Americas which could produce satisfactory substitutes for certain purposes. So often the reason a product becomes established on a world market is not due to its inherent superiority, but because large supplies are known to exist and the people inhabiting the regions where they are obtainable can be depended upon to gather them regularly.

HENBANE

Henbane, *Hyoscyamus niger* L., is a member of the same botanical family as belladonna—the Solanaceæ. The principal alkaloid of its leaves and flowering tops, for which it is used medicinally, is hyoscyamine, the main alkaloid of belladonna. It also contains scopolamine, which is said to be used to prevent airsickness. The similarity of the two plants also extends to their culture and preparation for market.

While there are reported to be eleven species of Hyoscyamus distributed over Asia, northern Africa, and Europe, *H. niger* itself is a native of Europe. It has been introduced to the United States, where it has escaped from cultivation in a number of the northern states and has become a weed in certain localities, being found alongside roads and old rubbish heaps. In normal times the demand for henbane leaves has not justified the cultivation of much more than ten acres of the crop in the United States. It has, however, been one of the plants commonly grown by pharmacognosists in their medicinal plant gardens.

At the University of Minnesota, E. L. Newcomb and M. H. Haynes [3] obtained satisfactory field results by first germinating the *H. niger* seeds in seed-pans in a greenhouse and later pricking them out in flats, where

[3] E. L. Newcomb and M. H. Haynes: *Hyoscyamus Cultivated in Minnesota*, Amer. Journal of Pharmacy: January, 1916.

they remained until they could be transplanted first to small pots and later to the field after frost was past. Because of the hardness of the seed-coat of henbane, germination is very uneven. Newcomb and Haynes found that they could eliminate this difficulty without injuring the seed by stirring the seeds in concentrated sulphuric acid for two and one-half minutes and then washing them thoroughly with water. Such treated seeds germinated with fair uniformity in twelve to fifteen days.

Henbane may be either annual or biennial. The annual varieties may be spaced in the field fifteen inches apart each way, while the biennials develop more satisfactorily if planted twenty inches apart. As in the case of belladonna, the finest drug product is obtained when the plants are harvested in full bloom. The drying of the leaves is carried out in the same way as for belladonna, and a favorable yield may be about 600 pounds per acre.

IPECAC

Ipecac is the root and rhizome of *Cephælis ipecacuanha* (Brot.) A. Rich. and *C. acuminata* Karst. of the family Rubiaceæ, of which coffee is a member. It is the source of the alkaloid emetine used in the treatment of amoebic dysentery. Ipecac also has emetic properties. It is one of the more important drugs contributed to medical practice by the Indians of the western hemisphere tropics. The plant itself is a low herbaceous shrub found among the ground-covering plants which survive the relatively deep shade of the tropical lowland forest. *C. ipecacuanha* is native to Minas Geraes and Mato Grosso, Brazil. In the trade the root and rhizome of this plant are known as Rio or Brazilian ipecac. *C. acuminata* is native to Colombia, Panama, Costa Rica, and Nicaragua and is usually labeled in the trade according to the country of origin.

As yet the largest source of supply remains the western hemisphere, where all the product is obtained from wild sources in the forests. The forest reservoirs are showing distinct signs of depletion, however, and ipecac would be a profitable crop to produce by cultivation if satisfactory techniques could be developed. The United States-Nicaraguan tropical agricultural experiment station at El Recreo, Nicaragua, has recently initiated a study of this problem.

At present a description of the best methods of cultivation is impossible, but certain remarks as to apparent conditions for its satisfactory growth in the forest can be given. It requires deep shade and a moist, friable, well-drained, acid soil high in humus content. The forest floor where it is found is covered with leaf litter and is always relatively cool and humid compared to such neighboring areas as have been cleared of forest for agricultural purposes. An annual rainfall of approximately 100 inches occurs where it is native. The ground does not at any time become excessively dry.

When the plant is gathered in the wild, enough root or rhizome sometimes remains in the ground to produce a new plant. The plant is slow growing, requiring two to four years to attain a marketable size. By then it may have developed one to four roots, or sometimes more, weighing about one ounce when dried.

Ipecac may be gathered at any time of the year, but to provide the best conditions for regrowth of the plant from root and rhizome remaining in the ground; the harvest should take place during the months of most frequent rainfall. Then the roots and rhizomes are more easily removed from the ground without breakage; care should be taken, if it is desirable to maintain the stand, to leave some propagating material in the soil. To bury the stem of the plant slightly, with a few leaves attached will serve as a method of propagation if done with some care.

In Nicaragua wild ipecac is gathered by grasping and pulling on the stem of the plant while prying out its roots and rhizomes by loosening and lifting the ground with a sharp stick shoved under the roots. Since most ipecac is sold on a wet basis by native diggers in Nicaragua, it is kept covered with either wet leaves or soil until enough has been gathered to take to a local buyer, who then dries it in the sun or in a storage room. The roots and rhizomes are very thin and dry rapidly.

NUX-VOMICA

Nux-vomica seed, obtained from the fruit of *Strychnos nux-vomica* L., of the family Loganiaceæ, is the source of strychnine, an important circulatory stimulant and common rat poison. In the United States considerable amounts of strychnine are used annually by government rodent control agencies and their cooperators to exterminate field rodents such as ground squirrels, prairie dogs, and kangaroo rats.

Nux-vomica seed is gathered from wild trees growing forty to fifty and even one hundred feet tall. These have been able to supply all of this product the market has demanded. Getting the seed is a spare-time enterprise for the natives of the regions where the trees grow wild. In India the natives go into the forests when the fruit ripens during the summer rainy season. The bright brownish yellow fruit is about the size of an orange. It contains a gelatinous pulp in which are embedded a small number of thin button-like seeds about ¾ inch in diameter. The seeds are separated from the pulp, washed, and dried in the sun. They are sold by the natives to small merchants, who accumulate sufficient quantities to market to exporters.

The value of *S. nux-vomica* seed in normal times is so low that it would hardly pay to plant these trees with the thought of exporting the product. However, there are so many places in the tropics where the rodent control problem is an important one, both from the standpoint of crop damage and the danger of house rats to health, that the inclusion of this tree among the species selected for reforestation would appear desirable. In such a way, a cheap local source of rodenticide would be provided with the possible opportunity of exporting the product should the market become more attractive at any time.

PAPAIN

Papain is the dried juices of the leaves and the rind of immature fruits of the papaya, *Carica papaya* L., of the family Caricaceæ. Papain contains a proteolytic enzyme which is used in greatest quantities by the meat processing industry as a tenderizer. Relatively small amounts are used for medicinal purposes.

While the papaya, a western hemisphere native, is one of the common plants of the tropics, it frequently exists not because it has been intentionally planted but because it has grown up in house yards from seed discarded with kitchen refuse. People usually take care not to cut down these plants once they have started to grow.

Although it may grow from five to fifteen feet tall, the papaya is not a tree but an herbaceous plant. It may reach maturity and produce fruit in less than a year's time. The plant may continue bearing for several years, although it usually produces smaller fruits as it advances in age. Papaya is sensitive to soil fertility. Best growth and production are obtained only on well-drained soils high in organic matter. It has been observed to grow especially well near refuse piles or where compost heaps have stood. The size of the papaya, its yields and the quality of the fruit are markedly influenced by these soil conditions. When set out in groves the plants can advantageously be spaced from ten to fifteen feet apart in an hexagonal pattern. The spacing distance should be determined by the fertility of the soil; more land should be allowed for better growth when the land is rich.

Individual papaya plants usually bear only male or female flowers; therefore considerable land and expense may be wasted on staminate plants set out in groves. The agricultural experiment stations in the Hawaiian Islands have carried on research on strains of the fruit and its propagation to obtain larger percentages of the female fruit-producing trees. In some regions papaya leaves are attacked by a leaf-blight with the appearance of a mosaic disease. Also the fruit may be attacked by a fly which deposits its eggs under the rind, with the consequent development of larvæ and spoilage of the fruit.

Several processes for extracting papain have been developed. The most common and crudest method is to make a series of shallow longitudinal cuts into the rind of the immature fruit while it is still on the tree. From these cuts a white latex oozes and will eventually dry so that it can be scraped off. Unfortunately, in the process of drying, sufficient fermentation takes place to reduce the enzyme content of the dried product considerably. Annual yields of about three and one-half ounces of dried latex per plant have been reported.

Rogers McVaugh gives a popular résumé of papain production in the July 1943 issue of *Agriculture in the Americas*. A short bibliography is appended to his article.

PSYLLIUM

Psyllium seeds, obtained from *Plantago psyllium* L., *P. arenaria* Waldst. et Kit., and *P. ovata* Forsk., are used because of their indigestibility and bulking properties in certain cases of chronic constipation. The mucilage extracted from the seed is employed as a bandoline and a cloth sizing material.

While psyllium seeds are produced on a commercial scale in a number of European countries, United States imports have come principally from India. Inasmuch as there is a rather good market for a limited supply of this product, it would seem to merit experimental attention on the part of a few enterprising land-owners in certain highland areas of the hemisphere tropics. Approximately 2000 acres could supply the normal annual United States requirements.

P. psyllium is grown in the region about Carpentras in southeastern France. The plant prefers light friable soils, and the seed bed should be well prepared. Seeding may be done in the fall, but spring sowing is said to be preferable.

A successful crop usually requires a heavy application of a complete fertilizer especially high in phosphorus. Shallow seeding is done, at the rate of six or seven pounds to the acre in rows two feet apart. The crop is cultivated twice during the early growing season. The plant has a semi-trailing habit of growth. In France it is usually sown before March 15 and harvested before the middle of August at a time when about three-quarters of the field has a light golden color. Since psyllium has a tendency to shatter, harvesting is done early in the morning to avoid as much loss as possible.

Psyllium mucilage is extracted from the seed by boiling it in water, in which the mucilage is readily soluble. *P. psyllium* and *P. ovata* produce a superior clear colorless mucilage. There are two standard types of the commercial seed:

1. Seed known commercially as black, French, or Spanish psyllium seed and obtained from *P. psyllium* and *P. arenaria;*
2. Seed produced in India from *P. ovata* and known in trading circles as white or blond psyllium seed, Indian plantago seed, and ispaghula seed.

The mucilage content and consequently the demulcent qualities are highest in *P. ovata.* Yields of *P. psyllium* in France are reported to range between 800 and 1400 pounds per acre, according to the season and the care the crop has had.

SANDALWOOD

The heartwood of the trunk, limbs, and roots of the tropical sandalwood trees, *Santalum album* L. and related species of the Santalaceæ family contain an essential oil highly regarded by the perfume industry and used to some extent in pharmeceutical preparations. Fine-ground sandalwood is used in incense and sachets.

Pound for pound there are probably few woods which have so high a market value as the heart of sandalwood. The tree is native to India, Malaya, the East Indies, and Hawaii. The exploitation of Hawaiian sandalwood was a very important industry in the early part of the nineteenth century. Most of it was shipped to China, where it was used as incense. Unrestricted cutting in Hawaiian sandalwood led to depletion of the trees, although it is said that there are still specimens as tall as thirty-five feet and twenty inches in diameter on the island of Oahu. The chief source of world supply is now the Mysore Government monopoly in India.

It is reported that the sandalwood trees require at least fifty years to produce sufficient heartwood to make them marketable. Considering the value of the wood, however, which has sold at from $200 to $500 per ton, it would appear to be worthwhile to experiment with their culture in the western hemisphere.

The tree is semi-parasitic. Although it is capable of obtaining necessary water and nourishment directly from the soil, it has roots which grow into those of adjoining trees and obtain some of their nourishment in that way. Plantations of sandalwood are started with seed in forest clearings where sufficient shade and nurse trees are left for the protection of the delicate young plants. In Hawaii sandalwood has been reported to do well under cultivation when provided with such nurse trees as the Casuarina and certain species of Acacia. These trees are apparently satisfactory hosts for the parasitic roots of the sandalwood.

The soil of the spots selected for seed plantings should be well loosened to the depth of a foot and for a distance of three to six feet around the seed. The young sandalwood forest must be protected from grazing animals. Underbrush is regularly cut back until the trees are large enough to hold their own, and then only overtopping scrub trees should be cut. The seedlings are reported to grow about three inches the first two years and about a foot the third year. By the time they are five or six years old they have a trunk about one inch through. When the tree is about fifty years old, it is considered mature and may have a girth of two to three and one-half feet and considerable heartwood.

Since the wood of the roots as well as the trunk contains the volatile oil, the whole tree is uprooted when it is mature. The bark and sapwood are cut off and the yellowish brown heartwood is cut up into pieces about a yard long. The product is exported in that form. Upon its arrival in the United States it is chipped or ground and subjected to steam distillation. The yield of oil is said to be about 2.5 percent of the weight of the wood.

SENNA

Senna leaves, which are imported by the United States in large quantities because of their mild cathartic properties, are obtained from the leguminous shrubs *Cassia senna* L., and *C. angustifolia* Vahl. The principal producing area is the Tinnevelly region of India where *C. angustifolia* is grown. As in the case of so many imported botanicals, bales of senna leaves are occasionally adulterated with stems, seed pods, and even leaves of entirely different plants which are included because of their superficial resemblance and not because they contain any desirable medicinal qualities.

The cultivated senna of India is propagated by seed which is first germinated in nursery beds. In two months' time the young seedlings are about six inches high. They are then transplanted to the field, where they are usually spaced about three feet by three feet on newly prepared, weed-free ground. It is reported that new plantings are made annually. Harvest takes place three times during the growing season, the first about three months after the plants have been in the field. The leaves are stripped from the shrubs and spread out in the sun to dry. Yields as high as 700 to 1400 pounds per acre per year have been reported, but Tinnevelly averages are said to run 70 to 100 pounds per acre at the first picking, 150 to 200 pounds at the second, and 75 pounds at the third picking.

Success in planting this crop for commercial purposes in the western hemisphere would largely depend upon labor costs. In those countries where labor standards and wages are about on a par with the Far East, its cultivation might be attempted if well supervised and efficiently managed.

STRAMONIUM

Datura stramonium L. is familiar to farmers in many areas of the southern and eastern United States where it is commonly known as Jamestown or jimson weed. It is a member of the plant famliy Solanaceæ, of which both belladonna and henbane are members. The principal alkaloids of its leaves and flowering tops are the same as those of belladonna and its pharmaceutical uses similar. Unlike its relatives, however, stramonium may be more easily grown. It requires no greenhouse or coldframe germination and transplanting. The seed may be drilled directly in the field in rows three feet apart. After the plants are visible, they may be thinned to distances of twelve to fifteen inches apart in the rows. As in the case of belladonna and henbane, the potato beetle is the most common insect which attacks the crop.

When the plants are in full bloom, they may be harvested by cutting the entire plant off at the ground. As the plant is succulent at this stage, it must be dried in a manner similar to belladonna and henbane. Later the leaves and tops may be stripped from the stem and baled for market. Yields of stramonium leaves may range between 1000 and 1500 pounds per acre.

INSECTICIDAL PLANTS

Approximately 1200 different plants are reputed to be more or less toxic to insects. A few of these such as certain producers of pyrethrum, rotenone, and nicotine are sources of commercial insecticides. Although nicotine is poisonous to man in concentrated form, it may safely be used as an insecticide on food crops. Nicotine disintegrates upon exposure, and its residues, unlike those of arsenic and lead compounds, are non-poisonous to the human system. Pyrethrum and rotenone are widely used in household fly sprays and bug powders because, in addition to being powerful insecticides, they are non-poisonous to man. For these reasons they are also preferred by the growers of certain fruits and vegetables.

The common tobacco plant, *Nicotiana tabacum*, is the principal source of nicotine which is extracted by steam distillation from wastes discarded in the manufacture of cigarettes, cigars, and other leaf products. Since

UNITED STATES IMPORTS AND DECLARED VALUES, 1938–1940
OF THE MEDICINAL PRODUCTS CONSIDERED IN THIS CHAPTER*

Product	1938		1939		1940	
	Pounds	Dollars	Pounds	Dollars	Pounds	Dollars
Acacia	8,735,447	539,914	9,199,623	634,610	14,055,415	922,012
Aloe	578,197	161,812	865,304	231,703	801,300	238,904
Balsam of Peru	88,551	49,469	67,813	33,127	102,999	57,075
Belladonna	83,251	7,147	229,246	22,319	125,394	20,237
Camphor (natural)	1,502,800	565,730	1,974,734	652,325	1,110,172	487,509
Castor bean	114,072,566	2,046,163	162,610,861	2,882,087	237,788,672	5,665,252
Coca	464,512	82,984	590,180	110,152	830,425	155,440
Gambir	2,989,894	197,008	5,562,019	382,081	4,970,263	343,875
Gum tragacanth	1,074,100	594,577	3,064,676	1,263,959	3,712,716	1,692,168
Henbane	55,109	3,901	121,638	8,718	120,272	13,629
Ipecac	60,300	53,802	67,710	60,864	149,880	166,013
Nux-Vomica	1,083,330	16,546	2,458,047	49,652	3,467,829	62,087
Papain	232,237	343,874	273,159	335,910	225,408	286,500
Psyllium	2,636,361	276,829	2,183,742	199,823	2,437,875	262,950
Sandalwood	1,162,787	193,191	583,812	82,188	1,840,502	261,780
Senna	1,500,894	69,089	1,979,625	77,192	3,625,486	176,977
Stramonium	319,812	24,403	517,219	36,673	178,734	18,195

* *Foreign Commerce & Navigation of the United States;* U. S. Department of Commerce; Calendar years 1938, 1939, 1940.

common tobacco is too low in nicotine content to make its cultivation feasible for insecticidal purposes, there is no likelihood that the demand for nicotine will influence the acreage which might be devoted to *N. tabacum.* However, there are some strains of *rustica,* a close relative of common tobacco, which have been reported to yield five to ten percent and even more of nicotine. This plant is grown for insecticidal purposes on a significant scale in several countries outside the Western Hemisphere, notably in Russia and Germany.

While pyrethrum and rotenone crops are grown specifically for insecticidal purposes, as yet neither has been produced in sufficient quantity

PLATE 15. Upper—Cryptostegia rubber plant in Haiti
Lower left—Hevea rubber grove in Brazil
Lower right—Harvesting castilla rubber in Nicaragua

PLATE 16. Upper—An Ecuadorean farmer plants cinchona trees
Lower—Native cinchona tree in Ecuador

PLATE 17. Upper—Cinchona tree, Ledger type, in blossom
Lower—Drying cinchona bark for quinine in Ecuador

PLATE 18. Upper—Cottonwood trees of Arizona
Lower—Spanish-American farmstead in New Mexico

to satisfy a steadily increasing consumer demand. By offering attractive prices under long term agreements the United States has extended considerable encouragement to producers of these commodities in the Western Hemisphere during the war period. In the United States the use of these products is subject to rationing under a strict schedule of priorities. With the opening of the world market after the war the demand for these products produced in Latin America will depend almost entirely on their quality and the price at which they are offered.

Pyrethrum is botanically related to our ornamental chrysanthemums. Its dried flowers constitute the crude insecticide. Most of the world's supply is produced in Japan and in the British Colony of Kenya in East Africa where cheap labor is available for the tedious tasks involved in its culture and the hand picking of the flowers. While unskilled farm labor is equally inexpensive in most countries of the western hemisphere, experience has indicated that there are other crops which usually return higher profits to land-owners than pyrethrum. As a consequence, the acreage devoted to this crop in Brazil, Peru, and a few other Latin American countries has increased only slightly. Pyrethrum requires a temperate climate, which in the tropics exists only at high altitudes.

Rotenone is found in a number of plants belonging to the legume or bean family but commercial supplies are derived entirely from the roots of two genera, Lonchocarpus [4] and Derris. The derris grown for insecticidal purposes is native to tropical East Asia, the East Indies and the Philippines. Lonchocarpus is indigenous to the Amazon Valley, where it is extensively cultivated in Peru and on a very small scale in Brazil. Considerable effort has been made since the beginning of the war to introduce derris culture to several tropical regions of the western hemisphere. Preliminary experience derived from the small acreage established indicates that Derris will not be as profitable as Lonchocarpus unless the cost of production can be reduced by improved cultural techniques and the selection of strains with higher rotenone content.

Both Derris and Lonchocarpus require well-drained soil, a high, well-distributed rainfall, and a tropical climate. Numerous localities in the western hemisphere afford these prerequisites but they are usually overgrown by the jungle growth of tropical rain forests. The people living in these areas have few implements other than an axe with which to fell the forest and a machete with which to cultivate their crops. Furthermore, such regions of South and Central America are usually sparsely settled, and wealthy land-owners have avoided risking capital in their development.

The culture of Lonchocarpus in Peru is astonishingly successful despite

[4] Known by various common names such as "barbasco," "cubé," "timbó," and "haiari."

the rather haphazard manner in which it is grown on burned over stump lands. Yields have been large and profits so satisfactory that Lonchocarpus roots have become the most important export of the Amazon region of Peru. The total tonnage produced far exceeds that of rubber in Peru's Amazon territory despite the costly efforts made in recent years to augment rubber harvests.

Long before Chinese gardeners in Malaya discovered the usefulness of rotenone as an insecticide, the natives of tropical East Asia employed the roots of certain species of derris as fish poisons. They had discovered that when quantities of fresh, mashed roots were cast into a pool or small stream, the fish would be paralyzed and rise helpless to the surface where they could be picked up. The Indians of the South American tropics in pre-Columbian times likewise found that roots of certain Lonchocarpus plants would serve the same purpose. It is interesting to speculate upon how these widely separated peoples discovered the fish poisoning properties of two plants so closely related botanically and so similar in appearance when found in the wild state.

The Spanish speaking people of the western hemisphere commonly use the word "barbasco" for fish poison plants. Scores of these "barbascos" do not contain rotenone or any other substance of insecticidal value. Of all the known fish poison species a few belonging to the legume family have proved to be the most promising for insecticidal purposes. While beginnings have been made, a systematic study of all the legumes botanically related to the species known to contain rotenone or to those used as fish poisons has not been completed. It is possible that further investigation, although it would be difficult and costly, would reveal more suitable sources of rotenone and related substances than we now have. Therein lies an opportunity not only for the professional botanist but for the curious layman who may have the good fortune to live in regions where these plants are native. The method to be followed in bringing these plants to the attention of entomologists and chemists is the same as that indicated in the chapter on medicinal plants for those who take an interest in botanical drugs. The discovery of the insecticidal value of *Tephrosia virginiana*, the "devil's shoestring" of the southwestern United States, resulted from a study carried out along these lines. Subsequent research on this plant indicates that it may one day become a commercial rotenone crop in the southern United States. Entomologists at Cornell University have recently reported that "yam beans" obtained from several species of *Pachyrhizus* show promise of becoming important commercial insecticides.

As yet the ideal insecticidal plant from the standpoint of economical production has not been discovered. The ones now grown strictly for insecticidal purposes are reasonable in cost only because they are produced in countries where cheap labor is available. Abundant production, however, is restricted by hand methods. Theoretically a plant such as pyrethrum which produces its insecticidal ingredient above ground should be cheaper than root crops like Derris and Lonchocarpus. However, the culture of pyrethrum also involves considerable hand labor. Although a mechanical pyrethrum harvester has been designed, the fact that the flowers do not usually blossom simultaneously in tropical and sub-tropical latitudes limits its practicability. Also, the land on which pyrethrum is grown in the western hemisphere is often too steep or rough to permit the use of machinery. In theory the ideal low cost insecticidal crop would be one which could be planted with seed directly in the field and which could be efficiently harvested with machinery. If it would yield about 2000 pounds or more per acre of potent insecticide in one growing season there should be a possibility of producing it cheaply and in abundance without so much concern about labor costs.

If such a plant cannot be found, the hope for plentiful supplies of a cheap agricultural insecticide non-poisonous to man probably lies in the laboratories of chemists. A synthetic may be the answer. The discovery of DDT (dichloro-diphenyl-trichloroethane) is more than a ray of hope. Not only is it important in itself but it opens up a field for further discovery. How cheaply it can be produced remains to be seen. It is superior to nicotine, pyrethrum or rotenone in its stability, consequently it has a more lasting effect when sprayed on plants.

The use of botanical insecticides in the tropical regions of the hemisphere remains in its infancy. Logically one of the markets for these products should exist in the very countries where they are raised or where they could be introduced as crops. Just as the farmers of the southern United States may some day be able to produce rotenone yielding tephrosias for their own and local consumption, land-owners and subsistence farmers of the tropical countries of the hemisphere might also consider growing some of these crops for home needs. Fresh Lonchocarpus or Derris roots need only be dug, mashed and the juice mixed with water to prepare an effective insecticidal spray for a number of pests.

The following data outline only the more important details of the culture of pyrethrum and Lonchocarpus. Space limitation permits only brief reference to other major and minor botanical insecticides. Inasmuch as common tobacco is not grown specifically for insecticidal purposes a discussion of its culture is omitted. The chart at the end of this chapter summarizes the relative importance of these insecticides as reflected by the imports of the United States which is by far the most important market for insecticides in the hemisphere.

LONCHOCARPUS

The roots of the commercially important species of Lonchocarpus, commonly known as cubé, timbó, barbasco and haiari, contain the insecticide rotenone. Rotenone acts both as a contact and stomach poison. It is harmless to man in the concentrations used in household and agricultural insecticides. Lonchocarpus preparations are applied as dusts made of ground dry root mixed with talc or other inert materials, or as sprays. The sprays are compounded with extracts of the crude roots. Flea powders, fly sprays, stock dips and moth proofing preparations are made of Lonchocarpus roots and extracts.

In addition to its insecticidal properties, rotenone is a powerful fish poison. Lonchocarpus roots were first employed for this purpose by South American Indians before their insecticidal value was realized.

Commercial plantings in the Amazon region of Peru constitute the primary source of the world's supply. Smaller quantities are obtained from Brazil, Colombia, and Venezuela where there are few commercial growers but where rapidly dwindling stands of semi-wild reserves still exist which were established by Indians for fish poison purposes.

The principal species of Lonchocarpus used as sources of rotenone insecticides are *Lonchocarpus utilis* A. C. Smith, and *Lonchocarpus urucu* Killip and Smith. They are members of the plant family Leguminosæ to which peas and beans also belong. These plants grow well on a variety of soils ranging from sands to heavy clays. They do not develop well on lands which are occasionally flooded or which have high water tables. A fairly well distributed annual rainfall of 80 to 125 inches and a tropical climate are necessary for optimum growth. Other species of *Lonchocarpus* having less or no importance as insecticides occur in many parts of our hemisphere.

Lonchocarpus is propagated from stem cutting about twelve to fourteen inches long and one to two inches in diameter. It is the usual practice to set the cuttings directly in the field at distances of about six by six feet. Planting is done during a rainy season to avoid drying out of the cuttings which develop roots slowly. The cuttings are placed in the soil at a slight angle just under the surface of the ground.

There are about 7000 acres of Lonchocarpus plantings in Peru. Almost all the land devoted to this crop consists of little clearings recently cut out of the virgin Amazon jungles. Commercial production of the crop is relatively new, having developed only in the last ten to twelve years. Since the Amazon natives have only a few hand tools they can do no more in the way of land preparation than cut down the forest and burn the clearing after the leaves and small branches of the trees have dried out. The crop is planted directly in these fields while still strewn with charred logs and stumps. Lonchocarpus requires two to three years before it is ready to harvest. At that stage the plants are about seven to ten feet high and the plantings are dense thickets.

Harvest consists of cutting off the thick stems about one and one-half feet above ground with a machete. The larger part of the root system which is superficial is ripped out of the ground by pulling on the stems. Some of the larger roots must be dug individually. These are loosened to facilitate pulling by prying under them with a heavy sharp pointed pole to break open the earth and lift the roots. The roots are dried before they are baled for export. A small quantity of them is milled into powder before shipment. Yields vary between 1500 and 2500 pounds of air-dried roots per acre. The rotenone content usually ranges between four and six percent. Standard agricultural insecticides are usually one-half to one percent rotenone.

PYRETHRUM

Crude pyrethrum insecticide consists of the dried flower heads of the pyrethrum plants *Chrysanthemum cinerariaefolium* (Trev.) Vis., a native of Yugoslavia and *coccineum* Willd., which is indigenous to the Caucasus and northern Iran. These herbaceous perennials belong to the plant family Asteraceæ. Pyrethrum is one of the oldest and most widely used of the insecticides derived from plants. The dry pulverized flowers, known as "insect powder," have long been used for household purposes for controlling flies, cockroaches, bedbugs, ants, and other insects. Pyrethrum is the active ingredient in the recently developed aerosol insect spray which has been used so effectively to combat the anopheles mosquito in malarial regions.

Pyrethrum has been grown successfully on well-drained soils ranging from sandy loams to clays. The plant will survive low winter temperature, particularly when protected by snow. It will withstand considerable drought, although a lack of adequate rainfall during the early months of the growing season will reduce the yield of flowers. Pyrethrum is ordinarily grown from seed which is usually sown in seedbeds. The seedlings are transplanted to the field when they are five to six weeks old. They are usually spaced from twelve to eighteen inches apart in rows three feet apart or in check rows two feet apart each way. The plant may also be propagated by crown division. Pyrethrum is subject to damage by a number of leaf, crown and root diseases.

In order to obtain the flower at the stage of maximum toxicity the blooms are harvested before they begin to ripen when most of them are from two-thirds to fully open. They are usually picked by hand or with the aid of crude hand-operated stripping devices. In some places the plants are cut off with sickles and the flowers removed by drawing the flower stalks through a comb-like stripper attached to a bench.

Immediately after harvesting, the flowers must be spread out to dry. In regions where clear weather prevails this may be done in the open as in Japan, where they are spread thinly on straw mats. Elsewhere provision must be made for drying in sheds or preferably in heated chambers. In the commercial producing regions the dry flowers are packed under high pressure into bales for shipment. Proper storage of the flowers, whether baled or otherwise, is necessary to prevent deterioration which takes place rapidly.

Pyrethrum yields a small crop of flowers in the second year after planting in the field. Thereafter it may produce a normal crop for several seasons. Over a period of eighteen years the average annual yield of dried flowers on the Japanese island of Hokkaido was 350 pounds per acre. Commercial plantings in the eastern United States have yielded up to 1000 pounds per acre with an average of 700 to 800 pounds. However, in the western United States, at higher elevations, the yields are considerably lower.

DERRIS

Derris elliptica (Wall.) Benth, and *Derris malaccensis* (Benth.) Prain, are grown for commercial supplies of rotenone. These plants belong to the plant family Leguminosæ. These perennial vines are native to tropical eastern Asia and the East Indies. Derris is propagated with stem cuttings which may be either rooted in a nursery or planted directly in the field. Unless supported on trellises the vines spread over the surface of the ground. Plants must grow one and one-half to two years before roots are ready to harvest. Yields are about 800 to 1500 pounds of air-dried roots per acre. Average rotenone content is about five to six percent. Principal commercial sources are British Malaya and the Netherlands Indies.

ANABASIS

The leaves and stems of *Anabasis aphylla* L. are used for the extraction of the insecticide anabasine, which is in many respects similar to nicotine.

It is a small woody perennial native to Russian Turkestan, the Caucasus, and adjoining regions of neighboring countries. It may be propagated by seed or by cuttings of roots and stems. Yields are reported to range between 400 and 2400 pounds of green plant material per acre. Anabasis grows wild in comparatively dry regions on saline soils with a high water table to which the roots can penetrate. *Nicotiana glauca*, Graham, or "tree tobacco" also contains anabasine. It is being grown experimentally to determine its possible value as a commercial crop.

HELLEBORE

The ground roots and rhizomes of *Veratrum viride* Aiton, a native of the northeastern United States, and of *V. album* L., which is indigenous to Europe and Siberia, are used to a limited extent as insecticides. They are of some medicinal value as well. These plants are members of the Liliaceæ or lily family. There is little if any cultivation of these plants. The small amounts entering commercial channels are believed to be collected from wild sources.

LARKSPUR

The ground seed of *Delphinium consolida* L. of the Ranunculaceæ family has been used to a limited degree for the control of head lice. Certain of the Delphinium alkaloids are toxic as stomach poisons to a number of insects. They are also poisonous to human beings. The commercial exploitation of larkspur seeds as insecticides is not significant. The plant is an annual and native to southern Europe. It is well known in the United States for its ornamental flower.

QUASSIA

The species commonly called Quassia which are used for insecticidal purposes are *Aeschrion excelsa* (Sw.) Kuntze, a native of Jamaica and the Dominican Republic, and *Quassia amara* L., a native of tropical northern South America. Both are members of the Simarubaceæ. Quassias are trees, and the wood is the source of the insecticide which has been used only in the control of aphids, particularly the hop aphid. Supplies of quassia are obtained from native trees, there being no commercial cultivation of the species. Quassia is also used in the preparation of medicinal bitters. Drinking cups for medicinal bitters are made of the wood. Jamaica is the principal source.

SABADILLA

Sabadilla seed is obtained from *Schœnocaulon officinale* (Schlecht. and Cham.) A. Gray, of the Liliaceæ or lily family. While it is most commonly used in the control of head lice, it has been reported to be used as an insecticide by cattle raisers in Venezuela where the plant is native. In the October, 1943, issue of the Journal of Economic Entomology, Mathhysse and Schwardt report they found ground Sabadilla seed was the most satisfactory substitute for rotenone in killing lice on dairy cattle. The seed entering the trade is probably largely obtained from wild plants. Although it has been reported to be under cultivation no details are available. The United States imports a small amount of Sabadilla from Venezuela.

UNITED STATES IMPORTS AND DECLARED VALUES 1939-1941

Product	1939		1940		1941	
	Pounds	Dollars	Pounds	Dollars	Pounds	Dollars
Derris (root and powder)	2,897,561	323,617	3,220,972	360,572	4,101,405	503,739
Hellebore	39,440*	1,639	....	....	....	....
Lonchocarpus (root and powder)	3,001,149	290,653	3,345,843	310,862	3,897,404	393,729
Pyrethrum	13,569,300	3,173,604	12,591,210	2,949,211	11,020,506	1,842,346
Quassia	291,325*	3,742	340,540*	4,918	590,199	8,307
Sabadilla	93,977*	10,142	75,758*	8,829	100,131	13,405

* Port of New York.

8

Biological Control of Insect Pests

By *C. P. CLAUSEN*
ENTOMOLOGIST IN CHARGE,
FOREIGN PARASITE INTRODUCTION,
UNITED STATES DEPARTMENT OF AGRICULTURE

AS the Messrs. Higbee and Lee have indicated, the culture and planting of some of the more promising drug crops, notably the rotenone-bearing plants, are motivated by the chronic need for defending crops from the ravages of destructive insects.

This is apropos of the fact that almost every beneficial new crop for the New World is accompanied or followed by one or more natural enemies. Usually these undersized hitchhikers, when relieved of their own natural enemies, flourish more readily in the new locale than the parent, or victim plant. Moreover, with our amazing new age of rapid transportation and travel and fading boundaries, the defense of crops from insects is also a premier challenge to international cooperation.

Dr. C. P. Clausen, a senior entomologist with our Federal Department of Agriculture, is the pre-eminent authority on the biological control of insect pests, which is essentially a strategy of employing natural enemies of natural enemies of migrating crops.

8

THE INSECT CONTROL problems of the western hemisphere are in large part a direct result of the agricultural development that has taken place during the past century. A very large proportion of the agricultural crops now being grown are not native to this hemisphere but have been brought here, some in relatively recent years, from Europe, Africa, and Asia. This applies to all classes of crops, as will be seen if the history of our grain crops, fruits, and vegetables is examined. Also an exceedingly large variety of ornamental plants has been introduced. A constant search is being made of all regions of the world for new plants, or better varieties of those already here, in order to increase production or to fill special needs. With the opening up of new territory, especially in South America, it is inevitable that the importation of seeds and plants into the different countries will continue for many years.

Unfortunately, this large-scale importation of seeds, plants, and plant products has had one very serious result. By this means many destructive insect pests have gained a foothold in the New World and have spread widely through many countries. This was especially true during the latter part of the nineteenth century, when the dangers of such importations were not so clearly recognized. Even today, however, with efficient plant quarantine services in operation, it is perhaps inevitable that some pests should be able to escape detection and succeed in establishing themselves. As an illustration of the permanent harm that results from the accidental establishment of pest insects from abroad, it has been estimated that well over half of the most important crop pests in the United States are of foreign origin, and that the number of plant-feeding species that have been recognized as of foreign origin approaches one thousand. Among these are all of the important pests of citrus, the sugarcane borer, the European corn borer, the coddling moth, the cotton-boll weevil, the Japanese beetle, the oriental fruit moth, and many others of outstanding importance. The situation is similar in other countries, though the actual number of established species may not be so great.

THE BASIS OF BIOLOGICAL CONTROL

The biological control of insect pests that attack agricultural crops involves the use of natural enemies to reduce the infestations below a destructive level. The natural enemies that are most frequently employed for this purpose are other insects that have become specialized in the parasitic or predaceous habit, and are able to live and reproduce only at the expense of other insects. This specialization has attained such a high degree that some species of parasites are confined strictly to a single host insect, while many others are able to develop only upon a group of closely related species. A parasite species that develops in a caterpillar is unlikely to be able to attack the larvæ of beetles. This being the case, there can be no danger that in another country they will modify their habits and become plant pests.

In its native habitat in the country of origin, a plant-feeding insect usually does not occur in sufficient abundance to cause serious injury. In a great many instances this condition is due to the occurrence of a series of natural enemies that serve to hold it at a relatively low level. However, when the pest insect becomes established in a new country, through various channels of trade, it usually happens that the parasites which attack it are left behind. As a result, the pest insect is freed from one of its principal checks and, accordingly, in the new environment it is able to increase without restraint and become much more destructive than in the country from which it came. Thus, the woolly apple aphid is much more injurious in South America and other parts of the world than in eastern North America, from whence it came. The Japanese beetle is vastly more abundant in the United States than in any section of Japan, where it originated. The objective in biological control, therefore, is to obtain the various natural enemies in the country of origin and to establish them where the pest has gained a new foothold. In this way it is hoped that the same condition of equilibrium at a low level that exists in the country of origin will be established in the new country. The citrus blackfly, which was so destructive to citrus in Cuba and nearby islands and in Central America before the importation of its parasite, is never injurious in tropical Asia, its native home.

While it cannot be said that there is no possibility of successful biological control of native pests, yet it must be admitted that the chances of such an outcome are very much less than with those of foreign origin. The native insects, almost without exception, are already attacked in all of their susceptible stages by a series of parasites and predators. The importation and establishment of additional species of similar habit is consequently unlikely to aid appreciably in increasing their total effectiveness. It is quite possible, however, that the native parasites do not occur throughout the range of the pest insect in a given country, and in such a case their colonization in the sections where they are absent would be worthwhile.

An outstanding advantage of biological control over other methods, such as spraying, dusting, and the like, is that the initial cost is usually the only cost. After the parasites have been imported and widely established, they increase and exert whatever measure of control is within their capabilities, and little or nothing can be done to increase their effectiveness. A fully successful parasite controls its host year after year without further cost, whereas with chemical control, measures against serious pests must be applied every year or several times each year, thus constituting a continuing annual charge against the crop.

It needs to be pointed out and emphasized that in no instance can there be absolute certainty in advance as to the outcome, in terms of degree of control, of any parasite introduction program. No matter how effective a parasite may be in the country of origin, its transition to a new and superficially identical environment subjects it to influences which, though apparently minor in themselves, may prevent the species from accomplishing the purpose desired. This is well illustrated by a tachnid fly, *Centeter cinerea* ald., which was introduced into the United States from Japan for control of the Japanese beetle. Climatic conditions in the locality of origin and of release were very similar; yet in the United States it has proved to be of no value in control. This is in marked contrast to the condition in northern Japan, where the parasite is responsible for effective control of the pest. In the United States the times of appearance of the fly and the beetles are not properly synchronized and, as a result, the great majority of the flies have emerged and died before the peak of emergence of the beetles.

There are instances, however, in which the outcome of an introduction can be anticipated with considerable confidence, and the issuance is based upon previous experience with the same insect in a considerable number of countries. An excellent example is the vedalia, *Rodolia cardinalis* (Muls.), which, during the past fifty-five years has been introduced and established in forty-five or more countries of markedly diverse climatic and other conditions. The consistently satisfactory result in the control of the cottony cushion scale by this beetle warrants an optimistic attitude regarding its introduction into any region where citrus, the crop most seriously attacked by the scale, is grown commercially.

In all biological control work involving the importation of beneficial insects from other countries, it is essential that suitable precautions be taken so that no harmful species will escape and become established. This is accomplished by handling the imported material in special quarantine insectaries until the beneficial species can be segregated and the remainder destroyed. In order to accomplish the introduction of some parasite species, it is necessary to make shipment while they are in the early larval stage within the living hosts, and in some cases the host is a different pest species from that which is to be controlled. Every precaution is thus necessary to prevent the escape of living individuals of such insects.

There is another danger in connection with importation which is of equal importance. A considerable number of insect parasites attack, not the pest insects themselves, but the beneficial species that are parasitic upon them. These are generally called secondary parasites, and it is obvious that they should be recognized and destroyed. The field control of a pest insect by an effective parasite might be entirely prevented by the establishment of one of these secondary parasites, as it might destroy so large a portion of the beneficial form that the latter would be unable to increase its numbers sufficiently to effect control. The habits of these secondary parasites are so exceedingly varied that it is often very difficult to distinguish them from the beneficial species. Because of this, it is essential that each species being considered for importation should be studied with great care before any releases are made in the field. Among the parasites reared from a pest insect it will often be found that more than half are secondary in habit and are therefore harmful.

THE TIME REQUIRED FOR CONTROL

Another question that is often asked relates to the length of time required for an introduced parasite to bring about field control of the pest insect. Contrary to general opinion, the period is relatively short in the case of species that are fully and consistently effective. An examination of the information on this point, and covering all of the twenty-five or more instances in many parts of the world where pest species have been thus controlled, reveals that a period of only three pest generations after initial release of the parasites is required before actual control in the field is accomplished. This applies, of course, only in the immediate vicinity of the points of release.

The course of events with only partially or occasionally effective parasites is markedly different and uncertain. These species are not fully adapted to the conditions that prevail in the new environment, and consequently react to changes—especially climatic ones—in various ways. They may increase very rapidly immediately after release and show promise of controlling the pest insect, only to subside even more quickly and possibly disappear entirely. Conversely, an introduced parasite may become established but remain scarce and ineffective for a period of years and then suddenly increase to an enormous extent. This is only temporary, however, and they sooner or later subside to a low level. These sudden increases are associated with periods of optimum climatic conditions, which usually cannot be accurately defined. No reliance can be placed upon such species, as their periods of effectiveness are unpredictable and of uncertain duration.

There is another group of parasites that, after establishment, bring about a fairly high degree of effectiveness year after year, but are short of satisfactory control. These species are unquestionably of considerable value but it is exceedingly difficult to express this in terms of reduction of crop injury. A fifty-percent kill of some pest insects may produce approximately that amount of control, whereas in other instances the benefit may be very slight.

THE RELATION OF BIOLOGICAL TO CHEMICAL CONTROL

The question often arises as to the relation of biological control to the usual spraying, dusting, and other chemical and mechanical control practices that may be employed against the pest insects. Do these measures supplement each other, or are they mutually exclusive? No single answer will suffice to cover all pest problems and control practices. We know that the application of several lead arsenate sprays each season for the control of the coddling moth in apples results in the virtual elimination of the parasites of this pest, whereas it has little or no effect upon *Aphelinus mali* Hald., the very effective parasite of the woolly apple aphid, which infests the branches of the same trees. In the latter instance, however, the parasite is very seriously affected by application of oil sprays against other pests during the dormant period. Various other parasites and predators are highly susceptible to tartar emetic, cyolite, and other insecticides.

When a parasite has been introduced and shows considerable promise of bringing about control of the pest insect, the question often arises as to the steps to be taken with respect to the chemical control methods, such as sprays, that are in use. Obviously, if the parasite is highly susceptible to the sprays, it will be unable to increase and to control the pest so long as the sprays are used. In such cases, it is advisable to discontinue spraying on a test plot in order to give the parasite an opportunity to demonstrate its effectiveness. When the capacity of the parasite to bring about complete control has been proved by such tests, the general abandonment of spraying is warranted. This may involve an interim period during which some injury, preventable by spraying, occurs, but with fully effective parasites that period is never long. This cannot be avoided if the full potentialities of the parasite are to be realized, except in instances where another insecticide, not so destructive to the parasite, can be employed.

THE EARLY HISTORY OF BIOLOGICAL CONTROL

It will perhaps be of interest to give a short account of the early work in the biological control of insect pests and a review of the positive results that have been attained by this means. This will give assurance to those who are unfamiliar with this type of control that it is a practical means of dealing with insect pest problems. Like other methods of control, it has its limitations, and like them is not applicable in all cases.

The real beginning of biological control work was in 1888, when Albert Koebele was sent to Australia by the United States Department of Agriculture to obtain enemies of the cottony cushion scale (*Icerya purchasi* Mask). This insect, which was native to Australia, had become established in California and was so destructive to citrus that the welfare of that industry was seriously threatened. A predaceous beetle *Rodolia cardinalis* (Muls.) commonly called the vedalia, was found to attack the pest in Australia, and large numbers of them were collected by Mr. Koebele and shipped to the United States. They were reared and distributed in large numbers, and within two years of the time the first shipment was received the pest insect was under complete control throughout Southern California, and it has remained so ever since. This spectacular result attracted attention throughout the world and provided the stimulus for similar work on a wide range of insect pests in many parts of the world.

During the period of more than fifty years that has elapsed since the importation of the vedalia for control of the cottony cushion scale, biological control has come to be recognized as one of the promising lines of approach to the solution of insect pest problems, more especially in relation to those of foreign origin. It has been developed most extensively in the continental United States, Hawaii, Australia, New Zealand, Fiji, and Canada. During the more recent portion of this period many other countries have initiated biological control projects, so that there are now very few that have not at least made a beginning by importing and colonizing the better-known parasites that have proved to be effective in adjoining countries.

A review of the biological control projects undertaken in the different countries during this fifty-year period reveals that at least twenty-five species of pest insects, many of them of major importance, have been satisfactorily controlled in one or more countries. The majority of these have been in island areas located in the tropic zone. This is believed to be due to more equable climatic conditions existing there, which give the imported parasites optimum conditions for development throughout the year, lacking entirely the vicissitudes associated with the winter period in temperate regions. Important among them may be mentioned the sugar-cane leafhopper and beetle borer in Hawaii, the coconut scale, coconut moth, and coconut leaf-miner in Fiji, the citrus blackfly in Cuba and adjoining islands. The temperate region, however, is not lacking in equally successful projects, among which may be mentioned the cottony cushion scale on citrus in California and many other countries, the citrophilus mealybug on the same fruit in California, the spiny blackfly of citrus in Japan, and the woolly apple aphid in many countries.

The extent to which some of these natural enemies have been distributed over the world will surprise those not in close touch with this type of work. The vedalia beetle, previously mentioned, has been imported into approximately fifty countries for the control of the cottony cushion scale and has become established in all except three; in the great majority of countries it has been equally as successful as in California. The parasite of the woolly apple aphid, native to North America, has been colonized in forty-five countries and is known to be established in at least forty, in many of which it has successfully controlled the pest. Other parasites and predators have been distributed to nearly the same extent.

BIOLOGICAL CONTROL IN THE UNITED STATES

During the past fifty years there has been a very considerable amount of work done in the field of biological control in the United States that is of direct interest and importance to the countries of Central and South America. In the control of insect pests affecting citrus trees, the work of the California Agricultural Experiment Station is outstanding. The citrophilus mealybug, *Pseudococcus gahani* Green, has been effectively controlled by parasites imported from Australia, while the infestations of the common mealybug (*P. citri* Risso) have been much reduced in severity. Effective parasites have also been established upon the long-tailed mealybug (*P. adonidum* L.), a pest of less importance than those already mentioned.

Of special interest is the apparently satisfactory control that is being accomplished with the black scale (*Saissetia oleæ* Bern.). The problem has been the most important of those on citrus in California since the control of the cottony cushion scale, and the search for effective parasites in nearly every part of the world has gone on for almost fifty years. Finally, a parasite was obtained from South Africa that has shown itself capable of controlling the pest. The infestations in a number of sections of Southern California have been reduced to a non-injurious level, and it now appears that this control will be general over the main citrus-producing area within the very near future.

The United States Department of Agriculture has been engaged for many years upon problems affecting a variety of fruit and field crops. The results, in general, have not been so complete as those mentioned above for several citrus pests; yet the natural enemies that have been utilized have brought about, in a number of instances, a considerable reduction in the severity of the infestations. In the case of the oriental fruit moth, a very destructive enemy of peach, the colonization of the native parasite (*Macrocentrus ancylivorus* Roh.) originally found only on strawberry leaf-roller in a limited area, has reduced fruit infestation in many sections from more than fifty percent to twenty percent or less. This is of particular value considering that it has not been possible to develop other practical methods of control. There are, however, a number of areas in which, for some unknown reason, the parasite is ineffective.

One of the most promising of recent projects for the biological control of fruit insects is that on the Comstock mealybug (*Pseudococcus comstocki* Kuw.), which is a serious pest of apples. A number of parasites from Japan have been released in infested orchards during the last few years, and satisfactory control has been effected in some of them. While it is too early to determine the final outcome, the prospects of eventual control over the entire infested area are very bright.

The alfalfa weevil, which is of European origin, became established in the western states about forty years ago and became very destructive. One parasite that was imported from Italy consistently destroys a high percentage of the weevil larvæ, though it is difficult to determine the actual value of the parasite in terms of crop protection. It is agreed, however, that the presence of the parasite, in conjunction with a change in cutting practice, has reduced the pest to a relatively minor status.

The possibilities of biological control of the sugarcane borer, a serious pest of that crop in the southern United States as well as in practically all of the cane-producing countries of the western hemisphere, has received some attention. A considerable number of parasites have been imported from South America and the West Indies, but of these only the Cuban fly, *Lixophaga diatraeæ* Towns., has become well established. This was accomplished only in southern Florida, where it apparently has brought about quite a reduction in the infestation.

For many years it was believed that worthwhile results could be obtained through the mass release each year of an egg parasite, *Trichogramma evanescens* Westw. An extended experiment was therefore undertaken in Louisiana, covering a three-year period. It developed that such releases had no effect in reducing the infestations. While this was conclusive insofar as Louisiana is concerned, where cane is an annual crop, yet it is possible that the outcome may be more successful in the strictly tropical areas where cane growing is continuous and there is no extended winter period to interfere with increase of the parasite. Such results have been claimed in Barbados and Peru.

BIOLOGICAL CONTROL IN LATIN AMERICA

In the aggregate, a very considerable amount of successful biological control work has been done in the West Indies and Central and South America, though there it is usually not undertaken on so large a scale as in the United States and Canada. For the most part, these efforts have been upon pests which have been shown elsewhere to be subject to effective control by natural enemies. Thus, the vedalia beetle, which was so successful against the cottony cushion scale in the United States, has since been established in Cuba, Puerto Rico, Mexico, Guatemala, Venezuela, Ecuador, Brazil, Uruguay, Argentina, and Chile.

A number of effective mealybug parasites have also been established in several countries. *Coccophagus gurneyi* Comp. is established on *Pseudococcus gahani* in Chile, *Pseudaphycus utilis* Timb. on *Pseudococcus nipæ* Mask. in Puerto Rico and the general mealybug predator, *Cryptolæmus montrouzieri* Muls. in Puerto Rico also. The woolly apple aphid parasite, *Aphelinus mali* Hald., is recorded as established in Costa Rica, Colombia, Peru, Uruguay, Argentina, and Chile, while *Prospaltella berlesei* How., a parasite of the white peach scale, has been successfully colonized in Brazil, Uruguay, and Argentina. Several parasites of the black scale of citrus have been established in Peru and Chile. The citrus blackfly has been very satisfactorily controlled by *Eretmocerus serius* Silv. in Cuba, Jamaica, Haiti, Panama, and Costa Rica, and during the past year has been imported and established in Mexico.

A number of the most effective parasites of the oriental fruit moth have been colonized in Argentina and Uruguay, and two of them, including *Macrocentrus ancylivorus*, are reported to be established in the latter country. There is some question, however, regarding the usefulness of this parasite in countries other than the United States, as an alternate host to carry it over the winter appears to be essential. The strawberry leaf-roller fills this requirement in the United States.

PROMISING PROBLEMS

The pests mentioned above have all been satisfactorily controlled in one or more countries through importation of their natural enemies, and consequently, they represent the most promising opportunities for effective immediate results. It would, therefore, be highly desirable to introduce the parasites of these pests into every country in which the latter occur, and at as early a date as possible. In addition to the mealybug pests mentioned above, effective natural enemies are also known and are available for use against the common mealybug *Pseudococcus citri* Risso, the long-tailed mealybug *P. adonidum* L., and the Comstock mealybug, *P. comstocki* Kuw. Another pest that is known to be especially susceptible to biological control is the coconut scale, *Aspidiotus destructor* Sign., which occurs generally in the tropical region.

There are several other pests in South America of which a certain degree of control may be expected, though probably not sufficient to eliminate entirely the need for spraying. A very high parasitization of the cabbage worm, *Pieris rapae* L., can often be obtained by *Apanteles glomeratus* L. and *Pteromalus puparum* L., both of which are of European origin. The San Jose scale is often heavily attacked by a series of parasites in the United States, and these appear to be responsible for holding the pest in check in some sections.

The sugarcane borer, which has already been mentioned briefly, is a serious pest in all cane-growing sections of the Americas. Aside from the work on Trichogramma and the apparently successful use of Lixophaga in Cuba, a considerable reduction in the infestations has been obtained in British Guiana through the colonization of the Amazon fly, *Metagonistylum minense* Towns. This fly has been imported into a number of other countries but has not yielded a satisfactory result. The outcome of such efforts against this pest must be looked upon as uncertain. The importance of the problem, however, would justify attempts to establish Lixophaga, Metagonistylum, and the several species of Theresia in the countries where they do not now occur.

DIFFICULT PROBLEMS

The insect pest problems that have been discussed in the preceding paragraphs are the ones which show most promise of solution by the biological control method. There are, however, a considerable number of other pests, one of them of major importance to agriculture, that for various reasons are not considered likely to yield practical results. Some of these, such as the locusts, are native species that already have a full series of parasites and predators attacking them, for which reason there would probably be very little practical benefit from the importation of additional species.

The aphid pests of field crops are often very destructive, and some of these are of foreign origin. In these cases, the difficulty that has been encountered in attempts at biological control have been due to the different temperatures required by the aphids and the parasites for their development. The aphids are in general able to develop and reproduce at temperatures five to ten degrees lower than those required by the parasites. As a result, these aphids increase to pest status in the spring before the parasites are active, and it is not until midsummer, after a large part of the damage is already done, that the latter are able to bring them under control. If, however, the field infestations, in the absence of parasites, have a tendency to persist through the summer, there still might be some advantage derived from the importation of the parasites.

The pink bollworm of cotton is a major pest in most of the producing areas of the world. In virtually every country where it has been established for some time, it is attacked by a number of parasite species. These presumably are native forms occurring on other insects, that have adapted themselves to the bollworms. In no instance, however, have they brought about any appreciable degree of control. Attempts at biological control have been made in Egypt and the United States, and in the latter country at least seven species of parasites from Africa, Korea, Hawaii, and South America have been imported and released in considerable numbers during the past ten years. As yet, not a single species has become established. A search of other parts of the world may reveal species that are capable of holding the pest in check, but none of those now known is considered to be promising.

There are a considerable number of insect pests of fruit trees that are very destructive and which have been the subject of extended attempts at biological control, but without success. The codling moth is an outstanding example of this group. This insect causes a large loss of fruit, up to fifty to ninety percent, in all parts of the world where it occurs, and it is present in all apple-producing countries except those in the Asiatic region. The frequent application of poison sprays that are necessary for control results in the almost complete elimination of the natural enemies. Because of this, it is useless to consider the colonization of any new enemies so long as spraying is continued. In the absence of the sprays, the parasites may destroy fifty percent or more of the larvæ; yet this is not sufficient to prevent serious crop loss. No parasite has yet been found that is sufficiently effective to reduce fruit injury to the point where spraying will be unnecessary and unprofitable.

The red and purple scales are serious pests of citrus in many parts of the world, and the search for effective natural enemies for colonization in California has been underway for nearly fifty years. This search has covered nearly all of the tropical and subtropical sections where citrus is grown, but no parasites have yet been found that are of any value in control.

The fruitflies of the family Trypetidæ are serious pests of citrus and a number of deciduous fruits. The well-known Mediterranean fruitfly, which attacks citrus, mango, peach, grape, coffee, and many other fruits, is found in the Americas only in Brazil, Uruguay, and Argentina. The many extensive attempts at the biological control of this pest in Hawaii have shown that the extent of parasitization is dependent upon the thickness of the pulp of the infested fruits. Oranges, mangos, and peaches have a deep pulp in which the maggots are embedded, and a large portion of them are located so deeply as to be beyond the reach of the ovipositor, or "sting," of the parasites. For that reason, satisfactory biological control cannot be accomplished when the pest occurs in such fruits. However, in a fruit such as coffee, where the pulp consists only of a relatively thin layer, any maggots that might be present are within reach of the parasite and subject to attack throughout their entire period of development. It is reported that a satisfactory degree of control of this pest in coffee was obtained in Hawaii through several species of Opius.

The same difficulties as mentioned above are encountered in any attempt to control the fruitflies of the genus Anastrepha in Central and South America. This genus is native to that region, and a considerable number of native parasites have been found to attack the different species in the various countries in which studies have been made. Some of the parasites that attack the Mediterranean fruitfly may be able to develop upon Anastrepha, but there is no reason to believe that they will be more effective than the species already present.

THE UTILIZATION OF INSECT DISEASES

One phase of biological control that has not been adequately investigated thus far is the utilization of disease-producing bacteria, fungi, viruses, and parasitic nematodes. It is well known that a great many important crop pests are periodically decimated by outbreaks of disease, and they are consequently of great practical importance. These outbreaks most frequently occur when the pest infestation is at its peak, and the sudden decline of such infestations is often attributable to disease rather than to the action of other natural enemies. It has been generally assumed that these disease outbreaks are associated with the overcrowding and starvation incident to heavy insect infestations, and further, that their occurrence is strictly dependent upon the existence of specific climatic conditions that permit a maximum increase of the organisms. If this is true, there will then be little opportunity to utilize the disease-producing organisms in a control program, as it would be obviously impossible to provide the required temperature and humidity in the field, even if the optimum conditions were known with a reasonable degree of exactness.

A number of efforts have been made, especially in Europe, to control insect infestations through the application of sprays or dusts containing spores of the parasitic organisms. In some instances a considerable measure of success has been reported, but the published data are not sufficient to permit an independent analysis of results. It has been claimed in the United States that the distribution of spore suspensions of the fungous parasite of the citrus white fly has yielded a satisfactory degree of control. This conclusion, however, has not been fully supported experimentally.

One of the most promising efforts of recent years is the use of several species of Bacillus in the control of the Japanese beetles in the United States. These organisms attack the grubs in the soil, causing what has come to be known as the "milky" disease, from the characteristic coloring of diseased grubs. It has been found that the application of eight to ten pounds per acre of a mixture of spores in talc, containing approximately 100 million spores per grain, will often bring about a reduction of eighty percent or more in the grub population in the soil during the season of application. Even in heavy infestations, such a reduction is sufficient to prevent serious turf injury. The results obtained have been consistent, which is in marked contrast to those in other attempts to utilize disease-producing organisms in insect control, and may be due to the soil environment, which is much more stable than that affecting the forms that attack insects above ground. The encouraging results in this work upon the Japanese beetle indicate that there is opportunity for equally successful utilization of such organisms against other pests.

Relatively little attention has been paid thus far to the nematode parasite of insects. It is known that many pest insects often suffer a high mortality from nematode parasitism, this in some instances being the most important of the various natural control factors that hold the pest insects in check. Attempts have been made in the United States to control the Japanese beetle by the release of large numbers of laboratory-reared nematodes, but no appreciable reduction in the infestation was obtained.

The practicability of utilizing this type of insect parasite has therefore not yet been proved.

OPPORTUNITIES FOR INTERNATIONAL COOPERATION

The biological control of insect pests is a field in which there is exceptional opportunity for international cooperation. This may take the form either of supplying colonies of effective parasites to countries that desire them, or of joint participation in projects that are common to several countries. An example of the first is the world-wide distribution of the vedalia beetle for control of the cottony cushion scale. Its effectiveness was first demonstrated in the United States. From there it was forwarded to twenty-three countries or geographic areas, and many of these in turn then served as centers of further distribution to many more. All of this was accomplished merely by shipment of small colonies of beetles by mail, through the cooperation of the entomologists in the different countries, and consequently, the costs of importation were exceedingly small as compared with other projects which have necessitated the sending of expeditions to the countries of origin. Such expeditions are usually necessary, however, on the part of the country that first undertakes biological control of a particular pest, as an extended search may be necessary before the parasites are found. It is only after they have been found, and have demonstrated their value in the new country, that exchange such as is illustrated above can be accomplished.

This international exchange of beneficial insects has been enormously facilitated in recent years by the development of air transportation. Virtually any part of the world is now accessible by air with a travel time of only a very few days. Because of this, the great majority of beneficial insects can be forwarded by air mail or express without requiring any attention en route.

The second form of cooperation mentioned above is the joint participation of several countries in projects to control pests of widespread distribution. The pink bollworm of cotton and the sugarcane borer, which occur in many American countries, are examples of insect problems that might be approached in this way. The work on the citrus blackfly was a practical example of such cooperation. This pest had become exceedingly destructive to citrus and many other plants in Cuba and other islands of the West Indies. Its occurrence there represented a real threat to the citrus industry of Florida and the Gulf Coast of the United States. The interest of Cuba was therefore in control, whereas that of the United States was in prevention of entry, the chances of which would be greatly reduced if the infestations in Cuba could be reduced to a low level.

The Departments of Agriculture of the two countries undertook a cooperative project for the importation of the natural enemies of the pest from tropical Asia. These were obtained and colonized in Cuba in 1930-31, and very soon thereafter the pest was brought under control. More recently, a heavy infestation developed on the west coast of Mexico; a similar cooperative arrangement was made in 1943 and the parasites were successfully established.

9

Forest Resources of Tropical America

By ARTHUR BEVAN
UNITED STATES FOREST SERVICE

IN the able discussions of rubber and quinine for the Americas, we have noted some of the significant fortunes of two renowned American families of trees which have done a great deal in deciding the destinies of nations and the rudiments of the age to which we belong. In the following chapter Arthur Bevan of the United States Forest Service provides a brilliant and eye-opening summary of the stupendous forest resources of the Americas to the south. These, too, are decisive resources which will almost certainly have much to do with shaping what our children and grandchildren will learn about the Americas.

Both as a distinguished authority on forestry and from recent and extensive study trips throughout the Americas, Mr. Bevan is exceptionally well qualified to write this chapter.

9

To THE average man tropical forests are immense, impenetrable jungles full of snakes and wild animals. They are immense, but in general they are not impenetrable, and the undisturbed tropical forest is not a jungle in the true sense of the word.

With the exception of Argentina and Chile, all of Latin America lies in the tropics or subtropics, and therefore the forests of this huge land mass are nearly all composed of tropical species. But it is by no means a uniform forest, and in fact varies, depending upon climate and elevation, to a greater extent than do the forests of the United States and Canada. Changes in type are much more numerous and more abrupt than in the temperate zones. In Latin America the mountain masses are larger and the elevations greater, so that varying conditions, both of temperature and rainfall, occur in relatively short distances, and all conditions from snow and frost to desert and hot humid climates exist. All these factors, in addition to soil, have a pronounced effect on the type of forest.

True rain-forest, the more general concept of tropical forest, probably equals or exceeds all other types, but only because of the huge valley of the Amazon River where this type predominates. Elsewhere in the American tropics the amount of rain-forest is rather limited, most of it occurring on the perimeter of the Caribbean Sea.

Ample rainfall and high average temperatures throughout the year are prerequisites to the growth of tropical and subtropical rain-forests. Mahogany and Spanish-cedar are the best-known and most sought after species occurring in this type of forest.

Tropical deciduous forests are more limited in extent but probably constitute the next largest area. They occur in areas characterized by distinct wet and dry periods and vary in composition with length of the dry season. They are deciduous because of the drought and not because of any marked change in the temperature; in fact, they often shed their leaves in the hottest time of the year. They are the source of primavera

(*Cybistax donnell-smithii*) and many other species more generally prized by the local inhabitants than in the world markets.

The Montane Zone, which forms the backbone of Central America and continues all down the western side of South America, contains innumerable types of forests, depending upon rainfall and elevation. It is in this zone that pure stands of timber are found in the tropics. Starting at the Mexican border, pines extend south as far as northern Nicaragua. From that point no more conifers or soft woods occur, unless planted, until southern Brazil and Chile are reached, where large forests of Parana pine (Araucaria) are found. Oak and other hardwood forests are common to this one, although much of the Andes at high elevations in South America is practically treeless.

Latin America, including all of Central and South America south of the Rio Grande, as well as the Caribbean islands, has a total area approximately two and three-fourths times that of the continental United States. The total population of these countries is about 132 million people, or about the same number as live in the United States.

According to the best information obtainable, forty percent of this entire area, or 3,325,000 square miles, is forested. If these huge forest areas were gathered into one unit, it would exceed the entire land area of the United States by ten percent. Brazil alone has a larger forest area than the 1,000,000 square miles of forest land in the United States, of which only three-fourths can be classified as commercial forest land.

With the exception of Argentina, Chile, and Uruguay, which have relatively small areas of forest, and El Salvador and some of the Caribbean islands which have been denuded, all of these countries contain large forests, much of them unexplored and their composition unknown.

Although these countries were discovered and many of them settled long before the United States, many mature stands of unexplored forest exist within relatively short distances of the heavily populated areas. The tendency of populations in Latin America is to concentrate in definite regions, principally because of inadequate transportation facilities and climatic conditions. Except in the inhabited sections, the only effective means of transportation is by the rivers, and only the larger of these in the lowlands can be used to transport bulky commodities.

Lands adjoining centers of population, or which can be reached by fairly good roads, by railroads, or by water, are almost invariably denuded of most forest cover. Forest products such as lumber, poles, fence posts, firewood, and charcoal in these populated areas are expensive and not too plentiful despite the fact that within relatively short distances there are untouched and often unknown forest resources. A good illustration of

Country	Total Areas Square Miles	Forest Areas Square Miles	Percent Forested
Argentina	1,078,278	193,750	18
Bolivia	537,792	200,000	37
Brazil	3,275,510	1,562,500	48
Chile	296,717	60,000	20
Colombia	448,794	237,200	53
Costa Rica	23,000	14,000	61
Cuba	44,164	7,812	18
Dominican Republic	19,332	13,275	69
Ecuador	275,936	91,406	33
Guatemala	45,452	18,750	41
Haiti	10,204	5,000	49
Honduras	44,275	37,890	86
Mexico	763,944	156,250	20
Nicaragua	60,000	45,000	75
Panama Including Canal Zone	34,216	20,000	58
Paraguay	174,854	43,000	25
Peru	532,000	270,000	51
Salvador	13,176	1,400	11
Uruguay	72,153	2,200	3
Venezuela	352,170	188,600	54
British, French and Dutch Guiana	208,812	168,000	80
British Honduras	8,598	6,020	70
French West Indies	968	311	32
Trinidad	1,862	930	50
Jamaica	4,780	1,195	25
Balance, Greater and Lesser Antilles	2,117	347	16
Puerto Rico and Virgin Islands	3,558	355	10
Total	8,332,662	3,345,191	40

this is the recent discovery of a pure stand of a species of white oak (*Quercus copeyensis*) in the mountains overlooking the valley in which the ancient capital of Costa Rica, Cartago, was built centuries ago. This mountain area is now being opened up by the Inter-American highway, and ultimately a twenty-mile drive will take one deep into this beautiful stand of oak trees, many of which are seven and eight feet in diameter, with trunks eighty feet to the first limbs. There are hundreds of thousands of acres of this forest, never penetrated or utilized up to the present time. Brazil also, despite her tremendous forest resources, has for years planted eucalyptus for ties and fuel for her railroads. Caracas, Bogotá, Quito, La Paz—in fact nearly all the capital cities of these countries—because of lack of transportation facilities, are without adequate supplies of forest products,

While the effect of forest growth on the conservation of water supplies, flood control, and erosion has long been recognized in the temperate zones, it has not been generally appreciated that these considerations are many times more important in the tropics. One has only to fly over areas of hilly or mountainous country from which the forests have been removed to appreciate the tragic and irreparable damage done by erosion. Most tropical soils are very susceptible to erosion, and the heavy tropical rainfalls insure an accelerated rate of erosion comparable to that of the loess regions of China. A cover of vegetation is the only thing which will check this erosion, and of all types of vegetation, forest growth is the best and nature's own method of control.

The leaching effect of tropical rains upon plant nutrients is notorious and is so severe that in hilly and mountainous country the soil deteriorates rapidly. There the crops can be grown profitably for only two or three years, when the land is abandoned and allowed to go back to weeds and vines, and then gradually to brush and forest growth. From one to two decades must elapse before such land has recovered its fertility to an extent that it is again suitable for cultivation, and then once more it must be laboriously cleared before it can be cropped. The necessity for clearing new lands to obtain crops to provide subsistence and income has led to the almost universal practice in the tropics of "shifting agriculture." This practice has been condemned by all scientific agriculturists, but no general solution has been worked out nor has much active research been directed toward determining the methods and techniques which should be applied to prevent such land abuse.

Pressure of population in Latin America will almost certainly increase rather than decrease, so that the practice of shifting agriculture will become a growing and more acute problem. People must live, so laws to prohibit farming of land on steep slopes will not work where there is population pressure. Therefore, the development of farming methods to mitigate damage and to insure the rapid rehabilitation of such lands is of urgent and paramount importance. The British system developed in India, called "taungya," is a move in this direction. This system, however, actually was developed as a method of reforestation of lands deforested or not carrying a commercial stand. The system consists of moving natives to areas which require planting, and having them clear the land and plant forest trees. In return they have the right to grow crops on the land for one or two years, during which period they are obligated to tend the plantation. After the plantations are established, the people are moved to other areas and the process repeated. Thus the land is returned to valuable forest growth which under the British plan would be maintained

PLATE 19. Upper—Mahogany logs for export from Mexico
Lower left—Mahogany from Guatemala
Lower right—Balsa logs in Costa Rica

PLATE 20. Upper—Famous bamboo grove in Jamaica
Lower left—Bamboo planting in Puerto Rico
Lower right—Planting bamboo, Tropical Experiment Station
in Puerto Rico

PLATE 21. Upper—Building bamboo corral in Puerto Rico
Lower—Draining land with bamboo pipe

PLATE 22. Upper—Structural bamboo in Puerto Rico
Lower—Articles made of bamboo

as permanent forest, removing such lands from agriculture forever. This is hardly a solution to caring for growing population or the problem of shifting agriculture.

In Puerto Rico, an adaptation of "taungya," known as the "parcelero" system, was tried out. In this case, a native family was settled permanently on a piece of land. The same plan of planting forest trees in conjunction with the growing of agricultural crops was tried with the idea that on the area of land allotted, a rotation would be followed, whereby a portion of the land would always be available for crops. The parcelero system had the advantage that it was planned primarily to settle the holder and his family permanently on a piece of land. His livelihood would come not only from the subsistence crops which he would grow principally, but also from the forest products which he would harvest off the land and adjacent forest. The rotation between farm crops and forest trees would check erosion and insure the continued fertility of the soil. The parcelero system has not worked out entirely as its initiators contemplated, and a great deal more research will be required before it can be said to be a solution to the problem of shifting agriculture. From a land-use point of view, there is no more important problem to be solved by agriculturists and foresters. As the economy of most tropical countries is pre-eminently agricultural, its solution will have a major effect on their political and economic welfare.

In temperate zones, forest land and wood-lots are an adjunct to agricultural crops—an important one it is true, providing not only additional revenue but many wood products essential to the maintenance of the farm and the protection of the crops. In the tropics, however, in addition to some important uses, forest cover is a direct and necessary element in the growth of many of the most valuable crops. Coffee and cocoa are usually grown under forest shade which not only protects the crop from the blazing sun but aids in preventing erosion. Members of the legume family are generally used for such purposes because they add fertility to the soil through their capacity to fix nitrogen and make it available to other plants.

It is doubtful whether the possibilities of utilizing forest shade for the growing of tropical crops has been explored as fully as is warranted by the benefits which accrue. Other crops might be equally benefited, and soil conservation alone would warrant investigation and research in this field. Cinchona (quinine), rubber and abacá (Manila hemp) are, to all intent, new crops to the western hemisphere which might profitably be grown under shade. In introducing new crops from other parts of the world, people are prone to apply the habitual methods and techniques without analysis of the economics which led to these systems, such as cost of labor, type of soil, etc.

Cinchona is a good example. The Dutch in the East Indies prior to the war had what amounted to a world monopoly in quinine. The methods employed of growing Cinchona in orchard-like plantations for six or seven years, and then harvesting the whole tree including the roots, was adapted to their conditions of plentiful cheap labor and good land. Today, with the Dutch source of supply of this essential drug cut off from the world market, efforts are being made to establish plantations in the western hemisphere; and all such efforts are of the plantation type, using methods similar to those of the Dutch. It is extremely doubtful whether these new plantations can compete successfully after the war unless methods can be developed which will bring down the cost of production. This cannot be done by employing the same methods.

Actually, Cinchona is a native of the western hemisphere, transplanted to the East Indies and adapted and improved to meet their local conditions. In its original home it grows as a component of the forest and is not a dominant species. It is quite tolerant and grows well in the shade of the other species. Should these facts not be considered in introducing the cultivation of Cinchona into the western hemisphere, and the amount of shade for optimum growth determined? Growing under shade reduces the cost of cultivation, for shade keeps down weeds and vines which grow so rapidly and require such a tremendous expenditure of labor to control. Similarly, Cinchona sprouts vigorously when cut, and perhaps the Latin American system of harvesting should involve cutting near the ground level to obtain regeneration at no cost other than thinning the sprouts which result. Might not such a system reduce the cost of production? Then Cinchona might become a truly new crop for the New World and not disappear after the war is over because of high cost production as compared with other parts of the world. Abacá and rubber are two other crops which could be retained as profitable crops in the western hemisphere if new low-cost methods of cultivation can be developed.

In the immediate future, the vast grazing and pasture possibilities of the tropics of the western hemisphere will be developed. Science is overcoming some of the handicaps caused by disease, such as fever tick, and is breeding stock adapted to the climate. What is being done to develop the pastures and ranges to better adapt them for the raising of cattle? Pasture or range trees for shelter and shade, and even to provide a more balanced die for the stock, are of greater significance in the tropics than in the temperate zones. Here again there are wide possibilities in the intelligent use of trees. Mesquite (*Prosopis juliflora*) has proved valuable on dry sites by improving the pasture, providing shade, and bearing a profusion of seed pods which the cattle eat avidly as a welcome protein addition to their diet. The amount of research work to be done on the development and improvement of tropical ranges and pastures is tremendous.

The picture of tropical forestry in the western hemisphere today is, almost without exception, one of exploitation. Huge as these forest resources are, their utilization and management is an almost unknown field of endeavor. With the exception of a few well-known species such as mahogany, Spanish-cedar, primavera, and balsa, the physical properties of the majority of the woods, which run into the thousands, are unknown not only to world commerce but even for proper utilization within the countries in which they exist. We thus have the anomaly of these countries importing lumber to take care of domestic needs despite the forests existing in their backyards. The bulk of these forests are hardwoods but because of the lack of knowledge of the physical properties of most of the species, and methods of cutting and drying, only a small percent of the stand is cut. This leads inevitably to the destruction of much of the accessible timber, and it becomes uneconomic to cut these "high-graded" stands again, at least until such time as their value in use is determined and reaches a point where returns will justify exploitation. Cutting of the valuable species which occur scattered through the forest leads to their extermination, as they usually will not regenerate under shade. Costs of artificial regeneration under such circumstances will prove too high. Our ignorance of proper management and the silvicultural needs of these species is profound, but it is reasonable to assume that cutting could conform to a pattern which would insure the regeneration of the currently valuable species if there were knowledge of the real use and value of these presently non-commercial species. The forest products laboratories of the world could perform no more useful service than a determination of the properties and uses of hundreds of the more important tropical species.

For many years the world has been cutting more timber than the annual growth of all its economically accessible forests. The rate of depletion has been more rapid during the last five years of war, and we have reached a point where it is quite possible that we are faced with a permanent shortage of this essential resource. This is particularly true as to hardwoods, and there is no doubt that following the close of the war and during the period of rehabilitation of the war-devastated countries, the forests of Latin America which constitute the most important last great stand of hardwoods, will be faced with an accelerated exploitation.

If cutting is carried out by present methods, it will lead to dissipation of these resources and the recovery of only a fraction of the wealth which they could contribute to the countries in which they occur and to the economy and needs of the world.

The time to place forest lands under proper management is while there are still forests on these lands—such forests as can be properly and profitably exploited and pay the cost of regeneration and improvement of these lands. Every country which has permitted the destruction of its forest lands has learned the cost and bitter disappointment inherent in reforestation efforts. To its loss, tropical America already has sufficient evidence of the folly of such practices. In all areas of heavy population, forest devastation is complete, with the consequent high cost of even the simple forms of forest products such as charcoal, fence posts, and poles, so essential to the farmer and most of the city, town, and village dwellers in these countries. The resultant soil erosion, rapid run-off of rainfall, and silting of reservoirs for power and irrigation are present for all to see. It is to be hoped that the post-war years will not witness a vast expansion of this land-use abuse.

A large increase in the population of Latin America, both from natural increase and immigration from the war-torn countries, seems inevitable. If forest destruction is allowed to take its course, tragic results will inevitably take place to the detriment of a world seeking peace. There is not the slightest doubt that there is not only an immediate need for the care and management of the forest lands of tropical America, but also a need for the reforestation of denuded and eroded lands, particularly such lands in and near centers of population.

Here again we are handicapped by the almost complete lack of knowledge of how to reforest such lands in the tropics. It is true that efforts have been made in this field. However, to a great extent these have been predicated and carried out on the basis of techniques worked out in the temperate zones. Almost without exception the result has been a dismal failure. Tropical trees apparently will not respond to silvicultural methods worked out in other climates, for they require a technique of their own. Unfortunately, to date very little work has been done in the western hemisphere to determine the methods of planting and rejuvenation which will succeed. As an example, the United States Forest Service has carried out extensive plantings in Puerto Rico. Large expenditures were made for the reforestation program that centered around the planting of deforested lands. The first species selected was Spanish-cedar (Cedrela sp.) because it proved easy to grow in the nursery and after placing in the plantation early survival was high. These plantations which were of this single species later wilted and died. Other countries where plantations of this species have been tried have had similar results, so that today, as far as known, not a single plantation of Spanish-cedar exists in any country that can be called really successful; and yet there are plenty of illustrations of natural regeneration of individuals of this species which have shown remarkable growth. Obviously, the methods used have been wrong.

In the tropics we find entirely different climatic conditions from those existing in countries where reforestation has been successfully carried on. In the former case, there are no checks to disease and insect attack such as frost, and once started they can build up indefinitely until epidemic proportions are reached and the plantation is wiped out. In the actual tropics, that is to say, the areas in which rain-forest, or semi-rain-forest is found, nature has stayed away from pure stands, and such stands are unique. The forests are an extremely complex mixed stand and one in which epidemic conditions, either of disease or insects attacking a single species, would be almost impossible because of the occasional distribution of the species attacked. An exception to this rule can be found in the teak plantations in Trinidad, but this is probably due to the fact that in introducing this East Asiatic species, by the medium of seeds, none of its enemies were transported and fortunately no local disease or insect has so far found it an acceptable host. Undoubtedly, should some local or introduced pest find it an acceptable host, the present practice of planting in pure stands, successful to date, would have to be abandoned because there would be nothing to check the spread of the pest, and it would increase to the point where such plantations would be lost.

Returning to the Puerto Rican experience, following the failure of Spanish-cedar, plantations of mahogany and other species of high export value were attempted with very similar results. Apparently, nature did not scatter these species in a mixed stand for nothing, and it might prove worthwhile to follow nature's system.

It is extremely unfortunate that world events are rapidly leading to the time when exploitation of these forests will be greatly accelerated, while at the same time our knowledge of the science of regenerating and managing these tropic forests is not only pitifully small but is increasing at only a snail's pace. The World War has already accelerated cutting wherever the timber is immediately accessible, and practically all such cutting is done at the expense of the few species having commercial value and with no thought for the future. Thus the trend today is one of a rapidly increasing forest destruction and devastation. Unless this is changed, the outlook for the future is dismal. There is every indication that the world will be faced with a shortage of timber at least for several years following the end of the war, and already the eyes of lumbermen are turning toward Latin America with a growing interest.

The most important job for the preservation and prepetuation of this magnificent resource is to place these forests under sound management while there are still forests to be managed. In addition, there is the very important one of reforesting the denuded and eroded areas. As has been pointed out, these areas are adjacent to the foci of population from which habitation will continue to spread, to the detriment of the forest unless a program for the perpetuation of the forests is initiated soon.

For the past 400 years these countries have based their economy on agriculture, and the forest has had to make way for crops. This has not been too serious, although it has forced the people of these inhabited areas to pay an unnecessarily high price for the simple forms of forest products essential to their agricultural economy. An appreciation of forest values and their contribution to control of erosion on lands not suitable for agriculture and which are marginal even for pasture, would have preserved the trees and made these essential products available to the people at a moderate price. These are the lands which should be reforested as soon as possible.

These reforestation programs, which should be undertaken promptly, should be aimed principally at supplying local needs and not to provide high-value furniture and veneer woods for export. Fast-growing local species, preferably those which grow successfully on such sites, should be given preference, provided they will produce an acceptable product. Species which will coppice, that is, regenerate from sprouts thrown out from the stump when cut, insure perpetuation of the forest growth and are the most easily managed. Such stands near good markets will generally give a much greater financial return than any attempt to reforest these lands with slower-growing timber trees, the establishment of which, except on good agricultural lands, has generally ended in failure. Unfortunately, little or no attention has been given by scientists or others to tropical species except those with a high value for export, and much work remains to be done to determine the species most suited for such forest plantings.

Even before the end of the war the economic trend in these countries is to industrialization, and if only a part of the plans now being considered are actually carried out, this trend will be at an accelerated rate in the post-war period. The importance of forest resources will grow as industrialization takes place; in fact, without these resources such a change in basic economy will be seriously handicapped.

With many sources of strategic materials cut off, the years since 1941 have seen large areas cleared and planted to crops such as abacá, rubber, and others needed to win the war. Increased acreages have been planted to sugar, and the tempo of production has been at an ever-increasing rate. When the world is again at peace, and cut-off territories come into production, competition may once more cause the abandonment of large areas as it did after the last war. When the market broke in 1920, large areas of sugar-cane were abandoned in Cuba. These areas should not be permitted to become an impenetrable jungle of weeds, vines, and brush, but should be reforested to rebuild the soil and provide a valuable resource for the future. Such areas are provided with means of transportation and are thus readily accessible, and if made to serve a useful purpose, will be an asset rather than a liability.

As has already been pointed out, the lack of knowledge of tropical forests and species is the principal drawback to any comprehensive program for the management and utilization of these forests and the re-establishment of forest growth on denuded and eroded lands submarginal for agriculture. The primary reason for this is the complete lack of educational facilities to train men in tropical forestry who would be capable of leadership in this important task. So far, the few trained foresters who have an intimate knowledge of the problem are men who were trained in the forest schools of the temperate zones, and then gained their experience the hard way in the tropics, mostly by trial and error. The number of such men is very small and is hardly large enough even to train those necessary to carry out the tremendous task which lies ahead. Facilities for training tropical foresters and technicians are nonexistent in the western hemisphere today, and until provision is made to train them, particularly citizens of the countries in which these tropical forests lie, very little if any progress will be made. While the basic sciences and courses can be studied anywhere, conditions in the tropics are so different that the forest techniques and silviculture must be learned and taught in the tropics. Unless such training is provided, the progress of tropical forestry will be painfully slow, and we will see repeated in Latin America the forest devastation that has taken place in every other section of the earth inhabited by man. History is replete with man's frantic efforts to repair the damage he has done rather than to take steps to insure that such mistakes are not repeated. The forests of Latin America can be preserved and utilized for the well-being of its inhabitants and of the world at large. The answer is in the hands of the present generation. The future will be too late!

10

Silks from South America

By GEORGE E. ADAMES

BRAZILIAN OBSERVER, UNITED STATES DEPARTMENT OF AGRICULTURE
OFFICE OF FOREIGN AGRICULTURAL RELATIONS

GEORGE E. ADAMES, *the youngest of our contributors barely twenty-nine, has been variously associated with United States Government research agencies, including work as economist of Brazilian, Ecuadorean, and Haitian resources for the Department of Agriculture's Office of Foreign Agricultural Relations.*

Mr. Adames acquires his knowledge of and enthusiasm for silks honestly. He comes of a renowned silk-dealing family and has made extensive investigation of silk productions throughout the Americas from the vantage of a professional as well as a studious observer. In Mr. Adames' own words: "My grandfather, when sober, sold four million dollars' worth of silk fabrics a year but . . . he was never quite the same when the ascot tie and the fancy vest went out; and became quite disgusted with the advent of artificial silk, and retired . . ."

But the Adames grandchild, like many other well-accredited observers throughout several of the Americas, is in no mood to forsake hope for natural silks, which we will almost certainly have with us so long as we have silkworms, mulberry trees, and women.

10

"COME, *minha filhinha*, show us your pretty dress," Senhor Fernando said to his daughter, who had just come out of the house to the terrace where we had been sitting over a *cafezinho*. The coffee and cigars had been good, and Senhor Fernando and I had spent most of the afternoon talking about Latin America's future. Yolanda, tiny even in her fashionable platform shoes with soles an inch high, kissed her father and then stood by his chair with her hand resting on his shoulder.

"This dress, it is beautiful, *não?*" Senhor Fernando asked me. It was as beautiful as the girl wearing it; and the bright print seemed so suitable for her creamy skin and black hair. "This dress is silk," my friend continued, "and the silk of which it is made is a product of my country. It was spun by little silkworms there, and it was woven there, and dyed there, and made into a dress there. As I told you after luncheon, silk is becoming a very important commodity in Brazil." He pronounced it "Brazeeoo."

Silk has always been in important commodity everywhere, and is probably one of the few luxury commodities that have ever attained the dignity of becoming world staples. But in Brazil, as Senhor Fernando had reminded me, many people—farmers and industrialists alike—have been considering silkworm culture as a potential contribution to the wealth and development of their country.

As Yolanda sat down and poured herself a little cup of coffee—the *cafezinho* that is so important in Brazilian social usage—her father looked at her affectionately. "It is for my Yolanda and other girls like her that we are interested in silk. Not just so that all our girls may have silk dresses, you understand, but also because the silk industry may become a part of the greatness of our country in years to come. Brazil is bigger than your United States, you know, but it is not yet developed. We have begun a steel industry, and we have a textile industry. We have valuable resources in vegetable oils, and many of our farms are fertile producers of food. But there is much yet to be done—very much. Perhaps the raising of little silkworms will bring prosperity to some of us. For ten or fifteen years we have been trying and experimenting. We believe that we could raise more silkworms than could any other country in the world."

As he paused, I asked, "But will you? Will you exploit this possibility?"

Senhor Fernando reflectively tapped his cigar in the ashtray. "No, I do not think we will, *meu amigo*. I said we *could*. There are many reasons why we will not. One reason is that we could not find a very secure place in an openly competitive world market. During the war, Brazil remains the major source of silk in the western hemisphere, and so can ask, and get, high prices. After the war—no. In the eastern part of Asia are millions of people who can live on a few cents a week. They will probably remain the world's important producers, for they can produce very cheaply."

The big, affable Brazilian sipped his coffee, then went on, "And no one knows yet to what extent the synthetic fabrics will displace silk. Rayon did not do it; nylon might. I do feel that there will always be a demand for silk, a rewarding demand, so that some regions will be able to produce it profitably. Brazil may be able to contribute some silk to the world, or may be able only to produce enough for its own use. But Brazil is a wonderful country, and as I told you, it could produce enough silk for the world, even though it won't. All the conditions there are favorable: climate, space, everything; but our farm people would not live on the returns that people in other countries get from silk. It seems then, that it must remain a secondary crop to us, and that is too bad in a way, for we feel almost that we could do the silk industry of the world a favor."

Yolanda put her cup down, and felt of the stuff of her dress. "This is so beautiful, this silk. I think women will always prefer it to other fabrics. Just to know that her dress is silk makes a woman very happy to wear it. It is something genuine, something real; and no matter how beautiful the—did you say synthetic?—fabrics are, there is nothing like silk."

Her father smiled and said to me, "You see how women are? Always they want the best and the most expensive of everything. That is one of the things we are counting on in Brazil; for we think that women will demand silk, always pure silk, and that our textile designers can make patterns that will be sought all over the world, because they are Brazilian, and different."

"Then you think that you can keep this new industry of yours going—that it will remain profitable? You think that this war boom in silk will not dissolve within a few years?" I asked.

"No—or perhaps yes, if you are speaking only of a war boom. So many silk parachutes will not be needed, but more silk hose will be. The war boom will disappear, but you must remember that we have been expanding our silk industry over a period of many years, expanding it most during the past twenty years. It has a good start, and we can but hope that it will show progress."

Brazilians have good reasons for believing that this new activity may become a profitable one for a large segment of the population. Where cheap labor has been the secret of success in Asia, the Brazilian formula is based on productivity and yield. Japan used to produce—or still does—one, two, or at most four crops of silkworms a year. Southern Brazil can produce five crops with ease, while up in the equatorial north of the republic, in the Amazon region, it is possible with proper care to raise twelve crops of silkworms one after the other. It could be a year-round occupation, not just a part-time one, in that great undeveloped part of the country.

Brazil is not the only Latin American country that produces silk. Mexico was raising silkworms experimentally in the 1870's and 80's and is now planning on silkworm-raising as a national industry which will employ thousands of rural workers. Argentina's National Board of Education started in 1936 to stimulate silk culture in the northern provinces. Cuba, Nicaragua, and Venezuela have been evaluating possibilities of sericulture. Chile has tried to start the industry, although the chilliness of most parts of the country has operated as a deterrent.

Silk, originally a product of Asia, is said to have been first brought to the western hemisphere by Hernando Cortez, who, in the year 1522, managed somehow to bring silkworms and the slips of mulberry trees, the silkworms' favorite food, to Mexico. The mulberry tree, which must be near the silkworm as water must be near human life, is said not to be indigenous to this hemisphere; and probably the only excuse for transporting it to the fertile New World would have been the maintenance of silkworms.

North America was once thought to be the ideal home for silkworms, too. Before the present century, silk was strictly a luxury—something that only the very rich could afford. And sometimes even the rich could not afford it or get it, for it came from the East and transportation difficulties, piracy, and other factors kept the European market very short of the sought-after yarn. As long ago as the Roman era, the wearing of silk garments was restricted by law to members of the aristocracy.

To help maintain supply, silk culture and weaving had been started in Italy and France and Spain during the Renaissance, but the contribution of these countries was only a part of the European consumption. It was logical then as time went on, to consider the New World as a possible source for silk. James I of England decreed that silkworms should be raised in the New Virginia colony, and hoped not only to make the colony prosperous thereby, but also to extirpate the cultivation of tobacco, which he hated. Some silk actually was produced on the east coast of North America and sent to England, some of it to be used later in the coronation robes of King Charles II. As the years passed, an occasional Colonial dame would be found wearing a gown of native-grown silk. One such robe can be seen today in the National Museum in Washington, D. C. In 1759, 10,000 pounds of raw silk were exported to England from Georgia, and as late as 1825, silk culture was flourishing in Connecticut, could be found in Massachusetts, and had only recently disappeared from Pennsylvania.

It is an interesting historical fact that a silk craze hit the United States in the years 1828-40. It has been likened to the famous tulip craze in Holland, for most of the speculation was in mulberry trees, which were sold and resold at double and treble profits. People eventually came to their senses, realizing among other things that mulberry trees just were not worth the money that was asked for them, and that silk culture had actually been declining in the United States for years. About all that is left of the whole madness is some fine stands of mulberry trees in various parts of the country and some quaint books written to teach ladies to handle silkworms.

Silkworms can be raised in the United States. They are being raised today in Alabama, in California, and in many other parts of the land, especially where the climate is warm and not too humid. And there are occasional announcements that someone has just discovered a new, cheap way to reel silk and that the United States will be able profitably to grow its own silk. And such announcements are usually followed within a few days by the statement of some economist showing that silk culture as an industry would never show enough profit to tempt the North American farmer to give up his corn or his pigs or whatever. Unfortunately, for once the economists are right. The unit profit in silk, the return per cocoon, and the high cost of reeling seem to be unremovable impediments to silk culture in most places; and the United States will have to go on importing silk whenever there is any to import.

Brazilians think they have answers to some of those problems, however. Labor is usually cheap in Brazil—not so cheap as in many parts of the world, but cheap by North American standards. A couple of years ago, the best cook in Rio de Janeiro could be stolen from her mistress by anyone who would offer her a few cents more than $15.00 per month; and even now the bribe may have gone up to only $18.00 or $20.00. Farm labor, as everywhere, is cheaper yet; and in some places it can be had for even lower pay than the cook's.

It is true that such wages, low as they are, are still several times those in Japan. The Brazilian answer here is increased production. In Europe and Asia, it takes about forty-five days to rear a crop of silkworms from egg to cocoon. Brazil can do it in forty days, or in some localities in twenty-five days. Farmers can interlard five or six harvests of silk with their other crops; and working in a coolish brood-house with silkworms is patently more pleasant than working out in the hot fields during the long subtropical days.

They have been approaching it in the right way in Brazil, too, for silk specialists there recognize that there may be room for improvement in the output per silkworm. Two new Brazilian varieties of hardy larvæ have been developed by the Sericultural Institute: the "Brazilian super golden" and the "Campinas yellow," which produce high-grade fiber to meet North America's rigid standards.

Although the matter of silk culture has been approached scientifically only during the past two decades, Brazil's interest in silk culture seems to be about a century old. There seems to be some evidence that sericulture existed, perhaps only as a hobby, a hundred years ago in southern Brazil. During the third quarter of the century, there was a so-called Seropedic Society at the imperial court. The Emperor, Dom Pedro, was a member. But it seems that the society, although a patriotic gesture, was a futile one, one reason having been, according to some writers, that in those days of slow transportation silkworms lost their health during the long ocean voyage to Brazil. In view of the earlier success of sericulture in North America, however, this seems to be a specious excuse, and it is probable that popular interest could not be aroused.

Dom Pedro, by the way, was the kindly emperor who visited the United States to attend the Centennial Exposition in Philadelphia in 1876. Motion pictures lead us to believe that he made the trip solely for the purpose of bringing to light Alexander Graham Bell's telephone. It is interesting to note, however, that one of the Emperor's subjects, a Dona Maria de Rezende, exhibited silkworms and reeled cocoons at the Centennial Exposition, having traveled to North America, like the Emperor himself, in a great burst of good-neighborliness and national pride.

During that same period, however, Japan was entrenching itself as the world's great merchandiser of silk, for it was in the latter part of the nineteenth century that Japan wrested from China the foremost position in silk exportation. There may be some question, however, as to which country produced more silk; for although Japan's exports have been greater, some people believe that China's vast unreported production, a good part of which was utilized domestically, may have surpassed the Japanese output.

Be that as it may, from the middle of the nineteenth century forward, Japan's exports far outstripped those of the other countries of the world without serious competition from anyone. Since the days of the Renaissance, France and Italy, catering to the fashion trade, have produced a certain amount of the fiber which was woven into luxury fabrics of great price. European silk was never intended to meet the prices of that from Asia, for the entire operation, from egg to finished gown, was costly; but the European industry thrived even through the stiff world competition of the past fifty years because silk weavers were willing to be guided directly by high-style dressmakers. For example, a textile designer in Lyon would make up perhaps a hundred samples of fabrics for the coming season, submit them to the French couturiers, then make up quantities of the desired patterns, in many cases devoting his entire output of a limited pattern to the demands of one stylist.

In any case, silk culture as an industry died away in most other places than east Asia and southern Europe. The United States, of course, became the world's greatest weaver, absorbing seventy-five percent of the world output of raw silk. Brazil was just another customer, buying the finished fabric rather than the raw silk for weaving.

The late 1920's and early 1930's, in addition to the economic problems they offered, were also a period of great unrest and dissatisfaction. In those days, some of the agriculturists and manufacturers in Brazil, trying to conserve that country's precarious international credit, began to wonder why enough silk could not be produced at home to meet domestic demand. After all, for a century or more, Brazilians had realized that climatic conditions were favorable for raising silkworms and that sufficient labor was available. And so the interest in silk showed an upturn again. Characteristically perhaps, the growing Japanese colony in southern Brazil was the first group to make a success of raising silkworms on a commercial scale, and soon many Italo-Brazilians entered the field.

Brazilians do not like to discuss those first years of their commercial silk culture, for some reason or another. Literature on the industry hints darkly at foreign exploitation, monopolistic practices, competitive wars, and generally sharp dealings. It appears that the Japanese interests, perhaps operating on instructions from abroad, were attempting to monopolize the industry, to produce raw silk on almost a peonage basis and in the large to use Brazil's adaptability to the industry merely as a sort of adjunct to the economic requirements of Japanese residents in Brazil. That loyal Brazilians might unknowingly have become parties to this trend toward monopoly is understandable in view of such developments throughout the world, many of which are still being revealed. For example, as late as 1941, the Japanese are said to have controlled an estimated forty percent of Brazil's cotton production.

Federal subsidies were granted to the silk industry in 1927 and took the form of price support granted to producers of raw silk as well as to textile manufacturers utilizing the fiber. The law put the industry on the basis of a contest, with the subsidies to be awarded to the first few firms with an output or more than a specified amount of silk annually. Obviously, the result was that those silk operations already in progress received the benefits, while small new organizations were practically thrown out of the running, being unable to meet the established competition.

In spite of its obvious inequities, this law was not without some good results, for it focused popular attention upon the silk business and did stimulate a certain amount of production. São Paulo, the most industrialized state of Brazil, became the center of silkworm raising. It may be no coincidence, by the way, that this was the state with the highest concentration of Japanese among its people. Other states might have been more adaptable to the culture of silkworms, but proximity to industrial centers was a factor in silk culture as it has been in other Brazilian enterprises.

No matter what the factors in the growth of silk culture in São Paulo may have been, the Paulistas became aware of the intolerable situation of favoritism created by the federal subsidy of 1927; and finally the state created, in 1935, a Section of Sericulture in the Department of Animal Industry. Charged with the duty of developing silk production in all phases, the Section was so successful that in 1941 it was reorganized and expanded, and was given the dignity of a separate Service within the State Department of Agriculture. By this time, its duties were clearly defined. The Service of Sericulture was devoted to research, experimentation, stimulation of silk culture, and technical assistance to all who needed it, as well as to the production and distribution of mulberry slips and silkworm eggs; and in general it has since had a finger in every pie in the state that has anything to do with silk.

The work of the Service of Sericulture has provided an undeniably important stimulus to the speedy and controlled expansion of silk culture. In 1936, a year after its establishment, the Service bred (and presumably distributed) 32,000 grams of eggs. Two years later the figure had been increased by over 100,000, and by 1940 had reached the level of 200,000 grams of eggs. This was increased by twenty-five percent in the following year and was increased by 100 percent at the end of 1942, during which year 400,000 grams of eggs are said to have been produced.

Four hundred thousand grams, about 900 pounds, of silkworm eggs is a heap of potential silkworms. Official data are lacking, but the 1943 figure is said to have been in the neighborhood of more than a ton of eggs. Assuming that there are 500,000 to 700,000 eggs to the pound, Brazil would seem to be well on the way to having enough silkworm eggs to lay end to end for the creation of an interesting statistical image.

The mulberry tree deserves mention, too. Its leaves are the silkworms' preferred food, although the little sixteen-legged babies have been raised successfully on the leaves of such other trees as the Osage orange. Be that as it may, Morus, the mulberry, is caviar to the silkworm, and is what the silkworm is usually fed. One gram of silkworm eggs—the fractional part of an ounce—will hatch out enough worms to eat ninety pounds of fresh mulberry leaves, so that it is obvious that the tree is highly important to the industry.

Morus alba thrives in Brazil and is relatively free from disease. It is hard to estimate the number of mulberry trees there today. In 1940 there were said to be 10,000,000 trees of an age to bear sufficient leaves for harvesting; and by 1942 the number is thought to have been about 30,000,000. Anywhere from four to eight trees are stripped within one breeding period—a month, roughly—to provide food for only a thousand of the voracious larvæ.

Morus alba (along with *M. nigra* and *M. rubra*) is known not to be indigenous to Brazil, and it probably made its first appearance there a little over a century ago. Everyone except the specialists has forgotten the tree's distant Asiatic origin, and now it has become a part of the Brazilian landscape. Cuttings are supplied to responsible applicants by federal, state, and municipal silk-stimulating services. Practically all that is necessary to start a tree is to put the slip in the ground and keep it moist. It grows rapidly, and only pruning keeps it from attaining a height of about fifty feet. Some growers keep their trees down to about six feet for ease in stripping off the leaves; this is known as dwarf culture.

Leaves are stripped from the tree in a traditional manner which is efficient, quick, and easy on the tree. This stripping must be done with care and at just the right time of day. It cannot be done when the leaves are wet with dew, nor yet when the sun is high. Naturally, the leaves must be fresh when used, and uneaten debris must be removed from the trays of silkworms when new leaves are added. For the first few days of the lives of the larvæ, the leaves are chopped to the texture of pipe tobacco, but after that the silkworms will nibble off bits from the whole leaf. Anyone who has seen tent caterpillars in action will have some idea of how thoroughly the silkworms can consume mulberry leaves.

The size of a breeder's grove is, of course, his criterion for the number of eggs he requests for each breeding season. Calculating the number of eggs that his grove will be able to support, he applies to the nearest sericulture station for the amount he requires. Having received the eggs in the mail or by express, or having gone to get them, as the case may be, the sericulturist makes sure that his brood-house is ready for the crop. Cleanliness is assured by sweeping, even scrubbing; and in some cases, where there has been an outbreak of any of the several silkworm diseases or even a suspicion that disease has been present, disinfection of the brood-house and all equipment is desirable.

The Brazilians' name for the house in which silkworms fulfil their destinies is *sirgaria*. It can be any size, depending on the number of hands available for raising the *bicho de seda*, or silkworm. Generally, *sirgarias* may be thought of as wood or stucco buildings about the size of a two-car garage, with one door and a number of windows so arranged as to permit maximum control over temperature and ventilation. They must be dry and fairly warm, but not hot, and must be safeguarded against insect pests, mice, and rats. Another essential in what is called in Brazil the "creation" of the silkworm is cleanliness. Old uneaten portions of mulberry leaves must be removed from the trays at every feeding time— in the case of newly hatched larvæ, as often as six or eight times in twenty-four hours.

The interior of the building is dark and plain, with row upon row of trays suspended from the ceiling by ropes, or placed in racks. Somewhere in or near the *sirgaria* there is equipment for chopping the mulberry leaves when the larvæ are young enough to require macerated food. And somewhere, too, in readiness for the days when the silkworms spin their cocoons, are bunches of broom or slatted wooden racks or even excelsior for the silkworms to climb into when they prepare to enter their long sleep.

Eggs are usually distributed on cards which, when received by growers, look as if they had been dusted with coarse gray sand or poppy seed. An ounce of eggs is normally considered the unit of distribution, and may comprise some 45,000 eggs. The cards are placed in shallow trays or cardboard boxes and kept at a temperature of a little over 70 degrees. Within about ten days, the worms begin to come out from the eggs, and hatching from each lot of eggs may extend over a period of a few days. Sheets of stiff perforated paper are spread over the hatching trays and covered with finely chopped fresh mulberry leaves. The tiny silkworms, at birth usually only one-eighth inch long, climb up through the holes in the paper and start feeding. Successive hatchings are removed to separate ·trays, so that all the worms in one tray will fill out their life cycle in approximately the same time.

For about thirty days, depending upon climatic and sanitary conditions, silkworms do nothing but eat and grow. Their appetites are enormous, and their fat little bodies enlarge with amazing rapidity, lengthening from about one-eighth inch to three or four inches. Four times during the period of growth silkworms seem to become dreamy, and for perhaps twenty-four hours are uninterested in food. This occurs, generally on the fifth, eleventh, seventeenth, and twenty-third days after hatching, and at these times the silkworm sloughs off its old skin like a lady peeling off her gloves. This done, the silkworm begins eating and growing again.

Finally, sometimes near the thirtieth day after hatching or, in some cases, by the twenty-second day or so, silkworms become restless and refuse food. Their bodies become translucent and a pair of silk-making glands under the mouth swells. At this time the breeder provides branches of brush, broom, excelsior or even boxes; for these days, from the breeder's point of view, are the most important in the silkworm's short and busy life. Soon there is a great migration from the trays to the branches as the silkworms begin to make their cocoons.

Turning its body this way and that in a sort of figure-eight, catching a strand here and there, spinning a marvelous little nest for itself, the silkworm spends three or four days sealing itself into its cocoon. The finished product feels like a thin papier-mâché container, and may be white, creamy, or yellow. There is, in fact, reputed to be a system for breeding silkworms to spin colored cocoons, obviating later dyeing of the silk. However, the cocoon may be almost any size up to two or three inches long, and in it the silkworm, now become a pupa, lies dormant. If allowed, the pupa will hatch into a moth; and in the case of selected cocoons this is permitted, so that the race may continue. These moths lead a brief, busy, but very pleasant life, mating with eugenically fit partners. Then more eggs are laid on cards, under little paper funnels, and so the next generations of silkworms comes into existence.

Cocoons from which the moths have hatched, however, are usable in the silk industry only by manufacture into a rare coarse waste silk called "schappe." To make the slippery kind of silk which commands higher prices, the cocoons must be unrolled, or reeled. Since there may be a long time lag between the spinning of the cocoon and the reeling of the silk, it is necessary to kill the pupæ. This is generally effected by the use of heat, preferably dry heat, sometimes steam. Most breeders are not equipped to do this killing, or suffocating, as it is sometimes called; and in those cases the reeling-mill assumes the duty.

A reeling-mill, or filature, may be a shiny modern sort of place or it may be extremely primitive. The technique of reeling is based on the need for picking up an end of the master filament from the cocoon, joining it with the filaments from other cocoons, and twisting them on a reel. The resultant hank of fiber is, essentially, silk thread, but naturally it requires further industrialization by way of cleaning and sometimes dyeing before it actually enters the weaving industry.

First the cocoons are scrubbed, in order to remove the sericin, a gummy silkworm product on the outside, and to enable the operator to discover the master filament. Then four to fourteen—usually six—of these scoured cocoons are placed in a basin of water. Their filaments are twisted together and passed over supports; and simple machinery, more often than not hand or foot-powered, causes the cocoons to unwind. Depending upon the quality of the breeding stock and other factors, a skein of yarn may hold as much as 1000 to 1500 yards of silk, but perhaps only half of this is first quality. This is the raw silk of commerce, and when it is removed from the reels, it looks like a hank of white or creamy rope. Its industrialization and weaving has been a billion-dollar-a-year business in the United States alone, and for many years silk has been a world staple of prime importance alongside of wheat and rubber and other agricultural commodities.

Nearly all of Brazil's silk culture—probably ninety to ninety-five percent of the industry—is located in the state of São Paulo. Although silkworm raising has sprung up in other places in Brazil—in the states of Minas Geraes, Paraíba, Amazonas, and perhaps all over the eastern part of the vast country—São Paulo, the most industrialized of all the states, has kept first place. Commercially, the industry is only a little more than a decade old in São Paulo, but it has made its greatest strides there.

The number of reeling-mills in that state has increased rapidly, in step with the growing cultivation of silkworms. In 1940, three filatures operated, utilizing 273 reeling basins. In 1942, there were fifteen mills, with a total of 619 basins, while the end of 1943 found at least twenty-five mills with a total of perhaps 800 or more basins. It is probable that 1944 showed a further increase, although exact data are not yet available. Although production figures may often be inflated or minimized, no matter what the commodity, expansion in the number of establishments for the industrialization of that commodity may serve as a fair gauge of the business, and so it is with Brazil's reeling-mills.

Since eggs and mulberry slips are obtainable without charge from the various government agencies, few sericulturists bother to do their own breeding for continuation of the species. The work of sericulture, then, with raw materials supplied, and with the end-product—the cocoon—industrialized by other hands than those of the sericulturist, is relatively easy. For a few hours a day, never in the hot sun, the sericulturist and his family or helpers work outdoors, stripping the trees and bringing the fresh leaves to the sirgaria for distribution on the trays. The old leaves remaining from the last meal are removed and burned or piled on a compost heap, and in general, that is the easy pattern of the day's worw. The main disadvantage is that at times it may stretch out over almost a twenty-four-hour shift, when there is a large crop of worms to care for or when the larvæ are in one of their especially hungry stages.

The ease of work in silk culture naturally has a wide appeal and the state of São Paulo has emphasized the relatively light labor involved: ". . . the well-managed breeding of thirty grams of eggs . . . means a return of 675 cruzeiros ($33.75). This is a sum which a boy or a girl, a woman or an older man can gain with each 28-35 day breeding period. There can be at least four breeding periods a year, which means a return of 2,700 cruzeiros ($135.00) per year for relatively light labor; all this in the shade and with greater comfort than that of workers who have to labor in the open air, exposed to the rays of the sun."

On the other hand, Brazilian authorities are proceeding cautiously in arousing enthusiasm, for sericulturists are warned not to put all their silkworm eggs in one basket, so to speak. In all respects, federal and state governments alike endeavor to show farmers that silk culture just at present should be regarded as an adjunct to ordinary agricultural activities, and not as a quick way to make a fortune. Brazil has become wise in the vagaries of silkworms, for Latin America has experienced quick and fragile silk booms before.

The fact that even in the temperate southern part of the country, Brazilians can raise almost double the annual number of Japan's crops of eggs is important enough in itself; but the fact that women, children, and older people unfit for hard work can raise a crop of silkworms as well as their stronger countrymen can is important in Brazil. That country has been complaining for the past three and one-half centuries about the lack of manpower; and any occupation which the weaker members of the family can engage in for profit represents to the rural Brazilian mind a worthy activity.

The establishment of silk culture on a commercial scale accords with the Brazilian Government's efforts to diversify agriculture. There has always been a tendency in that country to depend heavily upon one agricultural activity for regional or national prosperity. In its Colonial period, Brazil produced sugar almost to the exclusion of other crops, and fortunes were lost when other countries began to compete in growing cane. Then for a time cotton was king, until the seat of monarchy was removed to the southern part of the United States. The story of coffee in Brazil is well known. Outstripping all other countries put together in the amount of coffee it produces, Brazil has sometimes found itself almost imploring the rest of the world to help rid it of the colossus it has created. *Fazendeiros* continued to plant coffee because they could not—or would not—plant anything else; their fathers' fortunes had been made in coffee, and many of the sons seem to have been willing to lose theirs in over-supply of the same commodity.

More recently, cotton has once again come to the fore in southern Brazil, the great agriculturally productive region of the country. Many former coffee growers took up the cultivation of cotton, sometimes as a supplementary crop to coffee and sometimes rooting out their coffee trees entirely; and in the same way, farmers are being encouraged by the Brazilian Government to consider silk as a subsidiary crop. São Paulo Service of Sericulture has cannily demonstrated that the profits from sericulture in that state are higher per acre than those from coffee and cotton.

There is, and even after the war may continue to be, a ready domestic market for silk in Brazil. A recent estimate placed average annual requirements of raw silk during a peace-time year in Brazil at about 1500 tons. Present consumption may be running at about one-tenth or more of normal requirements, or 160 to 180 tons, according to Silvado Bueno, executive secretary of the Comissão Brasileira de Fomento Interamericano. Production of yarn in São Paulo during 1944 may have amounted to anywhere between 200 and 300 metric tons, with possibly another 70 tons coming into the state from other parts of the republic, or approximately 275,000 pounds at most.

Compared with Japan's pre-war output of between 90,000,000 and 100,000,000 pounds of raw silk a year, Brazil's production is a puny figure, but Brazilians believe that it represents a good bid for future commercial activities. There is a controversy among local interests as to whether it may not be wiser to start now to plan a post-war course of self-sufficiency in silk, completely ignoring the export market and maintaining tariff protection for the young domestic industry.

Present trade activities indicate that Brazilian weaving interests are in fairly tight control of the situation, although here again there may be some tendency to monopolistic practices. Late 1943 saw the prohibition of exportation of raw or thrown silk, with the end in mind of consolidation of the position of local throwing and processing mills. Some silk piece-goods were exported during that year to the United States, selling on Fifth Avenue at $7.50 per yard, and silk hosiery from Brazil appeared in North America as well as in South Africa. In 1944 a decree relaxed restriction on exports to the extent of allowing twenty-five percent of the year's output of raw silk to be shipped abroad. Earlier in the year, the Comissão Especial de Seda (Special Silk Committee) had estimated that as much as a third of Brazil's raw silk could be exported, so that the twenty-five-percent figure in the decree represented a compromise. Nevertheless, Brazilian weavers and knitters protested that no raw silk should be exported at all; and that as small as the throwing industry might be in that country, the entire production of raw silk should have been retained at home so as to keep the mills in steady operation.

The industry is young and in the formative years, and its future is dependent upon the solution of its present problems. It appears that a few large textile companies have control over Brazil's silk production. It has been argued that concentration of commercial activities obviates wasteful competition; but there is also a group that storms at monopolies, saying that competition would provide stimulus for further expansion and some lowering of prices.

The importance of quantity in Brazilian silk production is debatable too, for there is evidence that quality has often been neglected for the sake of increasing output. There is little official inspection and grading of silk in Brazil, so that there is small coercion toward bettering quality. There are testing devices in the country, but so far as is known, only one reeler and distributor really attempts to make proper classification of the raw silk produced; and that firm's equipment is not available to competing firms, for obvious reasons. The state of São Paulo owns equipment, but apparently does not utilize it to the greatest advantage.

Price is another factor in the future of the silk industry. Just at present, Brazil is able to command and obtain high returns for silk in all stages of manufacture; and unquestionably these prices have been an incentive to expansion, from increased planting of mulberry trees to establishment of filatures. Farmers used to receive about 12 cents per pound for green cocoons—that is, cocoons with live pupæ in them. The most recent available figures show that the price is now more than $1.00 per pound. The lower price stimulated only limited interest in sericulture; but the higher price could not be maintained at such time as silk returns to normal supply throughout the world. It has been estimated that farmers could turn over a fair profit if they received about 25 cents per pound for cocoons; but even at this moderate price the cost of enough cocoons to reel a pound of silk would be equal to the price of the finished skein of Brazilian silk in 1939.

In other words, if what seems to be a fair price is allowed the farmer, the charges for raw material for reeling would equal the cost of pre-war reeled silk, allowing nothing for reeling costs or profit to the filatures. Many Brazilians feel the solution for this would be the establishment of high import duties on silk in all forms. In that way, the industry would produce only enough silk for internal consumption and would forget about export possibilities. With such a limitation on production, there could in time be improvements in quality, they believe.

An aspect of this picture which is not yet clear is the post-war relationship between Brazil and Japan. Would Japan buy Brazil's cotton if Brazil did not buy Japan's silk?

A third factor in Brazil's silk industry should have been settled years ago: the prevalence of diseased eggs. Some diseases of the silkworm are inherited and can be largely avoided through the exclusive use of properly inspected and tested eggs. Laws have been promulgated in Brazil with the idea of reserving egg-production to government agencies, but private enterprises have found loopholes and continue to be large-scale distributors. It should be noted that one of the latter is a Japanese-controlled group.

These and similar problems beset the industry. Some, of course, can be solved by decree; some of them must await the further development of the world situation before they can be fairly appraised.

Brazil is nurturing the silk industry as present circumstances dictate. Sericulturists are repeatedly warned that they cannot expect to get rich in a year or two of operation; and the government makes it clear that the best approach to silk culture at present is to maintain it as a secondary crop—to work part-time on it, but not to depend upon it alone for subsistence. So it has happened that the industry has expanded vastly without assuming the aspect of a craze, and yet it has not expanded so greatly that retrenchment, if necessary, would bring about serious economic readjustment.

For the time being, there is a well-paying market for products of the silkworm, and economic realignments of activities in the years to come, whether upward or downward, should not be hard to make. Improvements in quality can be attained and production can be stepped up later on, depending on demand; meanwhile Brazil is in a favorable situation. It is felt that commercial silk culture could be abandoned entirely without domestic economic dislocation, or it could be maintained at its present level as a handy source of supply. And even if Brazil does not aspire to first place as a world producer, there is always the attractive possibility that it could occupy the sort of position once held by France and Italy— that of a caterer to the luxury trade.

Senhor Fernando explained that to me very clearly when he said, "We can without doubt improve the quality of our silk, perhaps making it the best in the world, but we do not think that we will be able to compete with low-cost producers on a price basis. But . . ." and here he leaned forward, using his right forefinger to draw designs on the palm of his hand, "we have style, we Brazilians. Our country and our continent have been supplying inspiration to designers of clothes, of dishes, of houses, for years. What is to stop us from supplying new weaves and patterns of silk to the great designers of the United States?"

He sat back in his chair and beamed before answering his own question. "Look, *meu amigo norteamericano*, after this war, a Brazilian textile designer could make up a group of samples and sketches, put them on an airplane, send them to Nova-York, and within a week perhaps have them back again in his hands. On each would be pinned a little slip of paper saying, 'This we don't like—perhaps you can sell it in Africa,' or 'This is smart—our Hollywood branch will take a thousand yards,' or 'Please send as soon as possible five hundred yards of this in each of the following colors . . .'"

Senhor Fernando is a good businessman, alert and cosmopolitan. "And we have our own market in Brazil. Maybe we will have a campaign to 'Buy Brazilian.' Our same ladies who wear Brazilian diamonds would wear Brazilian silks. And our gentlemen would wear Brazilian silk neckties. There are many possibilities in neckties, you know, for England perhaps would buy necktie silks just as the United States would buy dress fabrics."

He laughed, a hearty, pleasant deep-throated expression of enjoyment of his own enthusiasm. "There are so many possibilities in this new crop of ours. It becomes very exciting to consider them."

I smiled and said, jestingly, "You'd better get into the silk business."

"It so happens," he said, with a twinkle belying the seriousness of his tone, "that we have a *fazenda* near Marilia, and there, two or three years ago, I had some mulberry slips planted. I have heard that the fruit is good to eat and," he confided in a low tone, "I have heard also that there are certain ways to utilize the leaves of these trees. Who knows? It may be worth an experiment . . ."

11

Bamboos in the New World

By *ATHERTON LEE*
DIRECTOR OF NEW CROPS,
UNITED FRUIT COMPANY

TO list silk as a new crop for the New World is reasonably accurate, though in some respects figurative. The ever-important bamboos are more literally new to the Americas. Here is a news-worthy summary of the initial fortunes and futures in the New World of another great family of Far East crops.

For many centuries bamboos have been among the decisive utility crops of the Orient—a widespread supplier of cheap houses, home-made furniture material, ornamental shrubs, rudimentary piping for water supply and drainage, and a valid reinforcing material. During many years of agricultural study and work in the Philippines, south China, and other of the Pacific tropics and subtropics, Mr. Lee has appraised the agronomy of bamboo and its many valuable uses in the daily living of tens of millions of people. More recently, as director of the United States Depart-ment of Agriculture's Tropical Experiment Station in Puerto Rico, and at present the director of the United Fruit Company's Depart-ment of New Crops, Mr. Lee is giving careful study to the fortunes of bamboos in the warmer Americas.

11

RESIDENTS or travelers from the Far East who are accustomed to bamboo in many uses in their every-day life are surprised when they come to the western hemisphere and find such little development and utilization of bamboo. In the Far Eastern countries such as Java, the Philippines, China, and Japan, probably more use is made of bamboo than of any other crop. It is used for floors, siding material, and roofs of houses; for corrals, fishing nets, irrigation tubing, bridges, baskets, and poultry runs; for furniture such as tables, chairs, beds, lamps, cigarette-holders, cases, humidors, ash trays, and almost countless other uses. Construction of bamboo in the Far East is durable, and some articles will last a lifetime.

Bamboo has also been used a great deal for landscaping, particularly in China, Java, and Japan. Because of their closely matted roots, many species are valuable for hillside plantings to prevent soil erosion. On the banks of brooks, creeks, and rivers they hold the soil in flood-times.

Here in the western hemisphere, in Ecuador and to a lesser extent in Colombia, a native bamboo which is a Guadua species is used for the construction of houses. This Guadua is a thick-walled bamboo suitable for houses and scaffolding but not so desirable for finer work such as furniture; however, some beautiful houses are made from it. We find Guadua species as far north as Honduras in Central America, although less use is made of it there. The common bamboo of the other countries of the American tropics is *Bambusa vulgaris*. It now seems probable that the failure to use bamboo in the western hemisphere as it has been done in the Far East, is due to the weakness of this common species *Bambusa vulgaris* and its susceptibility to boring insects.

Probably the first continuous work on the utilization of bamboo in this hemisphere was that at the Tropical Experiment Station of the United States Department of Agriculture at Mayaguez, Puerto Rico. Articles were first made from the culms of *Bambusa vulgaris* and quickly showed the lack of strength and the susceptibility to boring insects. The most damaging of these boring insects proved to be, not the comejenes or white ants, but the small powder-post beetle, *Dinoderus minutus*. Furniture made of *Bambusa vulgaris* within a few months would be riddled with this powder-post beetle. This at first dampened enthusiasm for the development of bamboo until it was recalled that this beetle is also widely distributed in the Far East. The conclusion seemed logical that there at least some of the bamboo species must be resistant to this insect. Efforts were therefore made to obtain as many as possible of these Far Eastern species.

Fortunately, Dr. David Fairchild, of the Office of Foreign Seed and Plant Introduction, United States Department of Agriculture, had traveled extensively in the Far East and had seen the value of bamboo there. He had initiated the importation of a number of species and had established them at Savannah, Georgia, at Coconut Grove, Florida, at Mayaguez, Puerto Rico, and at Lancetilla, Honduras. The investigators working at Mayaguez, with the cooperation of B. Y. Morrison and Robert A. Young of the United States Department of Agriculture, quickly assembled planting material of many of the tropical species from the other propagation centers. F. A. McClure, working at the Canton Christian College, had also become interested in bamboos and is now the world's pre-eminent authority on the previously confused taxonomy of bamboo species and their uses. His knowledge put forward much more rapidly the understanding of the bamboo problems of this hemisphere.

A laboratory method was first developed for testing the susceptibility to the powder-post beetle of the different newly introduced bamboo species. The selection of test pieces from the culms of bamboo was standardized. Then twenty such standardized test pieces of each species were placed together in a wire cage with dimensions about 1 × 1 × 2 feet. Five hundred powder-post beetles were then introduced into the cage. After thirty days the test pieces were removed and counts made of the channels made by the boring insects. The numbers of channels totaled for the twenty test pieces of each species gave a representative measure of the susceptibility of the different species. Usually test pieces of *Bambusa vulgaris*, the known susceptible variety, were placed in each cage as a basis of comparison. Harold Plank at the Puerto Rico Experiment Station carried these tests further and perfected them. By these tests some six or eight species were found to be highly resistant to boring insects, while a number of others, although sometimes affected, were much more resistant than was *Bambusa vulgaris*. Highly resistant species were *Dendrocalamus giganteus*, *D. membranaceus*, *Bambusa tulda*, *B. arundinacea*, *B. textilis*, *B. longispiculata*, and *Sinocalamus Oldhami*.

Using the same tests in cages, treatments to increase the resistance of susceptible bamboos were studied. First of all, it was found that old mature culms of *Bambusa vulgaris*, possibly six to eight years old, had much greater resistance to the powder-post beetle than young culms. Also it was found that soaking the culms in water for six to eight weeks greatly increasely resistance to the powder-post beetles. There was some evidence to indicate that sugars and other nutrient substances in the bamboo diffused out in the water, making bamboo less attractive to the insects. Also the eyes at the nodes of the bamboo frequently germinated when lying in water, and the resulting shoots apparently exhausted food materials from the culms.

A method of impregnating the culms with insecticidal materials was also attempted. The culms were cut at their bases and the cut ends of the butts immediately immersed in solutions of such chemicals as copper sulphate, zinc sulphate, creosote, and such preservatives. This method was partly successful but it was found that rarely would preservatives penetrate uniformly into the upper lengths of the bamboo. However, as a by-product from these tests it was found that merely cutting the culms and allowing them to stand in the bamboo clumps with the leaves on for a week or ten days, considerably increased the resistance of the culms to the boring insects. The selection of well-matured culms, cutting them and allowing them to stand in the clump with their leaves on, is the method accepted to date for handling bamboo to avoid damage from boring insects. Harold Plank developed the foregoing information on methods of handling bamboo culms. It is understood that foresters have similarly found that trees allowed to lie with their leaves on for several days after felling, have considerably greater resistance to rots and insect attacks than trees which have had their branches and leaves cut off immediately after felling.

By some of these means some of the oriental industrial species of bamboo which are not completely resistant to borers can be made sufficiently resistant to be utilized for farm purposes.

Kenneth Alvis, also working at the Experiment Station at Mayaguez, made some strength tests with some of these bamboos. He found that laminated pieces of *Bambusa tulda* had a breaking point of 52,000 pounds per square inch. Walnut, one of the representative hard woods of North America, was quoted as having a breaking point of 22,000 pounds per square inch. Soft steel, such as is used for re-enforcing concrete, was quoted as having a breaking point of about 60,000 pounds per square inch. It can be seen, therefore, that bamboo has great strength per unit of weight, as compared to other woods and materials. It should be added here, however, that Bart Reynolds in recent tests at the same Experiment Station has shown the value of bamboo as a re-enforcing material for concrete to be practically nil.

In Mayaguez a carpenter shop was developed which specialized in designing furniture and other articles made of bamboo. Some of the products of this shop are shown in the accompanying photographs.

Edward McIlhenny of Avery Island, Louisiana, is one of the group who years ago became interested in growing bamboo in the southern United States. He has figures regarding yields of pulp per acre from forest trees as compared to bamboo. According to his figures, a good stand of spruce in Canada would yield about eighteen tons of pulp per acre at the age of eighty years. In the southern United States a good stand of pine will yield about the same—that is, eighteen tons of pulp—at the age of twenty to twenty-eight years. However, he says that some bamboos will produce more than eighteen tons of pulp per acre after six years of growth, and thereafter will continue to yield annually at about the same rate. Since there are twelve growing months in the tropics as compared to but a few months of growth in the northern temperate zone, such figures appear logical.

Most bamboos are resistant to drought but without adequate moisture they do not put on much growth during such periods. The best environment for most bamboos is in full sunlight with ample moisture the year round, and apparently the warmer the better. Larger culms will be obtained with adequate nutrients than will be the case on poor soils.

Bamboo species vary as to their habits of seeding. Most species do not flower and produce seeds for many years. When they do flower, all stands of that particular species bloom simultaneously, produce seeds, and then usually die. This difficulty in securing flowering material is one of the reasons why identification of bamboos is so difficult.

Because seeding of bamboo is rare, propagation for the most part has to be by vegetative means. At the Experiment Station at Mayaguez a method of layering was developed in which a whole culm was excavated with as much of its roots intact as possible; the side branches of the culm were then pruned back, leaving only a few of the leaves. The whole culm with its roots was then laid horizontally in a previously prepared furrow and covered with soil. We found that the addition of nutrients to the furrows, particularly with nitrogen fertilizers or stable manure and frequently irrigated, especially immediately after planting, aided germination. By this means we often obtained ten to fifteen small plants per culm. The soft bamboos such as *Bambusa vulgaris* and even *Dendrocalamus strictus*, the solid bamboo, germinated rapidly by these methods. Bamboos

PLATE 23. Upper left—Harvesting abacá in Panama
Upper right—Fiber of abacá called Manila hemp
Lower—Retting Roselle fiber in Honduras

PLATE 24. Upper—Processing abacá fiber for bailing in Panama
Lower—Mechanical crushing of abacá plant

PLATE 25. Peppers at a packing shed

PLATE 26. Upper—Sorting chili peppers
Lower—Unloading peppers in the packing shed

with harder culms also germinated by this method but not so readily as the softer bamboos.

More recently Cobin, acting on a suggestion from McClure, has successfully germinated side branches of bamboo culms by placing their butts in sand in germinating beds. This method should be the cheapest for large-scale multiplication. Where there is an abundance of planting material, cutting off a culm on the outside of a clump and transplanting the stump with its roots, will in most cases establish a new clump.

I have tried to cook bamboo sprouts. The best species is one which grows best in temperate countries, *Phyllostachys edulis*. Of the tropical clump bamboos, *Bambusa vulgaris* is mentioned as being used in Java as an edible bamboo. I have tried it with all the different types of sprouts and methods of preparation, but have never obtained a palatable product. It is probable that in our American tropics where footstuffs are not so difficult to obtain as in some of the densely populated parts of the Orient, we will not need to resort to bamboo sprouts as food material, at least from *Bambusa vulgaris*.

It is certain that these industrial borer-resistant bamboos when utilized for furniture and various farm uses will do much to aid the standards of living for all peoples in tropical America. It is possible to visualize that bamboo will be as widely used as in the Far East, in which case it would become the most important crop in the American tropics.

12

Peppers for the Americas

By *A. T. ERWIN*
RESEARCH PROFESSOR OF HORTICULTURE,
IOWA STATE COLLEGE

A STAPLE food and flavor factor throughout most of the Americas, edible peppers are another distinguished American contribution to man's food supply and eating habits. As this chapter points out, peppers fulfil a dietary need for which there is still no substitute. Though one of the oldest of American crops and one of the few vegetables still found in the wild state, the edible peppers are making new and noteworthy entries in inter-American menus—new uses and developments of an ancient crop.

Dr. A. T. Erwin, Research Professor of Horticulture at Iowa State College and past president of the American Horticulturists' Society, here offers a brief summary of the important trends in the practical propagation of the food peppers.

12

THOUGH a minor commercial crop in comparison with corn, peppers nevertheless represent an important Latin American contribution to our diet. Like potatoes, they are a universal article of diet among all classes in the two Americas. Their consumption has greatly increased within the past two decades, for they fulfil a dietary need for which there is still no substitute.

Peppers are one of the oldest American vegetables of which we have any record. Safford found dried chili pods in burial urns in the prehistoric cemetery at Anicon, Peru. Likewise Peter Marty, in a report of Columbus' first voyage, states that they found innumerable kinds of "ages (peppers) one half as long—as a man's finger—the other round. They have hotte kinds of sharpness and biting."

Peppers represent a wide diversity of characteristics, including marked differences as to size, shape, and flavor of the pods. The plant is a native of tropical America and Mexico and is one of the few vegetables still found in the wild state. Botanically, peppers are closely allied to the tomato and belong to the genus Capsicum, which was first described by the botanist Tourneforte. The origin of the term is obscure. Some authorities attribute the word to the Greek root "to bite," but since the red pepper is an American plant which was unknown to old-world literature in the pre-Columbian period, this derivation seems questionable. Its derivation from the Latin *capsa*, "capsule" or "pod," seems more probable.

The peppers were formerly classed under two species, *Capsicum frutescens*, a woody form, and *C. annuum*, a dwarf annual form embracing the cultivated varieties. Later studies, however, indicate that *C. annuum* is merely a dwarf northern form of *C. frutescens* and was classed as an annual because it was tender and winter-killed. The genetic relationship also points to a single species. Varieties belonging to the various groups readily intercross and produce fertile seed.

Interesting genetic studies have been made bearing upon the inheritance of taxonomic characters of the genus Capsicum. Halsted concluded from crosses made between Birdseye, a primitive type, and a long-fruited garden variety, that the long-fruited is dominant over the oblate forms. Webber in a study of color inheritance, found that violet flowers are associated with a corresponding pigmentation of the stems, leaves, and immature fruit.

The flowers of the pepper are nectar-bearing and are visited by numerous insects which may be an agency for cross-pollination; hence the seed growers find it necessary to plant the different varieties some distance apart to avoid crossing. The flowers of the pepper are also self-fertile. Studies made by the writer indicate that the flowers of the pepper open rather promptly the first three hours after sun-up, though on days of high temperature this period is shortened. Dehiscence or the dissemination of pollen follows rather closely upon the opening of the blossoms, and fertilization takes place quite promptly. The flowers last but a single day except in periods of abnormally low temperatures.

The number of days from seeding to mature fruit varies widely with the different varieties. However, the time required for the pods to mature is not proportionate to the size of the pods. Some of the smallest-podded varieties such as the Tabasco require the longest time to ripen.

The pungency of the pepper is due to a volatile alkaloid known as capsaicin, which is formed in the ovary walls and transferred to the seeds. In general, the hot pungent types are preferred in the tropics, whereas the northern races show a preference for the mild, non-pungent forms.

Horticulturally considered, peppers are divided into two classes, sweet peppers and hot peppers. Sweet peppers are mild in flavor, have a large fleshy, thick-walled pod, and are more or less oblong. The mild peppers are of a later development than the pungent type. The introduction of mild, thick-meated varieties, used as mangos, has greatly increased the consumption of peppers. The hot peppers of which the cayenne is a familiar example, are characterized by a high degree of pungency, and the walls of the pods are rather thin as compared with the sweet type. The size of the fruit of this type varies from a small globular pod to one six inches or more in length. The classification of varieties as "sweet" and "hot," though a convenient one for the gardener, is inaccurate because many integradations in flavor exist. Broadly speaking, the large-podded, thick-meated sorts, such as the California Wonder, tend to be non-pungent; the pungent varieties are usually characterized by a long, slender, thin-walled pod.

A study of current varieties indicates that the type of calyx is the most constant character for delineation. Two types of calyx are found in the cultivated peppers, the one being cup-shaped and the other saucer-shaped. In general, the cup-shaped type embraces the hot, long, thin-podded varieties such as the Tabasco and cayenne. The majority of the mild, thick-fleshed varieties, such as mangos, belong to the group with saucer-shaped calyx.

Peppers are used in various ways but principally as a condiment.[1] For the latter purpose they are extensively used in the Latin Americas. Peppers were also prized by the aborigines for their medicinal qualities. A few drops of the juice placed in a patient's eye by the witch doctor were said to be effective in driving away evil spirits, while in grandmother's day a drop or two of the juice was a sure cure for the toothache and grandfather depended upon a pepper poultice for the bachaches. In warm countries peppers are esteemed as a digestive stimulant. "Axi (peppers) taken moderately help to comfort the stomach for digestion, but if they take too much, it hath bad effects," wrote Father Acosta.

Fried chili constitutes an important article of commerce. Mexico was formerly our main source of supply. However, production has increased rapidly in the Southwest in recent years, particularly in California, and at present the major portion of the domestic supply is produced in this country. The ground pods and seeds are found on the market as paprika, cayenne pepper, and chili powder.[2] From the variety Tabasco, native to the Tabasco River in Mexico, is derived the name for the familiar Tabasco sauce. The most rapid increase in the consumption of peppers is in their use as mangos. These are the large-podded, mild type. They are used in either the green or ripe stage for stuffing and salads. The California Wonder is perhaps the leading variety grown for this purpose.

The canning of peppers or pimentoes is a comparatively new industry and had its birth following the invention of a roasting machine by Mark Riegel in 1914. The purpose of the roasting is to remove the skin, the first step in canning. California and Georgia are important centers of the pimento industry. Green peppers are said to compare favorably with lettuce and other green vegetables in vitamins A, B, and C.

The culture of the pepper is very similar to that of the tomato. It is a heat-loving plant and requires a long season in which to mature. North of the Mason-Dixon Line the plants are usually started about a month ahead of transplanting time. Peppers do best in a well-drained, warm soil not too rich in nitrogen. An excess of nitrogen causes a tendency toward too much vine growth and delayed maturity.

---

[1] The red peppers, our common garden peppers, are not to be confused with the white and black pepper of commerce which belong to an entirely different family.

[2] See preceding footnote.

13

Flowers for the New World

By B. Y. MORRISON

IN CHARGE OF PLANT EXPLORATION AND INTRODUCTION,
UNITED STATES DEPARTMENT OF AGRICULTURE

FLOWERS are also crops. Spiritually, if not financially, the flowers that bloom at a farm doorway can be as beneficial to agrarian living as the fields and pastures beyond. A great many of our best-loved garden flowers came to us, in most instances more or less indirectly, from the Americas to the south. More are on the way, and unquestionably still more will come. Happily, the floral traffic is not limited to one direction.

B. Y. Morrison, who is in charge of plant exploration and introduction for the United States Department of Agriculture (and therefore for all of us), is a distinguished student and introducer of flowers, as well as hundreds of economic plants.

13

I F ONE were asked suddenly what flowers he grew in his garden that came from Latin American countries, he might be put to it to answer quickly and intelligently. This is not so much because we do not really know as because the plants have frequently come to us via Europe as part of the material brought by plant hunters combing the world for everything strange and beautiful. The richness that came back to Europe is reflected in astonishing measure in such books as *Curtis Botanical Magazine* and *Lindley's Botanic Register*—books upon which every student must call in full measure. As one thumbs through their pages, he is impressed by the numbers that are rich in North American plants, others in plants from the Cape of Good Hope, others in plants from the Latin American lands.

Today fewer flowers are grown in pots than in the days when there were fewer florists and when the idea was more in vogue that each gardener should bring together a fine collection of strange plants. Nevertheless, there still are many gardeners who do keep a collection of potted plants in their windows. Not all who grow them have any idea that all this activity is more or less a legacy of the 1800's, nor that many of the plants native to the Americas have come to us from Europe rather than from those regions where they first grew.

It is, therefore, more with the idea of recalling the original homes in Central and South America of many of these familiar plants than of making a complete inventory of them, that the following sections of this chapter have been brought together.

For those who live in parts of the United States where there are frosts, most plant material from these southern areas is naturally tender, and has to be either protected or abandoned. This means that many of us grow only annuals, except for such shrubby plants as heliotrope and lantana which can be grown anew each year as cuttings to make a mass of summer bloom, or angels' trumpets and lemon verbena which can be stored over winter in the cellar, or begonias and fuchsias which will grow in pots over winter with more or less satisfactory results. Bulbs, of course, are another matter. Some can be lifted and dried, as is the case with Mexican tigridias; others can be kept in pots like amaryllis and its allies.

Although the thought may make the fortunate gardener on the Pacific Coast sniff a little disdainfully, there was a time when those who grew plants in pots in the house without considering the composition of the picture in the window, but merely the need of giving each plant the right amount of sun, had a plant of two of abutilon, or flowering maple as the catalog of the period called it. It was not the pale lilac-flowered *Abutilon vitifolium* from Chile, with its coterie of admirers in Britain and California; it may have been either *A. insigne* from Colombia or even *pictum* from Brazil and the Argentine, although memory says neither, but *megapotamicum*. The spindling open tree-like shrub with its maple-like leaves and pendent lantern-shaped flowers of lemon-yellow, reddish brown, or even near scarlet-orange, does not prepare one for the vigorous shrub of the Colombian scene, literally covered with bloom unless too much overshaded by taller trees.

The maidenhair fern was often grown as a window plant in the old days. It caused many controversies about the amount and frequency of watering needed, whether the plant should be making new leaves all through the year or only in season, whether one should content himself with the common and long-suffering *Adiantum cuneatum* or should venture *Farleyense* with its larger fluted pinnæ and delightful bronzy pink tinting on the developing fronds.

In Florida and California one may see allamandas growing freely as they do in the tropics, either as near-shrubs or as heavy woody vines. For the greenhouse or the gardener who overwinters tender things in a pit or cellar, the very word will bring up the image of the trumpet-shaped golden flowers, with five broad lobes and haunting scent, rather than the picture of the vine or the leathery leaves. These plants have been so long in cultivation and have been so carried about by gardeners even in the tropics, that one forgets that they were described from and have their rise in Brazilian material, although for *Allamanda cathartica*, the note in *Curtis Botanical Magazine* says "a native of Cayenne and Guiana ... introduced to this country in 1785 by Baron Hake ..."

Anthuriums! Instead of the wet woodlands of Colombia, the word inspires visions of lady flower arrangers, stiff gaudy inflorescences in hand, glaring perhaps at the "container" and trying to decide whether the "material" should be stuck into the vessel in the jackstraw manner disguised with alien foliage, or be massaged into some purely conventional pattern that might be conceived as born out of the patterns of their faintly indecent spadices. Their sole virtue is their quality of lasting indefinitely once in bloom. They are long-lived plants when established, with rather good foliage. In the most esteemed sorts, the spathes of the flowers flatten out and show the raw yellow or red or tender pink of their inner surfaces, while the spadix curls its upward way like a calla lily or skunk cabbage. But surely few who gather *Andreana* here or who grow it in greenhouses will think of the Choco in Colombia—still difficult to travel—from which M. Triana introduced it before the arrival of André, for whom it is named.

The greenhouse man is best acquainted with the younger plants of *Araucaria excelsa*, but there are occasional specimens of the South American representatives of this interesting genus of conifers. They are the dominant conifer in South America, where that type of plant is extremely rare. The name itself should recall for all of us the Indian nation that once occupied the heart of the territory now called Chile—a tribe that furnished the theme for the greatest epic poem of the continent, not to mention endless difficulties for the intruding Europeans who meant to settle there. If one dare be fanciful, it is interesting to speculate on the theories which suggest that South American lands were once part of another continent, so that *A. excelsa* from Norfolk Island need not seem so remote.

Aristolochias are vines of all sizes, from moderately smallish ones to great plants that drape any tree they may invade. For the most part, their manner of climbing has no distinction and provides the gardener with a more or less amorphous mass. Their flowers, on the other hand, are another story. They consist essentially of a tube, which may be variously curved and inflated, and a flattish face that spreads out about the opening to the tube, so that the alighting winged guest may savor the stench that comes from the mottled flowers before he descends to greater intimacies. The ground color is usually a dull white that has never forgotten green completely. The colors overlaid, in mottlings, sandings, and specklings, run the gamut from light reddish chocolates to cholocate-browns so near black that one must look twice to be sure. For the literal-minded, they have common names like Dutchman's pipe and pelican flowers; for the garden sadist, they offer their bloated tubes for inspection, so that he may gloat over the number of carrion-interested insects which had their feast and then could not escape from the banquet.

Milkweeds are so widely distributed in the world that one does not always give them due praise. Many have dowdy lavender-brown flowers, but that is not true of all. Our own gorgeous butterfly-weed, *Asclepias tuberosa*, is an example; and, although there are those who do not feel the beauty of its orange-colored flower heads in the hot light of mid-July in a field that has already lost its lush June green, there are others who have pursued it through its variations to lemon-yellow and deep orange-red.

Perhaps this is not the species closest to the South American *A. curassavica*, but it will serve to suggest the color scheme of the latter, and it takes its place in the shrubby or weedy roadside or the moist grass sweep. In the greenhouse it is grown for the cut shoots which bear their flower heads along the upper portions of the stalks.

Only a courageous person would dare to touch the great family of the begonias without fear. How many have been brought into trade and cultivation, how many have lost their identity in the developments of horticulture that have been lavished upon them, how many are known only to the herbarium sheet and the taxonomist's prose or are merely trodden upon in the several countries in our continent where they grow, cannot be guessed. They are not peculiar to the western hemisphere, but the most casual traveler can see them throughout Central America, down into the moist woodlands of the west coast of South America. Brazil appears to be a great center for them, but in this day when the greatest use of begonias is perhaps developed about the horticultural races, it is difficult to tell how many and which of the American species are more than collector's items. But one may safely consider the common angel's-wing begonia with its silver-speckled leaves, warmed by the pink color of the veination on the undersurfaces, as at least one of the travelers from Brazil.

Whether or not the woody greenhouse collections of today contain specimens of brownea is open to doubt; but no one who has seen the new growths on *Brownea macrophylla*, with their tender pinky bronzes and the terminal flower with its strange full petals, will forget them.

In one of the old conservatories known to the writer, the floor of the parts planted to taller and woody plants was covered in sections by members of the Marantaceæ, an order which contains the arrow-root of commerce. Among the gayer highly colored members are the many species of Calathea and of Maranta itself. Dull purples and warm deep reds lighten the effect of the undersurfaces, and lines of silver mark the upper sides of the leaves. Persons who come along in the evening will note the plants with their leaves folded upward like hands in prayer.

As a first cousin of the true palms, Carludovica in its several species includes the plant from which the so-called Panama hat is woven. Its young leaf bases also provide the vegetable element of a delicious baked dish which resembles an escalloped eggplant with a faint suggestion of artichoke hearts. In nature the plant makes spreading colonies with the leaves borne about three feet high, giving quite a different appearance from that of the palms which have upright stems.

Latin America has given us the canna—by no means a conservatory plant, but one that has suffered many ups and downs in popularity, with periods when its varieties were many and others when they were few. As an element of the much-derided bedding epoch, it suffered the fate of many other good plants. One rarely sees it used in bold clumps in perennial borders; yet here its broad foliage gives the same note of relief from the fluffy masses of perennials as does the fine foliage of some of the species of Hosta, once known to us as Funkia and in its great white-flowered form, as the August Daylily. Tender to cold and requiring winter storage in the North, the canna in the South can become a bedraggled and unsightly part of the perennial border. But if it must take on a purely economic coat, it yields a starchy root which, in the wild forms, is eaten apparently with some reluctance by both man and beast.

Possibly the orchid has carried more plant hunters to the Latin American countries than any other plant. It has many representatives in the several republics, and the different genera have various claims on the affections of the collectors. Cattleyas are plentiful from Costa Rica southward through Colombia to Peru; epidendrums from Colombia to Peru and again in Brazil; gongora in Peru; lælia of florists' fame, and lycaste with its particularly beautiful white form in Guatemala. Macradenia, masdevallia, and maxillaria mean less to the layman, but miltonia has fine sprays of beautifully penciled flowers. Odontoglossum makes the visiting American gasp with pleasure when he finds it offered cheaply in the flower shops in Bogotá, and oncidium bears wonderful sprays of tiny, yellow, butterfly-like blossoms. Phragmopedilum hides in its name one section of hte lady's-slipper orchids, with flowers strangely beautiful in color and in shape. And there is a host more, many only collector's items. Perhaps one should mention stanhopea, which air travelers in season must know from the airport in Medellín, where it is often offered for sale, its spotted mustardy yellow flowers in strange contrast with the usual lavender range of the cattleyas.

Another old-fashioned shrub of greenhouse collections is *Cestrum parqui* from Chile, grown for its delightfully perfumed flowers which fill the evening air with their heavy scent. By day, their somewhat drab, greenish yellow color belies their evening seduction. It is nice to recall that they were first sent home by one Father Feuille, were later verified by Archibald Menzies, and introduced to Britain in 1787 by one Mons. Williams of whom we know nothing.

And while one speaks of heavy evening scents, there also comes to mind the three datura, known in many Spanish-speaking lands as Floripondio, although if one wants to use the seeds for binding a spell on one's unwilling loved one, there is a less lovely name. Northerners know this plant in summer gardens when its long white trumpets fill the mid-summer air with a heavy perfume like that of petunias; in the winter its stands stark and somewhat shriveled in the cellar, awaiting another spring, like many a gardener. Which country would claim it for its own would be hard to tell, so far has it traveled in cultivation.

For persons who like foliage in other colors than green, there are the Colombian and Peruvian dieffenbachias with their broad green leaves blotched or striped with white or gold. Many a specimen has stood and perhaps grieved inwardly from dark corners of hotels or restaurants.

With leaves that almost suggest the humble and long-suffering aspidistra, a quite different plant is *Eucharis grandiflora* from Colombia, where it is said to grow in deep damp woods. In the North of course, it is a greenhouse plant, although it is met in Florida. Its charms consist in the amazing whiteness of the flowers, the delicate perfume, and pleasant form recalling a narcissus.

In the good old days of conservatories, among the many plants that crept about on the earth floor—lush green things with strange names and stranger forms—were the Peruvian fittonias with the furry, almost velvety stems and the equally velvety leaves, perfectly veined in white, dull yellow, or even carmine.

Although Californians will dispute the inclusion of the fuchsia among the tender shrubs, the fact remains that if most of us are to have fuchsias we shall have to have them only in summer or else with winter protection under glass. The average city dweller knows the plant only as the potted specimen that he can buy in the spring, with its pendent flowers that gave rise to the old name of lady's eardrops; but under conditions that suit them, the plants vary from small weak shrubs to moderate-sized small trees. Not all are of equal beauty, and until quite recent times—perhaps even yet—the majority of the cultivated forms have come from *Fuchsia speciosa*. The days of the first hybridizing or even of the first raising of seedlings are now so remote that it would be presumptuous to be too categorical about this.

The same argument might be raised by the Californians on behalf of heliotrope. Of species there are many—some of them quite weedy and poor—but gardeners here know chiefly those of *Heliotropium peruvianum* and *H. corymbosum*. Modern growers may know only those forms of garden origin with huge scorpioid racemes of beautiful deep violet, but almost scentless flowers. Old-timers will always grow the forms with smaller blooms and that delightful scent for which the plant was always beloved. It was this plant that was sent "by the younger Jussieu to the Royal Garden at Paris where the plants produced flowers and seed; and for the curious garden of the Duke d'Ayen, at St. Germain's, I was supplied with some of the seeds, which have succeeded in the Chelsea garden. . . ."

The morning-glories are essentially Americans, with a range that takes them in one species or another from Canada to Brazil, with perhaps the greatest concentration in the purely tropical regions. Like all large families, this one is made up of individuals that vary in beauty and utility. If one were to single out two species for special appreciation, they probably would be the common morning-glory in its best forms and the variety known as Heavenly Blue. The former, *Ipomœa hederacea*, includes those selected forms known as the Japanese morning-glories; the latter is a selection from *I. tricolor*. This latter species is credited to Mexico in Bailey's Standard Cyclopedia of Horticulture, but it was as plentiful in the waste fields in Guatemala City as chicory is in some of our fields.

One still comes upon pot plants of the jacobinias, even in strange places far from city dwellers and conservatories where it began its non-South American career. The species one sees most frequently is *Jacobinia carnea*, which made its bow to cultivation about 1835.

The lantanas in cultivation are almost all American, even if they have become very much at home elsewhere in the world. The common form used so much in bedding, *L. Camara*, is an often nasty shrub in the wild, with rank growth and strong hooked spines that snag one's clothing and hands. It has been selected, however, until now its cultivated representatives are modest in deportment and stature, free flowering in a wide range of colors, and generally amenable. From time to time one also finds another South American species, *L. Sellowiana*, which was dear to gardeners in the days when hanging baskets were popular. It is lax in growth and throws long shoots of willowy habit, covered in time with the pinkish lilac heads of flowers. But who was M. Orro, who received it in 1822 from Montevideo, and why was it named for Mr. Sellow and not for the Herr Doktor who sent it to M. Orro?

All gardeners have prejudices. One of this compiler's is against the very beautiful national flower of Chile, which was written up in great style in a widely circulated American magazine and immediately became the subject of letters of inquiry from the most extraordinary parts of the United States with climates which in no way resemble those of Chile. Furious replies came back from nearly all. Be it said once and for all that the plant is not hardy to frost and will not tolerate high summer temperatures. The result is that one must grow *Lapageria rosea* in a very carefully regulated greenhouse or else live in some of the chillier coastal areas in California. It is a slender twining vine which, when well grown, will festoon the supports with slender branches laden with large drooping lily-shaped flowers, rose-colored in the type but with white as well as darker-colored variants.

Almost in the same category as heliotrope and of the same vintage is the old lemon verbena, which is no verbena at all but a very nice tender shrub with no virtue other than its lemon-scented leaves. It comes from the southern half of South America but is not hardy to cold. Northerners grow it in large pots and keep it in the cellar over winter, bringing it to light and warmth in the garden and giving it a good feeding to make up for the winter of hibernation. Its route to us was Chile to Spain, Spain to France, France to England, and then "the colonies," even if the date was after 1784. In California, it has a very utilitarian creeping relative that is used in lieu of grass and forms a silvery sward dotted at times with tiny verbena-like heads of dull pinkish white.

Less common in more recent years but belonging to the same group of plants for pots in house or conservatory, is the old manettia vine with its twining stems, heart-shaped leaves, and tubular flowers of bright red with a yellow band about the lip.

One is frequently called upon to identify a pot plant that when once established has many virtues—graceful growth, simple cultural demands, and a prolific flowering habit in midwinter. Because of the superficial resemblance to iris, many mistake it for that genus; but the proper name is marica and the Central to South American countries are its home. For the amateur, one of its intriguing characteristics is that it forms little plants in the axils of the bracts of the inflorescence, even in those cases where the flowers do not develop. These always evoke inquiry. To quote *Curtis Botanical Magazine* once more: "a native of the Brazils, where it was gathered on the island of Raza, near the mouth of Rio Janeiro, by Sir Joseph Banks; introduced her via Lisbon by the late Mrs. North. . . ."

Among the many plants that one may have known all his life without a thought as to origin is the parrot's feather, which has grown in many a pond and fountain in this country. Chile is its native home. While it is not one of the main plants in water gardening, more than one pool margin has been made attractive by the masses of its finely cut leaves of tender green on the ascendent stems that rise above the submergd portions. Our own two native species are less delicate but even so are worthy cousins.

While there are many species of oxalis from elsewhere, South America has provided a goodly share. The most common in cultivation is *Oxalis rosea*, though rock-garden enthusiasts have a special word of praise for *O. adenophylla* from Chile and particularly for *O. enneaphylla* from the Falkland Islands, which geographically come within the sphere of present consideration. Those latter species are more delicate, more refined, and much less invasive. Gardeners who think of lilies and crocus when they hear of Elwes, may be glad to add this oxalis to his records of collections.

Many an old window garden and conservatory had a pot or two of passion vines, and much is the lore, sentimental and otherwise, that has been written about the curiously made flowers of these usually handsome tropical vines. We have species native within the States, but there are many more outside our borders, with groups in the Andean regions and others that follow the east coast of the continent. Some have been brought into the country as ornamentals, including those species which are sometimes known as tacsonias; others have been brought in for the delicious fruits which are utilized in South America in the preparation of sherbet as well as sorbets. Since the species from the Andean plateau do not find a counterpart of their climate here, they often fail; but the species from the eastern coasts, provided they have no troubles from actual frosts, grow with more success.

The peperomias, many from Brazil, are also house plants that, perhaps, came into general cultivation in the time of conservatories. They have been successful enough under household conditions so that they are often found in the cheapest sales of house plants. They make a jolly rosette of succulent leaves, with reddish stems and heart-shaped blades of green, often feathered with silver. The flower stalks give the housebound citizen a faint idea of the truly tropical piper, from which our black pepper is derived.

Philodendrons, which belong to the great arum family, have many representatives in the Latin American countries, but most of them are so large that the home gardener will have little chance to grow them unless he happens to have an old-fashioned conservatory of huge proportions. These, with monstera, pathos, and similar aroids, have had a great vogue of late and make striking plants when they can be accommodated. Perhaps they never look so spectacular under artificial conditions as they do in the wild, with their huge glossy leaves shining from their tall stems that climb slowly up the boles of the jungle trees.

When you shudder at the combinations of bougainvillea, pyrostegia, allamanda, hibiscus, and the like which you see only too often in Florida and elsewhere, you may bow to the pyrostegia as Brazilian. Only one has come into common cultivation, and that a long time ago when it was grouped with the bignonias or trumpet-creepers. Left to itself and given all the room it may need to clamber over tree or building, it makes one of the most magnificent of all climbers with fine evergreen foliage and myriads of orange-yellow trumpets in season.

Although many a gardener knows that the famous potato is a good South American, he may forget that all solanums are not vegetables and that many have even more handsome flowers than the potato. The Californian would set him straight, of course, and point with pride to plants of the Costa Rican *Solanum Wendlandii* with its fine violet flowers, to *S. jasminoides*, a much hardier vine with showers of small white flowers most of the year through, or the less common *S. Seaforthianum* with its lavender blooms. Just how far these might be extended into other warm areas in the United States is still open to proof, but that matters very little.

Although they are still not very commonly seen, the various members of the genus Stigmaphyllon are coming into cultivation in the open in Florida. One of the species was for decades a regular offering among greenhouse plants in the North. They are more or less woody vines with a mass—almost a cloud—of smallish yellow flowers which superficially resemble the oncidium orchids, perhaps more in color and poise than in the formation of the flower itself. The genus is essentially tropical and is said not to enjoy pot culture. We shall probably not have the pleasure of seeing it until the Floridians forego some of the ranker-growing and more gaudy vines that are not commonplace.

Another relative of the humble potato which is seen quite commonly in California gardens from San Francisco southward and less often as a greenhouse plant in the East, is *Streptosolen Jamesonii*, which makes a very nice evergreen shrub covered in season with orange-red flowers somewhat resembling the blooms of the annual browallias so much planted for late autumn flowering in the East.

When the apartment-house dweller looks upon his or her glass of rooted wandering jew, he is plain green, green with white stripes, or the vinous red one with silvery upper surfaces, he may send his horticultural greetings to Latin American countries, even if the red form is Mexican and creeps (according to the books) across the border into Texas. Nothing much need be said of the wandering jews save perhaps a word of appreciation for their willingness to grow under often untoward circumstances and a suggestion that their structural beauties are often worth looking at. The writer still recalls a scene in Colombia when the red one, more properly called zebrina, had been planted and then escaped at will in a rocky wood. It had crept out over large rocks and formed dense masses of short ascending shoots, making a carpet much like that of the common polypody fern in our own north woods.

No one save the more intrepid would venture to discuss the palms that have come to us from the Latin American countries, for such is the controversy over their names in science that whatever one says is likely to be disputed. Suffice it then to say that there are many palms in these countries, many of which have been brought to our own land in one way or another for outdoor planting in the warmest parts, and for growth in pots in areas where people still grow plants in pots. They vary from robust trees to the more delicate forms which make part of the cover of the forest floor, under trees which give them perpetual shelter. For those who want to see them, there are fine collections in southern Florida and southern California.

Although they actually are worlds apart, it often happens that the same amateurs who like and collect cacti are also interested in the bromeliads and their allies. If one were to believe the evidence in old garden journals from Europe, this appears to be particularly true of the amateurs in the Netherlands, Belgium, and even more so in Germany proper. In the matter of collecting cacti, the Germans have been more than assiduous in the South American countries, perhaps particularly so where western Argentina borders on Bolivia and the other countries which make up the southern portion of the Andean plateau. This area is perhaps comparable with Mexico in the abundance and diversity of its species, but one must not forget the cacti that like countries where rain is not a rare event. Brazil and the West Indies in particular are the places from which such plants have come into cultivation.

The taxonomy of cacti has been the study of many eminent botanists who do not always agree with one another, so that the amateur may have the task of deciding which school of thought or of baptizing he will follow. The plants themselves are another matter and presumably bloom with complete unconcern as to how they may be labeled. As everyone should know, the first beauty of the cactus is the amazing structure of the plant itself. Even if many of them never flowered at all, they would be worthy of attention because of the shape, form, and coloring not only of the body of the plant but also of its protecting hairs and spines. The flowers which follow are, in many species, of astonishing beauty, with a fragility that makes a violent contrast with the plant so often adapted to a life of natural adversity. As could be expected, there are many members of the great host that are less beautiful, perhaps even ugly. It can probably be argued with some safety that well-grown plants in collections under glass are sometimes far more beautiful than the same species in nature, where the body of the plant bears the obvious record of every accident of life. This is also true in cultivation, but not if the cultivator knows what he is about.

The bromeliads, like the cacti, are esteemed for the beauty of the plant forms and for the brilliancy of the flowers in many species. Many are epiphytic but not all perch themselves on trees, and travelers in many places can recall hillsides where there were lines of plants as regularly disposed as birds perched on wires. One may, in season, come upon many a small cryptanthus in the five-and-dime stores or a full-sized *Puya chilensis* in some florist's shop, but it is to a good old-fashioned conservatory that he will have to repair in order to find a good collection of the many forms. If he goes in the right season, there will be flower scapes, many of them gaudily colored, with small or large flowers protruding, usually in contrasting color. To those who may not know them at all, one might say in generalities that the plants look somewhat like the overgrown top of a pineapple, with variations in the width of the leaves, in the patterns or the colorings, in the degree and kind of marginal serrations, and so on. For persons who live in truly favored climates in this country, such as in some parts of California and Florida, these natives, which may be Brazilian or from almost any one of the West Coast countries, make delightful hobbies. The beginner who has not yet decided upon the hobby for his declining years might consider either bromeliad or cactus with a favorable eye. Is there a special reason? Surely; one can go off and leave them in the proper season without having to worry about who will water them, and how!

As is the case with practically all the material from the Latin American countries, the bulbous introductions are for growth in pots in the regions where there is winter cold and out-of-doors where there is just the right combination of heat, light, and dryness. In general terms, California is more to their liking than the East, although the Pacific Northwest can do the gorgeous alstrœmerias to perfection. Zephyranthes will grow East and West, and even those living almost in the North, can grow the Argentinian *Triteleia uniflora* which will spread its carpet of grassy leaves and stud them with violet-tinted flowers in the North as well as anywhere. Perhaps the same cannot be said for the gorgeous Mexican tigridia in every year, but this relative of the iris will come through many a winter in these parts and save one the trouble of dry storage. The flat-faced gaudy beauties of the greenhouse amaryllis—hippeastrum to the knowing—have doubtless been touched up by many a gardening hand in the many years since the first wild forms left Brazil. What may have gone on in the way of intermarriages, licit and illicit, will doubtless never be known.

Not many gardeners bother to grow the ismenes or hymenocallis, but there are excellent species in each genus that should be more commonly grown, particularly in the milder parts of the country. Much has been written about the *amancaes* of the Incas—the golden yellow Peruvian daffodil of the old garden writers—but no one seems to do much boasting about success with it in this country.

Another rarity that has caused many a horticultural flutter is the so-called Chilean crocus, *Tecophilæa cyanocrocus*, which, of course, is not a crocus and does not particularly look like one, although perhaps if one were to see it scattered across the pasture, it might recall a crocus-studded lawn. The plants that have bloomed here, brought from Holland in the good old days, were of the most gorgeous blue color, like the shade of old delphiniums before the hybridists got so very busy with them.

Bomareas, which are scarcely any more bulbous than the altrœmerias or the cormous tigridia, are again for the cool Pacific slopes. In their more spectacular forms they make a fine clambering vine that likes to worm its way upward through the shrub mass and then toss out its heavy head of tubular to bell-shaped, yellow, rusty orange to rusty red flowers in a mass like that of a good hydrangea. There are the poor cousins of the beauties as in any other family, but one does not regret them so very much.

From the Andean ranges, perhaps with more bulbs having come out of Peru than elsewhere, are a number of rather nice minor plants like Eustephia with its crimson to scarlet pendent bells; Urceolina, of the same ilk but showier; Stenomesson with strong flower scapes and disappointingly colored tubular flowers; Phædranassa with tubular blooms usually reddish with green tips; and the charming small Crocopsis which has almost crocus-shaped flowers borne close to the ground, of the most lovely reddish orange.

Since the botanists refuse to give their sacred word as to the exact origin of the tuberose, one hesitates to mention it. But no one who has ever traveled in Mexico or in Colombia could possibly forget the armfuls that can be had for a pittance, nor the really wonderful beauty of the single form, which is more easily found than the double.

Out-of-doors there are the familiar annuals—so familiar indeed that many forget that they were once unknown in our gardens and could not be bought in seed packets at five and ten cents an envelope. They come from all parts of the neighboring republics, and their chief value to us is that they fill the hot months of our summer with masses of flowers, after the first fine flush of spring blooming has passed and we have not yet come to the cool nights of autumn when the dahlia grower looks with wary eye to see whether frost is threatening his constantly improving flowers. He never thinks of the spectacular but not very elegant dahlias that he might see along the highland roads from Mexico to Ecuador.

From the modern petunia, with its innumerable forms, colors, patterns, and habits of growth, it is a far cry to the plants depicted in *Curtis Botanical Magazine* or *Lindley's Botanical Register*. In the former, the editor writes of *Petunia violacea:* "This new and most distant species of *Salpiglossis* [1] was raised from seeds sent in the autumn of 1830, by Mr. Tweedy of Buenos Ayres, to the Glasgow Botanic Garden. . . . It promises to be a most valuable addition to our semi-hardy plants, but whether as an annual or otherwise, I am not in position to say. I have specimens of the plant sent to me by Mr. James Baird of Buenos Ayres, who gathered them upon the Uruguay, near the Rio Negro. . . ." From the same source and from the same country I possess another species of salpiglossis, which may be named and distinguished: "*S. linearis*, etc."

Lindley's plate and note which appeared in 1833 adds little to the data save "a native of Buenos Ayres, and like other herbaceous plants from the same country, quite hardy in England during the summer; in winter it required protection from frost. . . ." Lindley also saw clearly that the plant was a petunia and neither a salpiglossis nor a nierembergia!

Unlike the petunia which is the mainstay of the summer garden, the salpiglossis is one of our more difficult annuals, magnificent when well grown but sadly disappointing when unhappy.

Graham, in the *Botanical Magazine* in 1828, wrote in part: ". . . It first flowered in the garden of Mr. Neill, Cannon Mills, Edinburgh, from seeds sent by Dr. Gillies. . . . Both the species have flowered freely in the stove of the Royal Botanic Garden, Edinburgh in September, and will continue to do so during October, the seeds having been sent from the Cordillera, by Mr. Cruickshanks in 1826. . . ." The plants are now known to be native of Chile, and while there are other species, the one now common in cultivation bears the name of *S. sinuata.*

Scarlet sage, a brilliant plant not much in favor at present but still commonly grown, was introduced a few years earlier, in 1822. Aside from the notes in the *Botanical Register* (1822), there is little to add here. "Introduced by Mr. Lee from the Brazils into the Hammersmith Nursery [near London] where the plant flowers freely in the hothouse and for a long time in succession.

[1] Genuine Salpiglossis were known before Petunias and were once considered to embrace the genus Petunia.

"Recently observed by Prince Maximilian of Wied-Neuwied, and mentioned in his travels by the name we have adopted, but without description. There are native samples collected by Mr. Sello, in Mr. Lambert's Herbarium. . . ."

The years 1831 and 1832 brought good illustrations of the beautiful schizanthus, with its hosts of brilliant flowers suggesting orchids to many persons because of their shape and coloring, but more often thought of as butterflies. "A native of the Andes of Mendoza, whence we have specimens from Dr. Gillies. . . ." and "In addition to the two species of Schizanthi already given in most of our botanical publications, two species have lately been raised from seeds brought from Chili by Dr. Gillies, in the present garden of Mrs. Borg, at Porto Bella. . . ."

The period 1820-50 saw the publication of many pictures and notes about nasturtiums, but the first note of considerable garden importance was that in *Curtis Botanical Magazine*, to accompany plate 23, in 1787. This note accompanies a drawing of a vermilion-red form of *Tropæolum majus*, the prototype of the ordinary garden nasturtium of vining habit.

From the text might be cited: "The present plant is a native of Peru, and is said by Linnæus to have been first brought to Europe in the year 1684. . . . Elizabeth Christina, one of the daughters of Linnæus, is said to have perceived the flower to emit spontaneously, at certain intervals, sparks like those of electricity, visible only in the dusk of the evening, and which ceased when total darkness came on."

One wonders about Elizabeth Christina!

With the exception of the species commonly called canary bird creeper (*T. peregrinum*), none of the other species of nasturtium have become common in our gardens. Many of them have long-lived roots that will not tolerate our winter freezes. Reports of success with *T. speciosum* from the Pacific Northwest come in from time to time, but there is always difficulty in finding plants if one wants them. Its name in horticultural history is associated with that of William Lobb, the splendid collector for Messrs. Veitch & Sons of Exeter, England, who have fostered so much horticultural exploration and plant introduction.

As good Americans we should, of course, know about *T. tuberosum*, the *añu* of Latin America, where it takes its place among such root vegetables as the potato and the tuberous oxalis. The *Botanical Magazine* note of 1840 reads: "This interesting species of Indian Cress, of which the large tuberous roots are abundantly eaten by the Peruvians (according to Ruiz and Pavon) and, indeed, form a daily article of food, was first made known to me my specimens transmitted from Peru, by Mr. Matthews. They are No. 402 of his Peruvian collection. . . ."

Although for this writer personally portulaca will always be vividly associated with a stone-paved courtyard in Peking where its brilliant flowers lined every paving joint, common portulaca belongs to South America. In the *Botanical Magazine* plate 2885 (1829), the note reports: "It was discovered by Dr. Gillies, growing in the light sandy soil, in various situations between the Rio del Saladillo, or western boundary of the Pampas, and the foot of the mountains near Mendoza. On the western side of Rio Desaguardero plants were growing in general profusion, giving the ground over which they were spread a rich purple hue, here and there marked with spots of an orange colour, from the orange-coloured variety which grew intermixed with the others. . . ." It should be remembered that there are other South American portulacas but that few have flowers as large or as gay.

Among the writer's early memories of St. Louis, aside from the heavy-scented petunias, were his first experiences with four-o'clock, so much more romantically known as Marvel-of-Peru.

In 1797, *Curtis Botanical Magazine* said briefly: "From Peru, its original place of growth, this plant was introduced to Europe at a very early date; the names it bore on its introduction sufficiently testify the admiration in which it was held; it was well known to both Gerard and Parkinson. . . ."

Of flowering tobaccos there are no end among the fine plates of both the *Botanical Magazine* and the *Botanical Register*, but it would need a staff of taxonomists perhaps to say with authority what names they would bear now. The genus is American and the flowering forms have been known for a long time; the heavy scent that fills the evening air was appreciated then as now.

Of verbena there is little to say, since most of the common garden forms are a mongrel lot with some uncertainty as to the whole story of their hybrid past. The genus itself is American, with possibly the greatest number of species South American. From some recent taxonomic papers one might guess that the whole number of possible progenitors has not been collected from Argentina, Chile, and the neighboring states.

The calceolarias have suffered a similar fate, and in some of the old papers one can find a querulous note from purists who hoped the species might be maintained as they came from South America. The family is a large one, with tiny annuals, all sorts of herbaceous perennials, and even shrubby species. Here we rarely see anything save the modern descendants of the biennial forms that are grown for winter greenhouse flowering and are known to many folk as lady's-slipper, a common name used for various other plants as well.

Occasionally one comes upon species of calceolaria in the rock gardens of specialists, and news from the milder climates of the Pacific coast make one wish for similar growing conditions. As. it is, we must be content with library pleasures, remembering the years of work of Ruiz and Pavon in Peru, the travels of Humboldt, the infinite journeyings of William Lobb, the "invaluable correspondent, Dr. Gillies, of Mendoza," of Mr. Cruikshanks, who collected in "Chili" and sent his seeds to Edinburgh, even H. J. Elwes, who usually means crocus or lily, and so on.

Within the last decade, several nierembergias have come to the fore, but one always recalls the old and lovely *Nierembergia rivularis* named to recall its place of origin. "I have dried specimens from various places near Buenos Aires, where it was discovered by the late Mr. Tweedie upwards of thirty years ago. This collection describes it as a most lovely and fragrant plant, abounding by the sides of the Plate River, and only within high-tide mark, its flowers rising above the dwarf grass which grows in similar situations . . ." writes the editor of the *Botanical Magazine* for November 1, 1866.

Wm. Jackson Hooker, writing in the same book in 1831, mentions ". . . a native of Peru (*N. repens* R. & P.) and another of Mexico (*N. angustifolia* HBK.) and a third of Monte Video (*N. pubescens* Spreng.). To these I have the pleasure of adding a fourth, a native, like the last, to the vicinity of Uruguay, but with its botanical character nearly approaching the Mexican plants. . . ." One gathers up as well the fragment that "Nierembergia" is "In compliment to John Eusebius Nieremberg, a Spanish Jesuit of the Sixteenth Century who wrote a 'History of Nature.'"

And last of all, although there are many others, one might choose the late summer- to autumn-flowering annuals named browallia by Linnæus, whose beautiful deep blue to purplish blue flowers will always recall to mind the tale related in the *Botanical Magazine:*

"Named after John Browall, a Swede, Bishop of Abo in 1743. The intimacy and subsequent rupture between Browall and Linnæus were commemorated by the latter in the specific appellations which he bestowed on the three individuals of the Genus then known—*B. elata* expresses the degree of their union, *B. demissa*, its cessation; while the ambiguous name of the third species, *B. alienata*, while it intimates the uncertain characters of the plant, implies also the subsequent difference between the parties."

No chapter such as this could close without mention of both zinnia and cosmos, which come to us principally from Mexico, although the yellow cosmos which has had such popular acclaim in recent years was introduced not only from Mexico but also from various places in South America where it was cultivated as a garden plant.

If one thinks of the wealth of forms and habits that have arisen since the first seeds came into our garden world, and how happily these plants have become part of our life, what pleasant philosophizing might ensue!

For woody plants—that is, trees and shrubs that are of interest and value only when used out-of-doors—we are not so deeply indebted to the countries to our south, since practically none of the patterns of weather which one finds there fit well into the many which we have. Only in the coastal areas on the Pacific slopes do we approach the arid conditions of the west coasts in Mexico or from northern Peru to Chile, so that one must hunt in vain for good representative plants in any of the states in the East.

Among the acacias which have been so largely introduced into California from the Pacific Southwest are far more spectacular plants than the single representative from Latin American countries, *Acacia Cavenia*, usually assigned to Chile but looked upon by many as a mere variant of *A. Farnesiana* which is the huisache of Texas and many another spot.

Broad-leaved evergreen shrubs, small trees, and the like are always dear to the gardener's heart unless he lives in a warm region where they are commonplace, and then he sighs for the fleeting bloom and leaf of a northern spring and does not get them. What the Chileans may think of the plants included in the genus Azara we may never know, but in California there are several representatives that make useful, even if not very spectacular, additions to the evergreen masses. The commonest, of course, is *A. microphylla* whose pinnate branches give a fernlike quality to the general appearance of the plant. The flowers are inconspicuous but sweetly scented, yet the plant would never come among the first requirements in a planting list.

In one or two species rather widely planted in the warmest parts of the country, the genus Bauhinia in its general aspects takes the place of the Judas tree or redbud of the North, but the large and showy flowers are a very different affair. They have the indefinable something that makes the stupid person scream, "Oh, just like an orchid," as if all orchids looked alike! Unfortunately for this present chapter, the showier forms do not come from the Latin American countries, but we can hope that the plant collectors of the future will be willing to watch for seeds of the South American species with an eye to introducing them, although since they are reported usually from east coast of the South American continent no one dare predict their hardiness. Of those recorded, *Bauhinia Kappleri*, escaped from French Guiana into the West Indies, sounds the most attractive.

For probably all gardeners save those on the Pacific coast, the beautiful South American evergreen barberries are only matters of regret. Long in cultivation abroad, plants like *Berberis Darwinii* with its shining, small, holly-like leaves and brilliant orange-colored flowers have been the delight of all gardeners who could grow them, and the envy of the remainder. Its hybrids with the less showy *B. empetrifolia*, grown as *B. stenophylla* with several varietal forms, are all excellent plants but just as tender to cold. They survive in Washington, D. C., but make no show and are not worth the trouble to keep alive. Many of the forms that have been brought into cultivation of late are recent reintroductions of plants long known and once introduced and lost. The majority come from the higher elevations and find no counterpart in our many American climates with the wide range of variation.

Although there are other buddleias which are far less showy and more common in distribution, the Chilean *Buddleia globosa* with its tomentose leaves and globular heads of brilliant yellow to orange flowers is well worth a place in the few areas where it might survive. If one dared, he would try it in a warm position, sheltered not only from cold but from excessive light in winter. The other species from Mexico south and in Brazil sound even more difficult, but one need no longer think that the buddleias are entirely oriental in their origins.

In those parts of our country where the gardener, not to mention the real estate dealer, wants to make a great and flamboyant show to impress the winter-weary Northerner, no plant offers more eye-filling effects than the bougainvillea which you must now call "buginvillea" if you are a purist. Brazil is their native scene, but they are more or less world-wide now in frost-free areas for out-of-door planting and are not unknown in greenhouse collections whether planted in the ground and allowed to cover the roof or kept clipped in pots. Among the many horticultural forms are varieties named for British ladies, but one wonders why there is no Carmen Miranda!

Cantua is the invented Latin name which records the national flower of both Peru and Bolivia. It was apparently brought into European cultivation about 1850 and is magnificently figured in *Curtis Botanical Magazine* 4582. This compiler has seen it growing in California and in Peru, and still wonders why anyone is so thrilled about it, even after having been shown herbarium specimens to confound his opinion that it is not floriferous. The bush as it grew in both garden and wild had no charm of habit or grace. In season it is covered with funnel-shaped, two-inch-long, red to yellow flowers.

The cassias are very floriferous leguminose shrubs and trees with a wide distribution in nature and good help from gardeners. There are many species in the Latin American countries, all of which are not likely to find a climate to their liking here. Those that do are those which will endure something of cold, perhaps of drought in season, and at times soil characters not like those of home. The Argentinian *Cassia corymbosa*, which was doubtless sent down by one of the visiting Britishers, was figured in 1803. As one might suspect, this is purely a matter for the Californians and maybe Gulf States gardeners. The pink and golden showers of gardens, *C. grandis* and *C. fistula* respectively, again are plants for the coast. However, one should not be deluded by these showy species into any belief that all cassias are lovely; like the members of many other large families, they have their representatives that are not swans.

The eastern gardener may have to be satisfied with the Scotch broom as an example of the plant which has decided to wear a green skin to help its chlorophyll situation, but coastal gardeners can grow some of the fantastic colletias, all from South America. If one were to reduce the selection to one species, it might well be *Colletia cruciata*, which looks like the invention of some architectural draftsman with modernistic tendencies. The stems are flattened so that the lateral twigs look like triangular emanations from the main stalk, green and dull, with occasional flowerings, all in the morphologically correct places but nonetheless odd. As a matter of good measure, the tips of the twig growths are armed.

Doubtless all people who garden are amused by the stranger who comes to the neighborhood, all curiosity about the things which have been daily fare to the home folks. The daubentonias, now referred to as sesbanias by some, are represented fairly commonly in southern Mississippi planting by *D. punicea*, which makes a five- to six-foot open shrub with locust-like leaves and clusters of brilliant flowers which look all red, filled with stamens that spread outward as do those of nerines or the common azaleas of our eastern woods. The dull orange to brown seed pods that follow are not showy, although they are fairly persistent. Like many other ornamental shrubs, this plant is one of a family that is also represented in India and Africa.

Of the durantas which are credited as being in cultivation here, one might perhaps choose *Duranta Plumieri*, which seems to be an East-coast affair, reported from the Florida tip across the islands and from Brazil, with a bow in passing to Mexico. It has been given the rather silly common name of golden dewdrop because the fruits have golden calyces which close over the fruit itself, giving the general appearance of the not quite ripe fruits of bittersweet. Personally, the compiler much prefers the plant when it is covered with its loose racemes of lilac-colored flowers, but even so he would not stoop to call them by some invented name, preferring the perhaps pedantic memory that Durantes was a physician, and so perhaps a gardener, of the 1500's, and that Plumier was he who found the time to write the first descriptions of fuchsia.

In the genus Escallonia, which is described as "widely dispersed in South America," West-coast gardeners are provided with many good flowering shrubs. A fair number are hardy in the East, but like many another border-line plant which is tender not because of actual temperature but rather because the total weather pattern does not suit it, the escallonias tried so far were unhappy. They died back during the winter and left a bush that in no way suggested a normal specimen. The flowers, ranging in color from white to deep rose, may grow in terminal racemes or panicles or may even appear in tiny clusters along the stems. There are enough of them to give the plant the appearance of a wealth of bloom. In some cases, however, the whites are not pure and snowy like the whites of bridal-wreath or mock-orange.

Not all the eugenias are from this hemisphere, although many of those in cultivation have come from South America. The plants are usually handsome, with shining leaves, beautiful flowers distinguished for their numerous conspicuous stamens, and fruits which "can be eaten" but which to a northern palate are much better cooked or conserved. The romantic names of rose-apple, surinam cherry, pitanga, and the like should be no disguise, and the useful clove should be remembered as a member of the group although it is not American.

Members of the heath family are not too common in the Latin American countries, and the pictures that have appeared in the British gardening papers of the beautiful Chilean pernettya have always intrigued this writer. Seed has been forthcoming on various occasions, but although it responded to all the usual routine for ericaceous plants, of which we considered ourselves masters, there came a day when the plants would die without warning—a quick complete death, as if it were self-determined. No one could foresee it, but the blame has been laid on the weather which heaven knows is nothing like that of Chile!

Gardeners who may also be readers of Latin American literature will know only too well the *molle* under which many a romance has flourished or languished, or which may have provided its somewhat barren shelter to the shepherd on the even more barren hills of the highlands. But whether or not he will recognize it as the "pepper-tree" so commonly seen in southern California is a matter for conjecture. This tree with its often gnarled trunk, its slightly pendulous branches covered with drooping, finely compounded leaves, and its drooping racemes of pinkish red berries, prefers the arid part of our country rather than the more humid East. The latter, however, can grow the more tender *Schinus terebinthifolius* from Brazil, where it makes a fine contribution to Christmas gayety, with its heavily produced red berries. Unlike *S. molle,* this has coarse, pistache-like foliage and makes here a low stiff shrub.

Where they will survive, the tabebuias make handsome flowering ever-green trees, with fine large terminal racemes of showy flowers that roughly resemble those of the trumpet-creeper, except in color, which may be white, pink, or clear yellow. In some seasons, of course, the evergreen leaves are shed, since no evergreen leaf lives forever, and when this occurs in some uniformity the tree stands out like a northern tree, blazing with color. Travelers will encounter it from Mexico through Central American countries down into South America proper.

Like the tabebuias in general characteristics is the genus Tecoma, of which the most commonly encountered is *Tecoma stans*, sometimes de-scribed as a tall shrub, but certainly making a small tree, with fine grayish green foliage and terminal clusters of brilliant yellow flowers.

PLATE 27. Upper—A village cathedral in Guatemala
Lower—Blooming bougainvillea in Guatemala

Plate 28. A cactus in bloom

PLATE 29. Upper——A bullcart in Costa Rica
Lower left—Central America farm home
Lower right—Coffee picker

PLATE 30. Upper left—First Central America planting of bamboo
Upper right—Vetivert root provides finest perfume oil
Lower—"Heads" of African oilpalm now grown in Honduras

14

Cane Sugar Production

By P. HONIG
CHAIRMAN OF THE INTERNATIONAL SOCIETY OF
SUGAR-CANE TECHNOLOGISTS

LIKE our beloved garden flowers, and the many flowering or otherwise ornamental plants which may become garden favorites of the future, the sugar-yielding plants are coveted by all peoples and by no means solely for routine economic reasons. Cane sugar, the principal supplier of man's sweets, is a giant grass brought to the Americas from the Old World. The crop has survived and grown great in the New World largely because of plant materials and scientific developments provided and replenished more or less continuously by the Old World, particularly Java.

Sugar-cane progresses as a basic crop of the Americas. In particular Cuba has become, rather literally, sugar bowl to the world. But in the broadest sense, sugar-cane remains an international crop, and from a breeding standpoint a perennially new crop.

Dr. Pieter Honig, the distinguished Netherlands authority on sugars, is at present Chairman of the International Society of Sugar-Cane Technologists. Before the Japanese invasion of the Netherlands Indies he was director of the Java Sugar Experimental Station. In 1941 he was invited by the Netherlands Indies Government to organize a Rubber Research Institute. When Java was overrun by the Japs he was directed by the Governor-General to represent Netherlands Indies interests abroad and prepare for postwar reconstruction in those per-eminent agricultural islands. Dr. Honig is a native of Schnermerhorn, Holland, and a graduate of the Delft Institute of Technology.

14

SUGAR AS AN IMPORTANT FOODSTUFF AND GENERALLY A TAXABLE COMMODITY

THE TIME is long past since sugar was considered a luxury product. Nowadays agriculturalists, dieticians, doctors, and economists count it among the important foodstuffs, in the first place because it is easily absorbed by the human body and secondly because of its relatively low cost.

This inexpensiveness of sugar is not to be accepted as a foregone conclusion. In many countries sugar falls under fiscal legislation and is placed in the same category as such taxable commodities as liquor and tobacco. A detailed survey of sugar prices in the various countries would therefore show a great dissimilarity in quotations.

In 1937, retail prices per pound of white granulated sugar in certain countries were as follows:

United Kingdom	5.1
United States	5.6
Canada	5.9
Australia	6.6
Norway	7.2
Irish Free State	7.2
France	8.8
Czecho-Slovakia	9.5
Netherlands	12.1
Germany	13.7
Italy	14.6

The fact that certain countries, such as England, the United States, Canada, Australia, Sweden, and Denmark, have a yearly consumption of over 100 pounds per capita, shows the importance of sugar as an essential foodstuff.

WORLD AND NATIONAL CONSUMPTION OF SUGAR

The world total sugar consumption in the years preceding the war averaged some 30 million metric tons, two-thirds of which were cane sugar and one-third beet sugar. This would amount to approximately thirty pounds per capita yearly, for over 2,000,000,000 human beings. A further analysis shows that some of the important sugar-producing countries are among the lower than world-average consumers; in the case of Java in the Netherlands Indies the per capita consumption amounts to only seventeen pounds per year. There are several explanations for this phenomenon. It is not that sugar as a world commodity in certain tropical producing countries has a higher sales prices than the other commodities usually consumed by the great majority of the population. It is basically a food problem, since the people of these countries have, as a rule, a predominantly carbohydrate diet which has to be bolstered with fats and proteins. The public income has to provide for these requirements but it is not large enough for the purchase of sugar, which would henceforth become a luxury product in the people's diet. A survey of sugar consumption since World War I revealed some curious developments. The world sugar production has increased from approximately 16 million tons during the 1910-20 period to 30 million tons during the second decade of 1930-40. Cane sugar, as well as beet sugar, was included in this increase. During these two decades the cane sugar production rose from an average of 11 to 12 million tons to approximately 21 to 22 million tons, and the beet sugar production increased from 5 to 6 million tons to some 10 million tons.

The increase in cane sugar production was the largest in volume as well as in relation to the general increase. As far as the world supply of sugar was concerned, the greater self-sufficiency through home production in sugar-importing countries and the relatively small increase in sugar supplies in the sugar-exporting countries, has been of great importance.

From World War I through the 1935-40 period, the sugar production of the importing countries has increased from 6 to 15 million—that is, some 10 million tons—while the sugar production in exporting countries increased from 10 to 15 million tons. The main feature in the development of sugar production during the period between the two World Wars proves to be not only a great increase in the total sugar production but also a powerful impetus of the sugar production in most of the importing countries.

Countries which exported beet sugar, particularly Germany, Czechoslovakia, and Poland, have been mostly affected by the restrictions imposed on the so-called free sugar trade. But cane sugar exporting countries, especially Java and Cuba, also had to reduce greatly their sugar production during the period 1925-35. For every individual country the interchanges in the productions of cane and beet sugar during the period between wars have been much greater than appear from above mentioned approximate data.

In studying the world sugar situation over a longer period, the question comes to mind of what caused the great boost in sugar production after the first World War. The principal cause was the sugar shortage after the war, which led to the increase in production in the western hemisphere, especially in the Caribbean. Other factors have been: first, the early rehabilitation of agriculture; second, a great development in sugar technology; and third, the exploitation of cane and beet varieties with a higher production per acre. Moreover, the national policy in various countries was the protection of their local sugar production.

This protective policy was generally practiced during the second period between the two wars. From 1920 to 1930 the increase in sugar production was due to the technological development and the exploitation of new territories for sugar production, which made a low price possible; after 1930, however, when the prices of most agricultural products were falling, the sugar industry, in many importing countries, expanded under the protection of tariffs, quota, and other government-supported regulations.

Between 1930 and 1940, the world sugar production, under various kinds of government protection, increased from 12 million to 20 million tons. In other words, two-thirds of the world sugar production can be counted as a protected branch of agriculture.

THE GEOGRAPHICAL ASPECT OF SUGAR PRODUCTION

Sugar-cane is considered a tropical product, although its area of production ranges up to a fairly high latitude in subtropical countries. Its equivalent, the sugar beet, is limited to temperate zones. Under a free world economy the beet sugar industry would probably be unable to maintain itself at home in the face of imported sugar. This is due largely to the higher yield of cane sugar per areal unit and to the much lower wage standards in cane sugar producing countries.

A sugar surplus is apparent in Asia and a shortage in Europe, the latter caused mainly by the imports of sugar supplies into Great Britain.

The western hemisphere is almost self-supporting in sugar, except for the United States, which before the war, purchased about a million tons of the surplus production from the Philippines. This causes the sugar-exporting countries in the Caribbean to try to find a market for some 1 to 2 million tons elsewhere, mostly in Europe and North Africa.

In normal times the world sugar production and consumption are distributed about as follows:

PRODUCTION AND CONSUMPTION IN 1000 SHORT TONS DURING THE YEARS
1937–1940

North and Middle America	9,000	8,000
South America	2,500	2,000
Western Hemisphere	11,500	10,000
Europe, including Russia	10,000	13,000
Asia, including Philippines, Java	10,000	8,500
Africa	1,200	1,000
Australia and Fiji Islands	1,000	500

The Asiatic surplus, especially the Philippine production, is exported partly to America, and the Java production to Europe.

THE SUGAR INDUSTRY DURING THE WAR

The situation created during the first years of this war is probably such that hardly any sugar shortage may have occurred in continental Europe. Russia was self-supporting before the war. Markets have changed, but the production set-up, its agricultural structure as well as its factory installations, cannot have suffered much up to this date. The greatest losses to production will have occurred in European Russia, but we know from the last war that the rehabilitation of a once-established production of beet sugar will not be a long process.

The war has little influence on the African sugar industry, which is cane sugar production only. Very much the same holds true for the western hemisphere where, except for a slight regression in the beet sugar production in the United States due to the manpower problem, and a slowing down of production in the Caribbean for lack of shipping space during the years 1942, 1943 and 1944, there can hardly be a question of disorganization or injury to the productive capacities of these territories. Once sufficient labor is available, sugar production in these countries will regain its highest pre-war level within a year.

We have had no data on sugar production during the last two years out of Japan and the Japanese-occupied territories of Manchuria, China, Indo-China, the Philippines, and the Netherlands Indies, which before the war produced some 5 million tons of sugar and whose potential production from available areas and factory installations would amount to 6½ million tons, while their pre-war consumption was from 3½ to 4½ million tons. This means that before the war production largely exceeded consumption. It remains to be seen how this problem has been solved and what measures have been taken in this respect by the Japanese authorities.

In war-times it is easy enough to stop any branch of production by not planting or not harvesting the crop. But we wonder what has become of the factories, whether they have been left intact or whether they were dismantled because the installations furnished valuable war material? In this latter case we will be confronted with a rehabilitation problem.

THE BALANCE BETWEEN PRODUCTION AND CONSUMPTION

The regulation of world sugar production according to the demand is a problem of international importance. It has long been a question how to achieve a balance between the production and the consumption of this world commodity.

The International Sugar Agreement was concluded for this purpose, among seventy-five percent of the sugar producers. By this Agreement a system is devised establishing a yearly quota of production for the sugar-exporting countries, in order to prevent any ruinous price-crash on the world market. This has become a necessity since the present potential production of factories and plantations, or plantation prospects, exceeds the world sugar consumption by approximately twenty percent. In adding up the capacities of all installations in the various countries producing cane and beet sugar from all available raw material, we should obtain the sum total of 35 to 36 million metric tons of potential sugar production for the years 1938-39.

Attempts have been made to come to an adjustment. The International Sugar Agreement has certainly accomplished some good work in this respect. The fact remains that in various countries sugar consumption could be higher for the improvement of public health and balanced diets. In order to reach this goal, world production would be made to function completely, but considerations of national financing, fiscal policies, and such other measures as compose, now and most certainly after the war, the realistic elements in the economy of each country seem to prevent the fulfilment of the world's need of this essential foodstuff.

It is to be hoped that the international collaboration will be restored after the war and that the first example of successful production regulation of an agricultural commodity will prove the practicability of such an agreement.

ORGANIZATION OF THE CANE SUGAR INDUSTRY

The expansion of the processing factories into large centralized installations marks the development of the cane sugar industry during the twentieth century. This development was caused by the modernization of equipment and the rational application of driving machinery as well as by the evolution of the beet sugar industry toward the end of the nineteenth century.

Competition then between cane and beet sugar ran high when the unprotected cane sugar industry in the tropical countries was faced with a highly protected, and for export even subsidized, beet sugar industry in Europe. This completion, fostered by fiscal and technical regulations, was eased by the Brussels Sugar Convention. Heavily subsidized and located in highly developed countries where scientific working methods became more and more popular, the beet sugar industry soon surpassed cane sugar production in the years 1880-90. In the tropical countries, the cane sugar industry reacted by modernizing the technique of its processing factories and by establishing experiment stations for the promotion of scientific research. Because of these improvements, the cane sugar industry was in a position to compete with beet sugar during the years preceding the first World War.

In most countries today the processing of sugar is done very much along the same lines. An economic production is obtained the world over by factories with 1000 to 4000 tons daily capacity. In most cases the raw material is gathered from territories within a ten- or fifteen-mile radius from the factory and brought in by truck or narrow-gauge rail lines. The sugar-cane processing takes place in accordance with weather conditions and varies in seasons which extend from 60 to 200 days. One factory can consume the sugar-cane from a planted area of 3500 to 13,000 acres. In general, this is the technical organization devised for the cane sugar industry.

Seventy-five percent of the total world production of 20 million tons cane sugar a year is processed in centralized installations as roughly described above. The total number of such sugar factories today amounts to approximately 800. They are generally located in subtropical countries of which the most important regions are the Caribbean, Hawaii, Formosa, and the Ganges Valley. Among the sugar-producing tropical countries are Java, Brazil, Peru, and the Philippines.

This form of technically rather intricate plantation industry was made possible by the great progress in the output of machinery, the mass production of rolling stock, the rationalization and standardization of appliances through the free and international exchange of data, which mark the sugar industry. Had it not been for this free exchange practiced for decades and a by-product of the otherwise unrealized free world sugar trade, the sugar industry could never have reached such heights and achieved such economic production in the countries most fitted for it.

The technical organization of the modern sugar industry develops parallel to the agriculture. The selection of sugar-cane is very significant and offers some of the most beautiful pages of applied natural science to the research worker, showing how, through systematic study and the planting of selected varieties, tremendous progress was made in the density of production per planted area. On Java the average sugar production per hectare amounted to 60 quintals in 1880 and increased to some 170 quintals of raw sugar. Among the factors responsible for this progress are the improvement in agricultural experience and its consistent use in well-chosen planting time, breeding, and the choice, quantity, and application of fertilizers, but above all the selection of high-producing cane varieties.

The first-mentioned factors may well have been responsible for one-third of this progress, which leaves two-thirds of the credit to the selection of sugarcane varieties. This is neither the time nor the place to give a detailed description of this selection work. We should like, however, to point out that the possibility of reproduction of cane sugar through seed was first proved on Java and on Barbados in 1889. The normal way of reproduction is by cuttings.

The discovery that cane sugar could be produced from the seed led to experimentation in cross-breeding, which became an important assignment in the Java experiment stations. Research was primarily concentrated on the finding of disease-resistant varieties. On Java various types of cane diseases had to be combated, which was detrimental to production. The first step in this direction was to cross-breed resistant varieties with low, or sometimes even no, sugar content. Wild species with the normal plantation variety, called "noble" in sugar terminology as distinct from the wild varieties of the Saccharum species. From this crossing, disease-resistant seedlings were obtained which were called the first nobilization of wild cane. In crossing these once more with a noble variety, a second nobilization is obtained, which is usually known for its good resistance to disease. A third nobilization containing one-eighth of the wild cane characters has proved to be disease resistant and equal to the highest yield of the noble susceptible varieties.

For years the Java experiment stations worked in this fashion and for a long time without much practical result. It deserves mention that several times in the board meetings of the Java experiment station, putting a stop to the selection work was suggested because the results were inadequate in comparison with the expenses entailed. Fortunately this advice was not heeded; consequently, the crops obtained from the work of the Java sugar experiment station and classified under the initials POJ (Proefstation Oost-Java) followed by the registration number, are now to be found in almost all cane sugar installations the world over.

This cross-breeding was done at other places than on Java. There are a fair number of experiment stations. Some varieties were bred by the Hawaii experiment station (indicated by the letter H), in Coimbatore, India (letters CO), Barbados (BA), Canal Point, Fla., United States (CP), and others.

It may be said without exaggeration that more than fifty percent of the sugar-cane used in the whole modern sugar industry originates from the varieties bred in the Java sugar experiment station of Pasoeroean, which amounts to one-third of the total world sugar production. This is all to the credit of the Java sugar industry, since it proves that this experiment station lived up to the ideal of free exchange of information and data, going beyond a merely theoretical adherence to the principle.

It must be pointed out, however, that the world-wide distribution of these varieties was not only to the benefit of the Java sugar interests, but contributed to the whole world production, which increased from 2 to 3 million tons, or seven to ten percent, without an expansion of the planted areas, through the selecting undertaken and donated by the Java sugar industry.

What have been the consequences for Java? The potential overproduction of sugar may be called a result of this increased areal production of POJ sugar-cane. The repercussion on the Java sugar industry itself has been that because of the restriction of the free sugar trade,—although this did not concern cane sugar producing countries only,—the Java sugar industry had to reduce its production from 3 to 1½ million tons. In other words, it had to cut down its own production in return for the production increase it had donated to the other cane sugar producing countries.

Several times the suggestion has been made that such important agricultural achievements as the selection of the most productive varieties should be protected by international regulation—some sort of breeders' protection of the property, like the one offered by patents to the technical inventor. It would be of much greater value if it were internationally agreed not to take any economic measures against the interest of those countries, and their industry and agriculture, which had been the originators of such inventions.

Paradox is no exception in present-day international trade. The development of technique and agriculture meets with general approval. It is considered important that good plant material be freely exchanged the world over. The principle of a free exchange of data is generally accepted in theory if not in practice. Should, therefore, the obtained results be taxed or otherwise restricted to the detriment of one of the parties concerned, friction and disagreement will be unavoidable. Notwithstanding the call for more freedom of exchange, this situation has arisen frequently.

We advocate the free exchange of information among research workers in all industries because it fosters mutual confidence in each other's aims and satisfaction in individual achievement. But it is often difficult to persuade the manager responsible for the economic interests of his enterprise, to honor the free exchange principle when other countries and rival concerns retaliate with protective measures and secrecy. Free exchange must be reciprocal and can be of value only if universally accepted.

THE FUTURE OF THE CANE SUGAR INDUSTRY

The cane sugar industry can be expected to increase in the various countries after the war without necessarily occupying larger planted areas. Production can still be considerably increased through the use of the most productive cane varieties. In this respect systematic agricultural research can yet introduce great improvements.

Better transportation and more effective industrial installations will also contribute to an enlarged production in most counties. Through these factors and renewed plan on the formerly restricted areas, the cane sugar production can be increased from 20 to 25 $\pm$ million tons a year during the next decade, without claiming any new areas. In order to attain this, the free exchange of information should be rehabilitated, the more so as this is the wish of cane sugar technologists the world over. This rehabilitation will have to enlist the support of the international economic policy. The resolutions taken at the Hot Springs Conference on Food and Agriculture stressed the significance of this exchange.

A peculiar aspect of the sugar production technique is, that of the approximate 6 million tons of cane sugar appearing and traded on the world market, at least three-fourths is delivered in the form of raw sugar and is refined into the final consumption product in the refineries of the consumer countries.

The immediate finishing of the cane sugar for consumption would be feasible in the local sugar installations. In countries where sugar is used by the retail trade in a specially adapted wrapping and the refineries have become packing installations, their function as distributors is more or less justified. Otherwise the sugar refineries in the present advanced stage of sugar technology, notwithstanding its defenders by the investors and the laborers employed in this industry, can be considered rather outmoded. A thorough analysis will show that a partial liquidation of the sugar refineries would serve the purpose of offering a cheaper product to the consumer.

15

American Plants for the Americas

By B. Y. MORRISON

IN CHARGE OF PLANT EXPLORATION AND INTRODUCTION,
UNITED STATES DEPARTMENT OF AGRICULTURE

THE continuing epic of the plant hunter, the skilled scientist who travels over the earth in quest of useful vegetation, is the stream-lined contemporary version of the Johnny Appleseed of an earlier America.

B. Y. Morrison, the distinguished authority on plant exploration and introduction, here discusses the transplanting of native crops from one part of our hemisphere to another.

Mr. Morrison points out that the interchange of plants within the hemisphere is sometimes more difficult and complex than interchange between far more distant points where respective climates are more closely similar. He reminds us that fields and gardens of the United States are not always easily hospitable to herbaceous immigrants—at any rate, not at first eager flush of arrival. Crop citizenship must come deliberately.

15

IF ONE considers the number of plant products which come to us from the Latin American countries, or remembers the extravagant way in which the riches of the Spanish Indies were once recounted, in comparison with the number of plants which have actually taken up residence in the United States and become a part of our agricultural life, one is more than surprised. Or perhaps one should say that he is surprised until he begins to consider how many carelessly conceived beliefs he has nurtured through the years.

One often reads, particularly in the papers of the Latin American agriculturists, "We have all the climates of the world," when what they really mean to say is that they "have many kinds of climates," which is quite another matter. This fond delusion is most often expressed by the Latin agriculturist when he insists that altitude can take the place of latitude, which is by no means true when one considers climate throughout the year. Altitude may add extremes of cold to the local pattern but presents other factors in duration of cold and/or heat, which are by no means to be compared with the weathers that accompany those same degrees of cold elsewhere in the world.

The American who lists the indigenous Latin American agricultural and horticultural plants which have become part and parcel of continental United States farming and horticulture will find them impressive but few. Potato, tomato, corn, peanuts, sweet potatoes, yams, and peppers are perhaps the most obvious, with minor items like strawberry, yuca or mandioca, chayote, and of late many grasses which are being studied for their use in the South, particularly in the Gulf States. Of the fruits, doubtless the most noteworthy is the avocado, with the papaya as the runner-up. Tobacco, naturally, must have a sentence to itself.

One can read any number of books on tropical horticulture and its allied fields and find descriptions that will make the imagination leap with interest; but when the time comes to examine the behavior of the same plants introduced into the United States, one is not moved to believe that they will invariably find a place in our own growing plans.

Two other things should be kept in mind in considering plants introduced from the tropics of this hemisphere, namely, that many plants native to one part of the tropics may have reached us from a very different point, since it is much easier to carry plants about the world within their own climatic pattern than to take them outside of it. Another somewhat similar factor is the result of the movements of peoples in the pre-Columbian era. There is no intention here to discuss the carrying of seeds or planting of stock of edible plants from one place to another by peoples who are not urban in the sense that we now use that term. In this latter case, the movements were quite as often from north to south and vice versa as in the east-west directions.

The oft-repeated story of the "Irish" potato apparently has not reached every ear, for there are many consumers of it in all parts of the world who do not realize that the potato, which they accept as something that has always been theirs, is truly South American, even if there are no records which will absolutely assure us on this point. These potato lovers also do not know that the species which has become the basis of so many dietaries is only one of many species of Solanum which bear tuberous and edible roots. Gradually the general consuming public is becoming aware that there are many kinds of potatoes in South America and some in Mexico, of which only the former enter into the local dietary and may in their turn become as highly improved in their general characters as is the present race of potatoes based on the original *Solanum tuberosum*.

The United States Department of Agriculture has made important collections of materials from the Andean region. The agricultural scientists of the USSR have done even more and in more recent times. Collectors from England have covered much of the same territory in search of the wild forms and more or less primitive varieties that are cultivated, as well as the selected forms from other local cultures. Whether or not these are to take a place in the production of a complex horticultural race or whether they must be improved within themselves remains to be seen. It should not be forgotten, however, that the weather pattern under which the Andean potato grows and thrives has practically no counterpart in the United States and that, unless aided by artificial means, the Andean potato is no happier here in the open than many of our own potato varieties are happy in the Andes. The general belief is that the potatoes in common use here are from tubers collected in the south of Chile, where there is a closer approximation to our typical lengths of day.

As is the case with the potatoes with which we are familiar, there are many clonal races of potatoes in the Americas. Among them they show not only differences in size and quality, but often in coloring. We have varieties here in which the pinkish color of the skin and the flesh beneath it make a pleasant appearance in the uncooked root. As yet we do not have in common use any potatoes in which the flesh is strongly yellow even after cooking, and we do not have forms in which there is a sweetish flavor in the degree that is present there. Although the traveler "down under" may be diverted by the potatoes in the marketplaces—potatoes with skins of every color almost to dead black, potatoes in many shapes, potatoes for which many prideful claims are made,—it does not seem probable at this time that any will be found that will grow for us in the United States just as they are, say on the Bolivian steppes.

The tomato is another instance in point. Like many another fruit eaten out of hand, the disposition of the uneaten portions, or the dropping of seeds, has led to such distribution that it is practically impossible now to say with arbitrary authority that the original distribution of the genus was this or was that. The original home of the tomato is generally believed to be in the coastal areas of South America, the higher Andean areas, and the Mexican *meseta*. Specimens have been collected from many other places, but whether they were native to the area or introduced is open to doubt. The genus Lycopersicon contains several species not of equal value from our point of view, but until quite recent years the major varieties of garden tomatoes have been evolved by selection from only one species.

The use of the small cherry tomato in breeding work has brought about a series of forms in which vigor, productivity, and resistance to disease are so conspicuous that the tomato breeders are now looking with renewed interest to all the wild forms and species.

Whether or not the tomato will become as docile in the hands of the geneticist as corn has allegedly become remains to be seen; but when one considers the very distinct varietal forms that are now coming into the market or to the testing plots, it would appear that the limits of the tomato possibilities have not been reached. When the geneticists in South and Central America have turned their attention to the creation of races for their own use, paralleling the progress we have made here but using other criteria in forming their goal, the range of tomato breeding may take another turn.

Probably because it is so indelibly fixed in our mind as Indian corn, the maize which the Indians contributed to our earliest settlers is indeed a plant which is peculiar to our continent, and moreover, to the pre-Columbian cultures. Here again there are varied opinions as to the original home of the corn as a wild plant and as to the story of its domestication and improvement.

Considerable popular pride is present here in the degree in which the corn plant has been improved. This improvement treats not only of the physical characteristics of the plant as reflected in flavor and productivity, but in the development of varieties which are almost specific to the several areas in which and for which they were created. If within the space of a lifetime or so, we have been able to breed corn varieties which seem peculiarly fitted to specific geographic areas, it is not surprising that the races of corn recognized in the countries to the south of us should be rather specific to those areas.

As one rides through the Andean plateau in Peru, for example, and sees fields of corn growing in temperatures about 50 degrees F., tattered in leaf from mountain hailstorms; as one is told that in the highlands of Colombia one needs ten months to grow a crop of corn; as one receives excited letters from amateurs about the large kernels of Cuzco and other corns, one can rationally deduce that the whole story of corn has not yet been told, either for us who are fairly well along on the road, or for our Latin American colleagues who are just beginning a conscious program of selection.

Although the peanut has had a wide distribution in world cultivation and for a fairly long period of time, there seems to be general satisfaction with the idea that its original home lies in the area embraced by southern Brazil, Uruguay, parts of Paraguay, and northern Argentina. The centers of production in the modern commercial sense of the word lie elsewhere. For the United States, the values of the peanut in terms of roasted nuts, expressed oil, peanut butter, feed for stock, and forage from the tops in the South come to a considerable total. The use of peanuts, in these or similar forms, is not limited to the United States, for this South American plant has by now seen the world.

Another plant which has spanned the globe and has done much to feed it, particularly in the parts where the individual has his own small patch of tropical stuff, is the sweet potato. There seems to be some evidence that this is a species of original distribution about the Caribbean. But, as reported before, it has been a long way from home and for a long time, so that now geneticists working with it have been importing from far-away lands the local types that have developed there, be they from Amani in Africa or Kobe in Japan.

The other great starchy vegetable product of the Latin American countries, the yuca or manihot, or mandioca or cassava, as you may wish to call it, has not found a secure place in our economy, for we are not quite tropical enough to have a successful planting in many places. There have been efforts to establish it in this country for the production of starch, but they have gradually disappeared until there is only an occasional inquiry received.

To place the strawberry among the important plants from South America that have taken their place in our agriculture is scarcely a proper statement. It is undoubtedly true that the strawberry came into cultivation with the introduction of the Chilean species into Europe, where the wild strawberry and the alpine strawberry were the only representatives up to that time. We may point out now that the same species is represented on our own Pacific coast, but it probably was not from plants of that origin that the upward trend in strawberry breeding took its rise. Nor need we be captious about the place taken in the work by the eastern species named for the state of Virginia, though by no means limited to that state. As an aside, it might be recorded that the strawberry in question comes from the same general part of Chile as does the potato that we grow most commonly in the United States.

Of the other vegetables that come to mind, one thinks of yams. If one means the sweet and juicy forms of *Ipomœa batatas*, these are no more than special clones or strains of sweet potato; but if one means the true yam or Dioscorea, they are plants for the most part from Africa. Those other starchy roots which we sometimes find in the markets, all somewhat resembling one another—taro, dasheen, yautia, and their kin—are not represented in the wild on this continent except in the case of the yautias which, being the most tropical of the lot and requiring the longest growing season, are least likely to make a place for themslves in the dietary of our people.

When one considers the years of work that were put into the launching of the dasheen, only to have it founder for want of customers who appreciated its special flavors, one is probably somewhat discouraged. In a degree this has been true of the chayote, a sort of delicious squash, tender as any midsummer cymling, which forms an important item in the fare of many Central and South American families. Since the plant has a perennial root which can be protected against cold and a vining top which will fruit from the first-year wood, it should add to the list of possible foodstuffs through the Gulf region of the United States even if the harvest is not too rich in proteins, vegetable fats, and the inevitable vitamins of the moment.

Perhaps we may turn with an interested look to our Latin American neighbors for grasses and other forage crops. As is the case with some of the ornamentals which we grow as annuals, there are grasses which can be treated in a similar fashion and which in favored spots will self-sow in such a way that their true habits are forgotten. Since in many cases all of the values of the indigenous grass species are not fully known to the Latins themselves, it is not impossible that we might be able to arrange a future program in which the common knowledge will reach a more rapid dissemination. The field is vast and the difficulty of finding funds to undertake so huge a scheme is formidable.

As in so many other cases, the original wild plant of tobacco has no close visual relation with the tobaccos that go into the industry which returns such large incomes to present-day farmers. Since the original tobacco is also a plant that had been carried about by the people who originally employed it in the pre-Columbian cultures, it is hardly possible to be too arbitrary about its original home. In addition to the species used for smoking, there are many other species of Nicotiana which are employed in minor ways in the several countries. One of them, *N. rustica*, is the basis of studies related to the insecticidal production of nicotine.

One moves perilously when he undertakes to assert that in the realm of fruits there is relatively little that has come to us from the other countries of the hemisphere, always remembering that we are speaking of things that have come to settle down and take their part in our agriculture. If one goes to the most favorable parts of the country—favorable only in their approximation to the conditions under which tropical and subtropical plants live and grow,—he may find a very impressive collection of species living in various degrees of felicity. Should his visit occur, however, in a season that has known several sudden cold snaps or a longish period of drought, the collection may not look so good as usual.

If one views the situation somewhat dispassionately, therefore, he can soon deduce that the avocado is probably the only tree crop that will come to any permanent place in our scheme of things within the continental United States. Forms have been found that will do more than survive. Preliminary selections have been made. A fair number of "hybrids" have been produced, so that the time-honored program of plant improvement may well be underway. For the factors that induce resistance to cold, there is the race of avocados usually referred to as Mexican, classified as *Persea drymifolia*, and curiously enough, those which are referred to in literature as the West Indian-Guatemalan group, from *P. americana*, which have larger size and in some cases unusual quality as well as less resistance to cold. If the avocado is as fortunate as other fruits have been, no doubt in time it will suffer as many changes of improvement as have all the other plants brought in from the wild.

The idea of bringing in material from the wild must lie behind much of Latin American agriculture for many years, insofar as we are treating of the natural wealth of those countries. Most of the people who go to the local markets in the other Americas and write wildly enthusiastic reports of the fruits offered for sale, are often too much carried away by their enthusiasms over things they have never seen before to have much critical judgment left for a capable appraisal of the material in its true market value. They also forget the confessions of the northern people who live in the tropics that there remains a permanent longing for the northern fruits with their acid tang, their crispness, their lively flavors, rather than for the satiety of blandness or sweetness.

Again we frequently forget that many a plant that might be brought to market as gathered from the wilds, when put into practical cultivation would not yield enough per plant or per acre in comparison with the cash crops of the area, to justify profitable cultivation by the generality of farmers.

So one may read of all the members of the Spondias tribe, the innumerable annonas, delightful passion-vine fruits, of guava, eugenias, feijoas, sapodillas, star apples, and dozens more. In every case they are worthwhile for the passing traveler to sample and are worth eating, whether out of hand or cooked as they best appear for the resident there, but there are limitations of soil and climate when we think of growing them in the United States. There are the conspicuous economic factors of producing them on a crop basis. There are also the very practical matters of difficult shipment as luxury fruits with a limited market and enough insect pests to bring them under the eye of the quarantine authorities.

There are enough people who know of the efforts to grow the papaya in this country to have some idea of the difficulties which attend it. Only under circumstances which suit it is the papaya an easy subject. In the tropical or subtropical countries where it grows, it is usually not raised on a crop basis but is gathered from whatever trees spring up. There is no question that the papaya at its best is a delicious fruit—one that would make a very welcome addition to breakfast or dessert fruits. But it still remains to be seen when we will have races of it that can be considered on a profitable basis here, or when we may have a steady and properly graded production there which will bear shipment.

Fewer people are acquainted with the efforts to establish the passion fruit on a paying basis. There has been the usual struggle, first to find the planting stock, next the areas best suited, and finally a public that would buy the product. Among the fellow travelers encountered in Colombia, where one is often served a delicious drink made from the fruits *Passiflora mollissima*, there are many who emphatically do not like the fruit drink. United States' experiments in growing passion fruit, mostly in California, led to minor successes, and then when the economic factors became pressing, the project was abandoned.

Guavas will always represent a minor industry, a home fruit in those parts of the country where they will grow and yield well. What one has to consider is that raising guavas in more favored parts of the world is much cheaper and more productive than in our own states and that it might be more intelligent to import one's paste and jelly unless one really craves the task of preparing them.

At repeated intervals the pineapple comes up for attention, particularly in Florida. There is no real doubt that pineapples can be grown in Florida and brought into good fruiting, provided they are planted in those few areas where conditions of soil, moisture, and temperature combine for the optimum. But here again, the greater ease of production under special conditions so far outweighs the reasons for local production as to make it uneconomic, leaving domestic pineapple growing a mere matter of satisfying one's personal pleasure. Such an arrangement would not of necessity preclude the possibility of finding in the range of the wild pineapples in Brazil, Paraguay, Uruguay, or other Latin American areas some form, perhaps even some specimen, which would be more suited to the combination of factors that we know here and which better provide the basis of a small industry. In that case, however, what would our present centers of pineapple production have to say?

With equal regularity and with even more persistence of late, one hears of the production of coffee within our domestic boundaries. There has been a successful fruiting of coffee in several parts of the United States, not once but several times. What we do not have is an extensive territory in which coffee would find all of the factors needed for its development in their ideal degree. Thus, it is not really prudent to consider domestic coffee growing on any other than the basis of the amateur's curiosity.

The banana is another case in point. Bananas do exist or survive within our continental limits, but scarcely more than that. Those which do the best are not the types of prime quality in comparison with the commercial banana of trade. There is another inter-American plant that comes in for recurring attention, the Paraguay tea or maté. This has a considerable consumption in the United States. The plant has been imported and has been shown to do very well in restricted areas in California, but the only nursery that was willing to keep a stock found in about two years that there were not enough sales to warrant maintaining it. Perhaps the news leaked out that there are surpluses of maté in South America?

During the war, many thoughts have turned toward the possibility of growing within continental United States some of the plants whose products we have needed acutely because of shortage resulting from war. The majority of them were tree crops, so that a long period before production had to be considered in any planning. As in the case of many of the ornamentals and food crops already discussed, limited numbers of these tree crops were known to have survived in many cases, but no one was willing to gamble that they could be put into cultivation on a basis that would be reliably competitive with other sources.

Enough has been written of the experiments with Hevea rubber in Florida to make it known that the tree has grown well there under rather artificial conditions made possible by careful selection of site and by care during the first years. It would be an intrepid person who would say, however, that we could or should undertake an immediate large-scale planting of Hevea in Florida. Cinchona has come in for similar attention of late, and even those persons acquainted with the short-term experiments of the Russians knew so little about them that they did not calculate the costs, nor bother to discover that the climate and soil of the area where the experiments were made did not compare with any of our own. Spices seem to catch the attention of the amateur, and spice could be had from our neighboring countries of the warmest wet tropics, with never a chill during the "winter." Resins, vegetable oils, fibers, tannins—all that type of product, as well as timbers—should be left to the truly tropical countries, even if the gifted amateur can take you to his garden and point out an apparently happy balsa tree, clove bush, oil palm, or what not.

16

Launching New Crops

By *V. C. DUNLAP*
RESEARCH DEPARTMENT,
UNITED FRUIT COMPANY

AS several of our contributors have noted, and as any agronomist —from amateur gardener to successful dirt farmer—will emphatically agree, the theory and practice of crop introduction are rarely the same. Until the new or renewed crop can be grown by every-day "practical" farmers, it is not really a crop at all, but merely an experiment. Any continuing crop requires human resources—the work, sweat, planning, interest, and devotion of the farmer or gardener.

Of all the Americans who are taking part in the practical introduction of economic plants, no one is qualified to speak with greater authority than Dr. V. C. Dunlap, director of the United Fruit Company's Research Department at La Lima, Honduras. With a degree in pathology, and an enviable record in scholarship at Cornell, Dr. Dunlap left his Maine home for the tropics some twenty years ago. During those years he has earned and held a place as a foremost practical scientist in tropical agriculture, shaping an outstanding career in that fascinating and complex field throughout Central America, the West Indies, and with extensive field work in equatorial Africa for good measure. For many years Dr. Dunlap has directed the widespread tropical research enterprises of United Fruit, which at present is the largest, most active and diversified tropical farming organization in the world.

Most of the following is taken from work reports of Dr. Dunlap and his associates made during the calendar year 1943, which was a particularly significant year in American tropical agriculture. It is noteworthy that many of the highly practical plant experiments of 1943, instituted as urgent war needs, are today succeeding as commercial field plantings.

Here without adornments are typical excerpts from one of the most noteworthy and newsworthy farming work records of these times. Dr. Dunlap's contribution was not prepared with a view of publication. That was solely the editor's idea.

16

Much of the work of this department is concerned with the extension of our cultivations of strategic crops for war use and the processing of their products. Among these we are cultivating considerable plots of the following:

VETIVER GRASS
(Vetiveria zizanioides)

This grass, known commonly as khus-khus, has been cultivated extensively in the past in India, Ceylon, the Philippines, the East and West Indies, and to a small extent in Louisiana. The chief use of the oil of vetiver has been in the compounding of soaps and perfumes. The oil is distilled from dried roots which are harvested when the plants are fifteen to twenty-four months old, and the yield runs from .6 to 2.0 percent (dry weight). Yield per acre is around 2000 pounds of dried root or twelve to forty pounds of oil. Besides being a source of oil, vetiver roots are used for weaving baskets and mats. Tied in small bundles they are sold in the West Indies for scenting wardrobes and closets and repelling clothes moths.

When the chief sources of supply were cut off by the war, the price of vetiver oil rose as high as $50.00 per pound. At this writing the quoted price is $25.00 to $28.00. Since a good return would be netted at these prices, we have increased our seed beds to 2.8 acres. Vetiver grows readily under local Honduran conditions. Old mats are divided into small clumps which should be planted three inches apart in a light, rich, sandy soil. After a few months the new plants completely cover the field and control all weed growth.

So far, our plantings are too young to produce oil of good quality, but trial distillations have been made successfully with our local equipment. The roots are placed in the still, barely covered with water, and distilled at low pressure for thirty-six to forty-eight hours. The addition of a small amount of salt helps. The oil is difficult to separate from the water in the condensing process, and considerable time must be allowed for this operation. The oil is yellowish brown in color and has a mild pleasant odor. It is of particular value as a fixative for perfumes.

AFRICAN OILPALM [1]
(Elæis guineensis)

Acreage cultivated in the Honduras Division as of December 1943, exclusive of seed beds for the 500-acre test plantations, consisted of 9.9 acres of mature palms and 51.0 acres not mature—a total of 60.9 acres.

From the twelve acres planted in 1942 and the thirty-nine acres planted in 1943, it is evident that it is not advisable to plant seed at stake or small plants (up to twelve months old) in the field, due to rodent damage, slow growth, and high cost of maintaining such areas through a long germination period and subsequent first year's growth. It was found that plants should be held in pots or nurseries for at least twelve months after germination and then transplanted to a permanent field location during the rainy season. Aside from rodent injury, no serious pests or diseases have been noted to date on new plantings.

During the year, 2994 heads of fruit from Birichichi Plantations were processed for pericarp oil. This was done in the La Lima, Honduras, mill with equipment loaned us by the Birichichi Plantations. From experience gained through use of this equipment, it will be possible to draw up plans for a more efficient unit which will eliminate much of the hand labor now necessary and result in more economical operation.

Better average results would have been obtained if nuts could have been processed on the spot, as considerable rotting and fermentation sets in during extended wait for carload lots and in transit. Also nuts processed were of miscellaneous varieties, many of which are of poor quality. Extraction results were as follows:

Number of bunches	2,994
Weight of nuts	55,668 lbs.

Pericarp Oil

Weight	8,616 lbs.
Percent oil to whole nuts	15.5
Oil per bunch	2.88 lbs.

In addition, 376 bunches from low-yielding varieties in our miscellaneous collection at Lancetilla were processed for pericarp oil for local sale, but yield figures on these are not representative because of small quantity, poor varieties, and harvesting out of season. A total of 890 pounds of oil was obtained from this source. Our palm oil is readily

[1] See Chapter IV.

accepted at the current price of 12½ cents per pound by the Fabrica de Manteca y Jabon Atlantida in La Ceiba, Honduras, for use in the manufacture of soap.

Work on a 500-acre planting of oilpalms is in progress. In Lancetilla 15,000 one- to six-months-old seedlings, recovered from leaf axils and under old trees, have been planted in beds. At San Alejo, 24,000 seeds have been planted in nurseries. Field planting began with the advent of the rainy season of 1944.

Only seeds and seedlings of the Java varieties of oilpalm are being used for propagation, as these varieties have been found superior in yield to all others in our Lancetilla collection. Two hundred pounds of this variety (approximately 21,000 seeds) were supplied to the Quepos Division, Costa Rica, in October, for the proposed 500-acre plantation to be established there. All Java seed from now on will be held for possible future propagation.

ABACÁ

In terms of acreage planted, harvested and processed, abacá, the banana-like perennial that supplies the strong resilient fiber commonly known as Manila hemp, is the largest and most widespread crop introduction effected in the American tropics during very recent times. Prior to World War II roughly 95 percent of all abacá fiber in commerce was produced in the Philippines, where the crop is probably indigenous. Most of the rest was supplied from the Netherlands Indies.

When the Japanese sweep overran all established abacá areas, the needs for the fiber became imperative for the United Nations. Abacá fiber makes particularly strong and resilient rope which is indispensable to ship operation and widely used in aviation, construction and various other wartime and peacetime industries.

The plant flourishes only in the true tropics and usually reaches harvest age within 18 to 23 months after planting. During the 1920's, with able cooperation of plant explorers of the United States Department of Agriculture, experimental plantings of several varieties of Philippine abacá were made on United Fruit Company lands at Almirante, Panama. United Fruit improved and maintained the establishment and by 1941 had increased the seed bed to slightly more than 2,000 acres.

This was the one source of planting stock available to the western hemisphere as of Pearl Harbor. On January 3, 1942, after the Philippines were clearly doomed, United Fruit entered into contract with the Defense Supplies Corporation and the United States Government for making large-scale Central American plantings of the crop, as a war emergency project.

Large plantings were promptly effected in Panama, Costa Rica, Honduras and Guatemala and planting stock was distributed widely among citizen farmers of various American nations. The company began immediate construction of decortication mills for supplying the fiber direct to the United States Navy. Immediately the fiber met and exceeded the exacting Navy specifications. More than 30,000 acres of high-yielding abacá is planted and much of it is now in harvest.

In Honduras our experimental program was launched in 1936 with test plantings of the varieties Bungulanon, Maguindanao, Libuton, Tangongon, Sinaba and Puteean. The varietal experiments are supplemented by experimental progress in pruning, fertilizer uses, surface and overhead irrigation, soil ranges, maturity experiments and various related experiments.

CASTOR BEANS

During 1942, seven varieties of selected seed were planted in Honduras as seed beds in abandoned banana areas. In 1943, Research Department plantings of 40.85 acres, and Cortes Farms area of 512.0 acres (a total of 552.85 acres), came into bearing, and harvesting and processing operations continued throughout the year.

In wet weather, downy mildew and sooty mold were very much in evidence, which caused considerable damage to flowers and young seed clusters and reduced the yield appreciably. A prolonged drought greatly retarded some areas, especially on heavy soils. Two recurring outbreaks of lacebugs caused considerable defoliation during dry weather. Some girdling by rodents also occurred.

In order to limit growth to a height suitable for convenient harvesting, several plots were pruned back to the second or third joint of the branches after harvesting of the first crop. It was believed that this practice would promote branching and increase second-crop production. However, such pruned areas proved very susceptible to ant, termite, and shot-hole borer attacks, which caused extensive die-back. Root rot was also more noticeable in areas which had been pruned.

At the end of the year, total producing acreage had declined to 179.3 acres, 373.55 acres having gone out of production.

After extensive study, we believe that under our local climatic and soil conditions these plants are naturally short-lived. The improved strains at first grow thriftily and under favorable conditions produce one or two heavy crops. The quick decline from this point seems to be a natural condition and may account for the early mortality experienced in all varieties. Root rot, borers, ants, and termites seem to be secondary rather than contributing factors. Climatic conditions were unusual during the year, and no doubt prolonged rains during the flowering period, as well as subsequent severe drought, affected large areas adversely.

Production of shelled beans varied widely. Yield of Farm plantings of Salvador Large varied from 229 to 451 pounds per acre, and Salvador Cafe from 119 to 473 pounds per acre. Average cost for maintenance and harvesting of Farm beans was $9.76 per acre. Statistics on plantings are as follows:

Variety	Acreage	Pounds Shelled Beans	Pounds Shelled Beans per Acre
Brazil Large	28.35	19,938	703.3
Salvador Large	1.10	1,456	1,323.6
Salvador Cafe	2.40	1,905	793.8
Salvador Medium	.50	483	976.0
Salvador Small	.50	97	194.0
Ecuador	4.00	444	111.0
Brazil Dwarf	4.00	439	110.0
Total	40.85	24,762	606.2

The plantings listed above produced a total of 7677 pounds of oil or a yield of 31.6 percent of the weight of the shelled beans. Beans were air-dried and bagged on the Farms, shipped to La Lima, and run through the drier in baskets. Continuous operation of the drier was required in wet weather when beans could not be thoroughly dried in the field. The sheller has a maximum capacity of 1200 pounds of shelled beans per twelve-hour shift. A total of 77.6 tons of shelled beans were processed. Best results were obtained by pressing the beans cold and re-pressing the cake hot. In this way two grades of oil were obtained, the cold-pressed oil being much lighter in color than the hot-pressed oil.

TUNG OIL
(Aleurites sp.)

Tung oil is one of the most important vegetable oils of the so-called drying-oil group. It is particularly well known as an essential raw material in the manufacture of varnishes and paints, and is also used in the water-proofing of wood and many other substances. Up until 1932, domestic requirements were derived almost exclusively from China, but since then a great deal of planting has been done in the southern states. The temperate Tung Oil variety, *Aleurites Fordii*, has been a failure here in Central America, but *A. triloba* and *A. trisperma* from the Philippines thrive and are long-lived. *A. montana* seems to do well for ten or twelve years.

SOYBEANS

Originally native to lower east Asia, soybeans, which theoretically can be grown wherever corn thrives, could unquestionably supply a most valuable source of protein food for the tropical American and his family, as well as a superior feed for his livestock. Our experimental plantings are to prove or disprove the soybeans as a valid crop for the citizen farmer of these warmer Americas.

Small plots of seven varieties were planted during the year, several of which show promise. The following table shows individual characteristics of each variety:

Variety	Seed Color	Percent Oil	Remarks
Avoyelles	Black	17.0	Poor results so far due to poor seed germination.
Mamloxia	Straw-yellow	18.6	Same as Avoyelles.
Porto Rico	Yellow	15.9	Very good results so far, although this variety is susceptible to mosaic disease.
Porto Rico Seminole	Straw-yellow	17.6	Fair producer but not equal to the variety P. R. No. 8.
Otootan	Black	17.3	Fair results have been shown as a forage crop.
Hamer (Santo Domingo)	Yellow	15.3	A fine variety, producing a good-sized bean. Disease resistant so far.
Laredo	Black	14.9	A small seed-forage variety giving poor results.

We have concentrated so far on building up a seed supply and have obtained a total of 178 pounds of seed from a very small beginning of four pounds. Of this total, forty-three pounds have been distributed to various individuals for trial. Fifty pounds were recently planted, and eighty-five pounds are carried in our seed stock for future planting.

Our observations to date, based on limited plantings, show excellent growth and yield on fairly heavy soil in the dry season where irrigation facilities are available. Good results were also obtained during a moderate rainy season. Best results require considerable cultivation. Some traces of mosaic diseases were noted and would probably be a factor to be considered in large plantings. The vector appears to be species of leafhoppers from infected local bean patches.

We are awaiting a shipment of several hundred pounds of selected Santo Domingo seed with which we will undertake plantings on a larger scale. Varieties which flourish in the United States are in general not suited to areas south of the Rio Grande. We are, therefore, obliged to build up our own seed material.

PLATE 31. Upper left—A nursery planting of teak trees in Honduras
Upper right—New planting of abacá
Lower—A newly harvested citronella grass

PLATE 32. Upper—Spanish-American nursery school playground
Lower left—Marbles
Lower right—Americans tomorrow

TIMBER TREES

In Honduras we now have a total of 81.3 acres planted to valuable timber trees, of which 61.9 acres have been planted during 1943. It is obvious that due to heavy depletion of natural stands during the past few years for local building, for railroad construction and maintenance, and for export, a serious shortage of good native timber will soon occur. In the La Lima area a shortage of trees for firewood is already in evidence.

Abandonments in banana farms serve as excellent opportunities for reforestation, for they are already drained and usually accessible. Large areas are available, and aside from their ultimate return, timber tree plantings should serve as inexpensive windbreaks, provide erosion control, and definitely benefit the soil.

For local reforestation the species of trees used should be adapted to the same general soil and climatic conditions as bananas. They should be able to dominate local forest weed trees after a few years. They should transplant easily, be free of serious diseases or pests, and stand a considerable amount of flooding or drought. They should be of rapid growth and show high production of good-quality lumber or fuel. So far it would appear that Teak (*Tectona grandis*) and Burmese Rosewood (*Pterocarpus indicus*) come nearest to filling these requirements.

A brief summary of Research plantings of timber trees is as follows: *Adenanthera pavonnia—Coralwood. Native to India and Burna*. A rich hard wood with great qualities of durability. Six feet in height at sixteen months from seed.

Casuarina equisetifolia—Australian Pine. Australia. A fast grower, fair for woodworking, good firewood. Very susceptible to parasitic growth. Twenty inches in height at eight months, 85 feet at eight years with diameter at breast height of 14.6 inches. At fourteen years, 104 feet high; diameter at breast height, 18.8 inches.

Cassia siamea. Burma and India. A highly decorative hard wood. Fast grower. Six feet in height at thirteen months from seed.

Cedrela mexicana—Cedar. Native. A very serviceable timber tree of many local uses. Young trees extremely susceptible to the twig borer, *Hypsipyla grandella*, which kills many trees and often causes die-back in older ones. Cannot be successfully grown in large stands because of attacks by this insect. Height 44 inches at eight months; 30 feet at twenty-eight months.

Tabebuia chrysantha—Cortes. Native. Excellent hard timber, very durable. Scarce at present. Height 6 feet at twelve months from seed.

Tabebuia pentaphylla—Macueliz. Native. A fine medium hard wood of many uses. Subject to attack by twig borers when young. Height 35 inches at six months; 7½ feet at twelve months from seed; 24 feet at twenty-eight months.

Harpullia cupanioides. East Indies and India. Fast-growing tree yielding good building timber. Height 6 feet at twelve months from seed.

Swietenia macrophylla—Honduras Mahogany. Native. 7.0 acres. The Honduras mahogany of commerce. Young trees subject to attack by twig borers and beetles. Periodic leaf-blight on some older trees, difficult to grow under plantation practice. Height 4 feet at eleven months; 85 feet high with diameter at breast height of 14 inches at sixteen years.

Swietenia mahagoni—West Indian Mahogany. West Indies. A valuable wood of somewhat better quality than the local species, but very scarce. Has not done well at Lancetilla, but is being tried out in drier regions. Height 30 inches from seed in twelve months; 67 feet and diameter of 10.5 inches at sixteen years.

Pterocarpus indicus—Burmese Rosewood. Malay Peninsula. 10.0 acres (some 400,000 seed in beds). A massive, fast-growing tree up to 85 feet tall, with diameter at breast height of 26 inches and covering an area 120 feet in diameter at age of sixteen years at Lancetilla. Yields a light, beautiful timber reputedly free from termite attack, also excellent fire-wood. Not particular as to soil—grows in sandy loam and in heavy clay. Withstands high water table. No serious pests or diseases, transplants readily with bare roots at age of twelve months when 52 inches tall. Grows rapidly from stakes in wet areas, growing 14 feet in twelve months. Seeds copiously with good volunteer growth, and cut stumps produce second or coppice growth.

Dalbergia cubilquitzensis—Honduras Rosewood. Native 17.1 ares. A native wood famed for cabinet making. Grows readily from seed in pots or nurseries. Forty-two inches tall at seven months. No pests or diseases in nurseries. Cannot stand prolonged drought when young.

Tectona grandis—Teak. Burma, India. 33.0 acres. Fast-growing tree, free of pests and diseases. Excellent, probably the best, hard timber, resistant to weathering, salt water, fire, and termites. Young trees suffer somewhat from high winds in exposed locations because of the large surface area of leaves, but partial leaf pruning for the first two years corrects this. Requires deep subsoil and only moderate rainfall. At age of one year, nursery seedlings are cut off an inch above ground and the root 12 inches under; these stumps are then planted in field. Growth is rapid when young—8 feet in six months, 26 feet in seventeen months with diameter of 3 inches. Sixty-four feet tall with diameter of 18 inches at sixteen years at Lancetilla, Honduras.

Eucalyptus hemiphloia, albens, and E. rostrata. Australia. Fast-growing tall trees yielding a very resistant hard wood. The first species also yields oil of eucalyptus from the leaves. Twenty-five inches tall at ten months; 104 feet at sixteen years with a diameter of 16 inches at Lancetilla.

Bamboo Varieties. Dr. Floyd McClure of the Board of Economic Warfare, previously with the United States Department of Agriculture in China, and a bamboo specialist, visited our Lancetilla collection in August. He gave us a comprehensive identification of our varieties which we did not have previously. The following list summarizes his information.

Name	Origin	Notes
Gigantochloa verticillata	Java	A good medium hard timber bamboo.
Bambusa tulda	India	A fine straight and tough variety. Suitable for props and construction.
Dendrocalamus sikkimensis	Northern India	Medium hard timber bamboo.
Bambusa Oldhami	Formosa	(Called *Dendrocalamus latiflorus* in the United States.) A medium hard timber variety.
Schizostachyum funghomi	China	Soft. Easily split. Used extensively in China for weaving mats which are used as house walls, fences, baskets, etc. Is extremely difficult to propagate. Long internodes.
Gigantochloa aspera	Java	An extra hard variety. Split sections used for ski poles and other light but extremely tough and durable articles.
Dendrocalamus strictus	India	The Calcutta cane of commerce. A very thick-walled slender cane. Suitable for props and construction.
Phyllostachys sp.	China	Fish-pole cane. Young shoots are edible. A very popular slender cane of many uses in China.
Guadua aculeata	Native	The local "taro."
Bambusa polymorpha	India	A medium hard timber bamboo.
Bambusa arundinacea	India	Easily grown and of ornamental value. Fairly good timber if cared for properly; makes excellent propagation pots.
Bambusa tuldoides	China	Similar to *B. tulda*, as the name implies, but more slender. Useful for stakes and light pole framing.
Bambusa vulgaris var. vittata	China	This is the yellow variety. Very durable but not so straight or smooth as *B. tulda*.

Extensive propagation of the better canes will be undertaken next year. *Bambusa tulda* and *Dendrocalamus strictus* would make excellent durable props, and when available in quantity would fill a large local need for construction of shelters, framing, fences, and trellises. Over 9000 propagation pots for African oilpalms were cut this year from mats of *B. arundinacea*.

ROSELLE
(Hibiscus sabdariffa)

This tropical fiber crop, a substitute for jute, is being tried out as a field crop for the American tropics to help replace former imports from India and the Pacific tropics. According to contract with the Defense Supplies Corporation we agree to plant, cultivate, harvest, and process twenty-five acres of roselle for fiber and twenty-five acres for seed.

The location of this experimental planting was at Santa Rosa Farm on light alluvial soil in close proximity to the Ulua River in Honduras. Preparation of the land includes underbrushing, cleaning, and windrowing, followed by plowing and harrowing. Planting for fiber was made at the rate of eighteen to twenty pounds of seed per acre in rows eighteen inches apart, with the use of a rise drill adjusted for this specific purpose. The same drill was adjusted to planting for seed with rows thirty inches apart, using approximately five pounds of seed per acre. A mule-drawn "middle-buster" was used advantageously for first cultivation, but later some hand and machete cleaning was necessary.

Leaf-cutting ants did considerable damage to young plants before their colonies could be eradicated with carbon bisulfide. A leaf-spot disease, apparently caused by a species of Cercospora, attacked the plants when they were about two months old, covering the leaves with ash-gray markings surrounded by a reddish halo. With increased infection these spots coalesced and caused the leaves to fall off prematurely. A considerable amount of root-knot (nematode injury) caused some stunting of growth. Scattered cases of downy mildew were encountered.

Germination took place five to six days after planting, and flowering was first observed four weeks later, lasting for a month or more. After heavy rains, standing water retarded growth and subsequent production in low portions of the planting.

Harvesting for Seed. After four and one-half months the roselle planted for seed, which had attained an average height of 113 inches, was harvested by hand. Subsequent dry weather made it possible to separate the remainder of the seed by flailing in the field. The seed was then cleaned and winnowed of chaff by means of electric fans. A total of 2239 pounds of seed or 896 pounds per acre was harvested from the twenty-five-acre plot. A floating process, to eliminate non-viable seed, cut the final total down to 1210 pounds or 48.4 pounds per acre of viable seed.

Harvesting for Fiber. This was carried out when the plants were eleven and twelve weeks old and averaged seventy inches in height. A power-drawn mower proved unsatisfactory, leaving stalks badly scattered and tangled on the ground, and most of the harvesting was done by hand. Following cutting, the stalks were bundled and hauled by mule-back to the retting canal. A concrete irrigation canal adjacent to the plot provided excellent retting facilities. Immersion of the stalks from ten to twelve days produced best results. Following retting, the bundles were washed and the stalks laid out in the sun to dry for one or two days.

Part of the dry material was then run through crusher rolls and a brushing machine prior to baling for shipment. These machines, designed and built locally, proved unsatisfactory. The remaining fiber, after retting, was separated from the boon by hand, washed in the river, sun-dried, and baled. This method was somewhat more costly than machine processing but the resulting fiber was free of splinters and of good quality. This project yielded 2940 pounds of fiber, or 117.6 pounds per acre. Cost of fiber production averaged $74.61 per acre or 63 cents per pound of fiber.

A second planting of twenty acres for fiber and five acres for seed was later authorized by the B.E.W. and was undertaken by the Agricultural Department to gain additional information on growth, harvesting, and processing. Growth was noticeably retarded by a prolonged dry spell. However, benefiting from experience gained previously, a better yield of both fiber and seed was obtained. This project yielded 1018 pounds of first-class seed after floating, or 204 pounds per acre. Fiber yield was 6018 pounds or 300.9 pounds per acre.

Summary. Roselle requires a fertile, permeable, and well-drained soil. Cool or wet weather retards growth.

Diseases and pests might greatly reduce or completely ruin plantings for both fiber and seed, unless control measures are adopted.

Mechanical processing of fiber was not a success with us but improved design of machines might give better results. Hand stripping, although giving better quality fiber, is very costly.

Local laborers look on the work in connection with harvesting, retting, and seed extraction with considerable distaste. Roselle probably cannot be grown profitably in Honduras because of attacks by disease, unpredictable weather conditions, and high wage rate. Small plantings might be made by isolated farmers but marketing would be a considerable problem in normal times.

OTHER FIBER-YIELDING PLANTS

Seeds from another tropical plant, from whose stalks a soft fiber is produced, were received from Ecuador and planted here to study in this locality. *Corchorus capsularis* (jute) is a tropical annual plant that grows straight with slight branching, quite similar to roselle. A small plot was planted August 4 and harvested November 25. The plants seeded heavily, and a fair amount of fiber was obtained. The growing conditions, rainfall, and soil seem very favorable for its growth here. As only a small amount of seed was originally received, it was impossible to carry on spacing experiments, so important to fiber and seed yields. New plantings are now underway.

LUFFA SPONGES

These are a vegetative substitute for marine sponges and are used for cleaning machinery, particularly on ships. The former sources were principally the Pacific tropics, now cut off by war.

Experiments have been continued this year with luffa sponges, using seed of the Japanese variety. Two plots of one-half acre each were planted, one in the dry season and one during wet weather. The dry-season planting proved most satisfactory, since rains damage the flowers of the plants, and insects and pests such as melon aphis, melon worm, and common rodents are more prevalent during the rainy season.

A light clay loam, well drained and located so as to facilitate watering during the dry season, gives the best results. The general layout of the planting and trellising should be arranged to assure maximum exposure to the sun. Heavy support posts seven feet high are spaced every twelve feet in inverted V formation. Small posts are then spread every three feet between pairs of main supports. Horizontals are spaced three, five, and seven feet from the ground.

Two seeds are planted at the base of each vertical post, and thinned out to one plant after germination. Training and tying vines to horizontals should be done with majao or banana fiber. Care should be taken in training the vines so that all the available space is used on the trellises. The reason for this is to allow maximum sun penetration. Male flowers should be pruned off until vines have covered all horizontals. Newly formed sponges should be examined and pruned out during the first week if they are deformed, pear-shaped, or coarse. Harvesting commences in from four to five months from planting.

Retting. As soon as sponges turn light yellow on the flower end, they are harvested and soaked in water from twenty-four to thirty-six hours.

The Japanese sponges are a marked improvement over the previous strains experimented with. The commercial type No. 1 grade, Japanese sponges are firm in texture, yet yield to ordinary pressure of the hand and have sufficient resiliency to withstand being bent and twisted without causing a breakdown of the fibers after several foldings.

Along with the new or experimental crops herein mentioned, the Research Department of United Fruit is carrying on active introduction and propagation experiments with derris, or tuba, an improved Malayan root crop which provides rotenone, one of the most valuable of commercial insecticides; cryptostegia, or Mexican rubber vine, a quick-developing source of natural rubber; extensive plantings of selected Hevea rubber trees, and Castilla, another native latex-producing tree of Central and South America.

Also being grown are several hundred acres of lemon grass and citronella, tropical or subtropical grasses which produce specialized oils for sprays, soaps, and menthols. (These crops were formerly grown principally in the Pacific tropics.) These grass oils are being processed commercially, and the crops are being grown by citizen farmers in many areas of Central America.

Other new crops for the American tropics, now in experimental and field propagation include tropically adapted peanuts needed to overcome the chronic tropical shortages of edible oils and to benefit livestock possibilities of the warmer Americas; tropically adapted cowpeas, as a leguminous cover crop; peppermints, oranges, grapefruit, mandarin, limes, lemons, tangerines, avocado, litchi, rambutan, mango, breadfruit, durian, and coconut. In addition are such "ornamentals" as roses, gardenias, and ornamental palms; experiments in growing kapok, the lustrous floss of the Ceiba tree; extensive research in bananas, and test propagation of many other plants which in time may become crops.

Index